Wings of the North

Wings of the North

A Gallery of Favorite Birds

Candace Savage

University of Minnesota Press
Minneapolis, Minnesota

Published by the University of Minnesota Press
2037 University Avenue Southeast, Minneapolis
MN 55414
Printed in Canada

Published in Canada by Western Producer Prairie
Books as *The Wonder of Canadian Birds*

Design by John Luckhurst/GDL
Cover photograph by Wayne Lankinen
Back cover photograph by Arthur Savage

The University of Minnesota is an
equal-opportunity educator and employer.

Library of Congress Cataloging in Publication
Data

Savage, Candace Sherk, 1949-
    Wings of the North.
    Bibliography: p. 179
    Includes index.
    1. Birds — Canada. I. Title.
QL685.S28   1985   598.2971   85-8655
ISBN 0-8166-1433-4

In memory of
Arthur Savage
1948–1981

His spirit soared,
and his love
lay light as a feather.

Contents

Scientific Advisors

The author gratefully acknowledges the assistance of the following experts:

Dean Amadon, Ph.D., Lamont Curator Emeritus of Birds, American Museum of Natural History

David A. Boag, Ph.D., Professor, Department of Zoology, University of Alberta

Richard Fyfe, Research Scientist, Canadian Wildlife Service

W. Earl Godfrey, D.Sc., Curator Emeritus of Ornithology, National Museum of Natural Sciences, Ottawa, Ontario

J. David Henry, Ph.D., Biological Consultant, Waskesiu, Saskatchewan

C. Stuart Houston, M.D., Radiologist and Naturalist, Saskatoon, Saskatchewan

Ross James, Ph.D., Associate Curator of Ornithology, Royal Ontario Museum

Paul A. Johnsgard, Ph.D., Foundation Professor, School of Life Sciences, University of Nebraska

Louise de Kiriline Lawrence, Author and Ornithologist, Rutherglen, Ontario

Ernie Kuyt, Wildlife Biologist, Canadian Wildlife Service

Edward H. Miller, Ph.D., Curator, Vertebrate Zoology Division, Provincial Museum of British Columbia

Robert W. Nero, Ph.D., Wildlife Specialist, Manitoba Department of Natural Resources

David Nettleship, Ph.D., Research Scientist, Canadian Wildlife Service

Henri Ouellet, Ph.D., Chief, Vertebrate Zoology Division, National Museums of Canada

John P. Ryder, Ph.D., Professor, Department of Biology, Lakehead University

P. Lynn Ryder, Department of Biology, Lakehead University

Robert W. Storer, Ph.D., Professor of Biology and Curator of Birds, University of Michigan

Miklos D. F. Udvardy, Ph.D., Professor, Department of Biological Sciences, California State University

Kees Vermeer, Ph.D., Research Scientist, Canadian Wildlife Service

Ultimate responsibility for the accuracy of the text lies with the author.

Acknowledgments

This book began twenty-five years ago with a gangly, freckle-faced boy named Arthur Savage, who lived on what was then the outskirts of Edmonton, Alberta. Every day after school, every weekend, he biked into the countryside for fresh air, freedom—and birds. He was older when I knew him, but the enthusiasm for bird life was still there, and his knees and elbows still got scraped each spring, climbing to the year's first magpie nest. This book was to have been a joint project for Art and me, and in many ways, it still is, despite the fact that he died before the work could be begun. Without him, it would not have come to be.

Recognition is also due to members of Arthur's family, particularly the Savages senior and the Hartsons, for their continued interest and their willingness to keep little Annie happy while her Mommy worked. Thanks, too, to my parents, Harry and Edna Sherk, for kindnesses too numerous to mention and for generally making life possible. Special thanks, as well, to Claire Pullman for making it easy to accept assistance when I needed it, and to Diana, for tolerance and forbearance beyond her years.

In addition, I am deeply grateful to the men and women listed as "scientific advisors," all of whom volunteered their time to review portions of the manuscript. Their willingness to do so reflects a dedication to their field of study that goes beyond mere professionalism. I owe a particular debt to Ross James, Paul A. Johnsgard, and Robert W. Nero, and to W. Earl Godfrey who gave me copies of his updated distribution maps before he published them. Sincere thanks are also due to Roger Tory Peterson for his foreword. My research assistants, Adrian Pritchard and Ian Sanderson, both exhibited great patience in performing essential but often tedious duties. A word of appreciation must also go to Marion LaVigne of Outcrop in Yellowknife, for the loan of a much-needed slide projector.

Finally, it is an honor to acknowledge the financial support of Alberta Culture, the Canada Council, and Edna E. Sherk.

Foreword

by Roger Tory Peterson

Canada and the northern United States boast an avifauna of about 550 species, eighty percent of which breed somewhere within this vast domain. To identify the birds of this varied galaxy one needs only a field guide, but to gain a deeper understanding of their behavior and ecology, one can turn to this book.

Candace Savage provides us with a selective overview of northern birds. Her book is a series of essays aimed at giving us the essence of at least one member of each order of birds and most of the bird families.

Some of the birds treated in depth are unique in their way; others are representative of a group. What bird symbolizes the spirit and solitude of northern lakes more than a loon? What bird is more droll than a puffin? What bird is more secretive and mysterious than Leach's Storm-Petrel? And what birdlet is more lovable than a Black-capped Chickadee? Birds are as different from each other as dogs are from cats — or from chipmunks. Candace Savage has sketched out their personalities in a series of well-written essays that are a pleasure to read, whether you are an armchair birder who reads but seldom watches or a gung-ho binocular addict who enjoys making lists.

The focus of these essays is on behavior and ecology. Their objective is to provide readers with new insights into some of the birds that they may know only by name and appearance. The environmental movement owes much to the perceptive birder who really watches, and also reads.

Introduction

Whatever surprises may await us in the outer corners of our galaxy, of one thing we can be sure: there is no other planet like Earth. Look at the variety of living things that surrounds us, a profusion of colors, sizes, shapes, and sounds. Consider the range of life forms that has been nurtured here, from simple, precellular viruses to human consciousness. And think, for a moment, of birds. In this class alone, there are about eighty-seven hundred living species, representing twenty-seven distinct orders, or evolutionary lines. Of these, eighteen orders and more than five hundred species occur in Canada and the adjacent states. Birds of the air and the ocean; birds that nest on cliff-sides and underground; birds that feed on carrion and on nectar from flowers; fish-eaters, fly-catchers, and sharp-beaked hunters; hermits that crave solitude and sociable creatures that breed in cities or in dense colonies; monogamists, polygynists, and female "liberationists": the diversity of North American bird life is dazzling.

In this book, we will not deal in detail with every species that occurs in our area. But we will discuss at least one representative from each of the eighteen orders, beginning with what is theoretically the most "primitive" group (the loons) and proceeding to the most "advanced" (the perching birds). Along the way, we will also include members of most of the major subgroupings within the orders, the taxonomic families. There are three families of raptors, for example—vultures, hawks, and falcons—and we will treat all three. There are a dozen large families of songbirds, and we will deal with eight. Since the members of a family are often similar, what you learn about the birds that are covered in this book will serve as a guide to the biology and behavior of other, closely related species. As far as possible, we will also deal with species that have broad, rather than localized, distributions, so that the information will apply wherever you go across the country. We'll also give preference to the familiar birds, like robins, bluebirds, and birds of prey—the ones you're most likely to see and

wonder about. And finally, we'll include a few species that are simply too interesting to leave out.

But before we get down to specifics, there is a general question that we need to think about. Just what are birds? What sets them apart from other organisms? The first characteristic that comes to mind is flight. A bird, we might be tempted to suggest, is an animal that flies. But then what do we make of flying insects? Let's try refining the definition: a bird is a vertebrate animal that flies. But then what becomes of bats and, come to think of it, where do we put ostriches and other flightless birds? Maybe we'd do better to begin with a different trait; thus, a bird is a vertebrate that lays eggs. But the problem with this is that it also applies to one mammal and many reptiles. No, there is only one attribute that meets our requirements, an attribute that is both unique to birds and universal among them, and that is the possession of feathers. Any creature that grows feathers is a bird, a member of the class Aves.

Strong, lightweight, and flexible, feathers are one of evolution's most successful inventions. Most birds have several kinds, including down for insulation, bristles to protect the eyes and nostrils, and "filoplumes," bare stalks with tufts at the end, which may have a sensory function. The most familiar type are the "contour" feathers, so called because one of their roles is to shape and streamline the body. Each contour feather has a hollow, central shaft, fringed on both sides by fine filaments, or barbs. The barbs in turn are edged with hairlike projections, or barbules, which are of two types: those that point toward the tip of the feather are simple threads, while those that point toward the base of the feather are equipped with hooks. The millions of tiny hooks grabbing millions of minute threads hold the fabric of the feather together. When the bird runs its beak along the barbs, it "zips up" the barbules. Feathers require a great deal of care—oiling, dusting, bathing, and tidying—and a bird spends many hours a day

The wonder of birds lies in their diversity, their complexity, the intricacy with which each species is adapted to its way of life. Shown here: a Great Blue Heron practicing the habits of alertness and stealth that make it an excellent hunter.

Taking care of their feathers is a major preoccupation for all species of birds. This Killdeer is spreading oil from a preen gland onto its plumage.

performing these vital tasks. Once or twice a year (usually after the breeding season and, sometimes, in the spring as well), the bird molts; that is, it gradually sheds its old, worn feathers and grows a whole new set—a process that, like breeding and migration, is one of the major expenditures in its annual energy budget.

Feathers are thought to have evolved from reptilian scales; in fact, birds still have scales on their feet. For this and many other reasons, there can be little doubt that birds evolved from reptiles. The oldest and most famous fossil bird, *Archaeopteryx,* would certainly have been taken for a pterosaur or small dinosaur had it not been for the imprint of perfectly formed feathers. Indeed, that is exactly what did happen to two *Archaeopteryx* fossils that have only recently been correctly identified.

Just how the transition occurred from scales to feathers and from reptiles to birds is unknown. Suggestively, about 90 million years before *Archaeopteryx* (or 230 million years ago), there was a lizardlike reptile that walked on two legs, had birdlike feet, and wore long, slender scales that were slightly ribbed. Were these the precursors of feathers, and was this animal, known to science as *Euparkeria,* the ancestor of birds? Some experts think so, and they also propose that *Euparkeria* and its relatives gave rise to crocodiles and dinosaurs. But there is a dissenting group of scientists who disagree. Basing their opinion on an array of anatomical features, they argue that birds did not evolve alongside dinosaurs from a common ancestor but instead derived from them, specifically from the brainy, birdlike ostrich dinosaurs. If this is true, it means that the dinosaurian line did not die out completely as we have thought. Instead its descendants are currently flitting through the shrubbery in your backyard.

No one knows whether feathers developed first for flight or for insulation, though the latter seems more reasonable to many experts. Effective insulation is one of the prerequisites for endothermy (warm-bloodedness), a characteristic shared by mammals and birds. Ectotherms (cold-blooded animals), like reptiles and amphibians, take their body temperature from their surroundings and are incapacitated

by cold weather. Endotherms, in contrast, generate and maintain their own body heat so that they can remain active in all but the most extreme environments.

In addition to their feather insulation, birds also developed an exceptionally efficient "heating system"—their digestive tract, which processes food quickly and with little waste. For the most part, they fuel this system with high-energy foods such as insects, fruit, and seeds. Their oxygen supply is also abundant, thanks to their four-chambered hearts (a feature they share with mammals, which prevents the intermixing of venous and arterial blood) and the structure of their lungs, which are bright red with blood vessels and honeycombed with thousands upon thousands of fine airways. Gas exchange occurs along the surfaces of all these passageways. What's more, the lungs are connected to a system of air sacs, usually nine in all, which extend into the body cavities. Through a series of complicated maneuvers, the air circulates through these sacs in such a way that stale, deoxygenated air is never mixed with the incoming supply, as happens in humans. As a result, the internal surfaces of a bird's lungs are constantly bathed in fresh air. Birds lack sweat glands, so their air sacs are also important as a cooling mechanism, since they provide a place where water can evaporate inside the body.

Interestingly, it is not at all uncommon for a bird's air sacs to extend right inside its skeleton. To become airborne, an animal obviously must be as light as possible, and birds have made many adjustments to reduce their load. For one thing, they generally have hollow bones, with no heavy marrow. The skeleton of the Magnificent Frigatebird, a creature with seven-meter wings, weighs just over one hundred grams, or less than the bird's plumage. Cross braces inside the bones provide strength without significant weight. Birds also have fewer bones than other vertebrates, some of their hand, foot, tail, and back bones having been discarded or fused over the course of their evolution. They have no teeth (coarse food being ground in the gizzard), no urinary bladder, and only one skin gland; most females have a single ovary. The reproductive organs of both sexes atrophy outside the breeding season, swelling again only when required.

Lightness and a high-fire metabolism, together with strong flight muscles, excellent eyesight, and good neural coordination, have permitted birds to take to the air and have made them the envy of humankind. Try as we will, we can neither equal nor fully understand the complexity of flapping flight. We do know that lift is achieved by the "forearm" of the wing, and that forward propulsion comes from the supple movements of the wing tip, or "hand," making a bird's wing equivalent to both the wing and propeller of an aircraft. But no one ever has (or perhaps ever will) come up with a precise description of all the forces at work from moment to moment as a bird swoops and turns and molds its feathers to the wind. Nor can we match the efficiency of bird flight. Take, for example, the Lesser Golden Plover, which annually flies nonstop from Labrador to South America, a distance of thirty-eight hundred kilometers, yet loses only sixty grams of its body weight. For a pilot in a small plane to equal this, he or she would have to make the trip on fifty liters of gas, instead of the usual five hundred.

It is this cheap transportation that makes it possible for birds to undertake long-distance migrations. All told, about thirty percent of the world's birds are migratory, though the percentage is much higher at our latitude. The reason is obvious: our severe winters. Who wouldn't leave if they could afford to? For most of us and most other animals, this is impossible, but we can and do shift to the best habitat that is available. Thus, people move inside, Deer Mice go under the snow, White-tailed Deer congregate in gullies and heavy cover, and so on. But birds, being exceptionally mobile, can pick and choose amongst the resources of the continent or even of the hemisphere. Given their powers of flight, it is not surprising that birds migrate. It would be surprising if they didn't.

If why birds migrate is not puzzling, exactly how they do it remains a mystery. How do they find their way unerringly over hundreds or thousands of kilometers, often zeroing in on precisely the same territory or nest site that they used in previous years? Scientists have recently discovered that birds have at least three kinds of "compass": they may navigate by the sun, by the stars, and/or by the Earth's magnetic field. Their magnetic sensitivity is literally a sixth sense and, incidentally, one which we may share; in the case of pigeons, the receptor is a tiny particle of magnetite between the skull and the brain. Superimposed on these three basic systems is a wide range of route-finding techniques, the importance of which varies from species to species. In some cases, first-time migrants follow experienced birds and learn where to go. But are the birds learning the physical twists and turns of the voyage, as some researchers have suggested, or will they remember landmarks and the general lay of the land? Visual orientation is no doubt important for most birds, and even such subtle cues as the direction of ocean waves may be useful. Some species are known to rely, in part, on the heading of the prevailing winds, and the sense of smell can be crucial, too, especially for sea birds. There is also a possibility that some species rely on infrasound (frequencies below the range of human hearing but audible to birds), such as winds off far-away mountains or waves on an ocean shore. These sounds travel long distances without alteration. Or perhaps birds can sense gradations in gravity or navigate by ultraviolet and polarized light. Many questions remain to be answered about both the nature and the operation of birds' navigational systems.

For the birds themselves, of course, these questions of "why" and "how" never arise. They do what they do because they feel like doing it. Although they are certainly capable of learning and making choices, much of their behavior is automatic. As Konrad Lorenz has pointed out, birds "have" behavior in much the same way as they have wings or eyes or beaks. It is part of their genetic equipment. Presented with a certain stimulus, they respond in a prescribed way. Suppose, for example, that a nesting tern is confronted with a strange chick. The adult immediately and violently drives the chick away; but if the youngster is then pecked by another hen, its cries of distress stimulate the first female to run to its defense! And if, in the midst of the battle, the chick touches its attacker on the breast, the adult's aggression immediately gives way to an urge to brood. Under normal circumstances, the tern's impulses to defend its nest and to protect and brood its young are switched on at just the

Many bird behaviors are "automatic" responses triggered by particular stimuli. The open gape of hungry nestlings, for example, is an almost irresistible stimulus for most adult birds. These are young Barn Swallows.

right times and enable the bird to rear its offspring successfully.

Most communication among birds follows this stimulus/response plan. Sometimes the signals are auditory: songs, calls, and various mechanical sounds such as bill clacking, foot stamping, and wing drumming. Often they are visual or audio-visual. The red breast of the American Robin is an aggressive signal; so is the red epaulet on the male Redwing. In conjunction with vocalizations and a set pattern of movements, such signals permit the members of these species to communicate their aggressive intentions and determine a winner without fighting. A distinct, stereotyped sequence of actions and sounds with which an individual elicits a response from another member of its species is called a "display." The movements used in displays are derived from functional behavior such as feeding and preening. When they become detached from their functional context, they are said to be "ritualized." Among birds, "body language" of this sort is commonly associated with courtship, nesting, and the defense of territories.

Over the millennia, the behavior of birds has been refined by natural selection, so that, under normal circumstances, it is as beautifully adaptive and appropriate as any aspect of their anatomy or physiology. Under abnormal circumstances, however, birds may not cope so well. What would happen, for example, to a bird that had evolved in isolation from predators, if it were suddenly attacked by human hunters? Never having needed to defend itself, the creature wouldn't have developed an instinct to flee, and being a bird, it could not quickly learn. This is exactly what happened to the Great Auk, which once bred by the millions on islands off our east coast, and is now extinct. A similar story could be told about the Passenger Pigeon, whose immense flocks once made easy targets for men with firearms.

Today, the threats to bird life may be more subtle, but they are no less menacing. It's an all-too-familiar litany of pollution and habitat loss. Pesticides, industrial poisons, acid rain, urbanization, the expansion of industry and intensive agriculture, and the mining of the seas all take their toll on birds and other living things. There are now vast oil slicks in mid-ocean and a thin haze of smog over the far North. Since 1600, it is estimated that 150 species or subspecies of birds have been lost, mostly because of human activity. Of these, over three-quarters have vanished in the last two centuries. At present, about 350 types of birds are in peril, more than two dozen of them in Canada and the northern states. And as Darwin once reminded us, "Rarity . . . is the precursor to extinction."

But all is far from lost. The Earth still glows with beauty and delight. Now is a time for commitment and collective action. It's a time to foster a new view of life on this planet, for just as we know that the Earth is not the center of the universe, so we must now learn that mankind is not the center of the biosphere. It's time for us to see birds and other creatures in a different light and to appreciate each species for its special excellence.

Order Gaviiformes

Loons

The quavering "laughter" of loons echoes through the gathering dark. A momentary silence, and the calls ring out again—clear, wolflike howls that speak of wilderness. For many of us, these haunting sounds number among the essential characteristics of this order of birds; but biologists take a more prosaic view (during office hours, at least). In their eyes, loons can be succinctly defined as "large, mainly fish-eating, foot-propelled diving birds." They point out that there are four species of loons in the world, all of which breed in the northern hemisphere, including Canada. Of these, three nest in the Arctic or subartic, and only one, the aptly named Common Loon, *Gavia immer,* is widely known.

Common Loons might be thought of as seals with wings, so thoroughly are they adapted to an aquatic life. Their leg bones are mostly inside the torso and far to the rear, with the ankles and feet extended, flipperlike, behind. This arrangement gives the birds power and speed underwater and permits them to catch almost any small fish, including swift-moving trout. (Their diet also includes crustaceans, amphibians, and, occasionally, the young of other water birds.) Their plumage is watertight and can be compressed at will to remove trapped air; when air is expelled from the respiratory system at the same time, the birds vanish underwater by degrees, back first, then neck, then head, until only a ripple remains.

Their diving ability is also enhanced by another adaptation—heavy bones. Unlike most birds, which have air-filled skeletons to help them fly, loons have marrow, which permits them to sink. And sink they do: the record-holder among Common Loons descended to a depth of more than seventy meters before getting tangled in a fish net. Loons also have a number of physiological adaptations that permit them to stay underwater for five minutes or more at a time, though dives of less than a minute are usual.

Evolutionary gains often entail a measure of compromise, and so it is with Common Loons. The dense bones that serve so well as diving weights make it difficult for the birds to get aloft, especially since the surface area of their wings is not exceptionally large. In fact, loons have the highest "wing loading" of any living bird. This accounts for the long, pattering run across the water that always precedes take-off. If a Common Loon comes down on ice or land, it is probably doomed. (Once airborne, however, loons fly powerfully.) Similarly, the aft-mounted legs, which drive the birds through the water, render them almost incapable of travel on shore. Barely able to stand erect, they hop, flop, and hobble, sometimes using their wings like walking sticks.

The only events in a Common Loon's life that force it onto land are copulation and nesting. Not surprisingly, mating is a brief, no-nonsense affair, and nesting usually takes place at the water's edge, in a site that provides quick access to a deep-water refuge. The ideal nesting place for Common Loons is a small, predator-free island, but they will sometimes accept an isolated mainland shore, a bed of cattails, or the top of an old muskrat house. Nests may be established in the same or adjacent sites year after year, and it is presumed that this represents reuse of the area by the same pair. It is suspected, though not proven, that Common Loons mate for life.

Returning to their old nest site is only one way in which Common Loons streamline their springtime activities. Raising a brood, from conception to independence, generally occupies four or five months, and the ice-free season on northern lakes is mercilessly short. Accordingly, the birds arrive immediately after breakup, probably already paired. Within as

Common Loon

little as five days after their return, or a month at the most, the pair will probably have a clutch of two dark, spotted eggs.

Although the parents are easily frightened off the nest in the early days of incubation, both become more committed with time. After about twenty-nine days, the eggs hatch, the young flounder into the water, and parenthood enters what seems to be its most anxious stage.

One sign of the heightened tension during the hatching period is a sudden increase in territorial disputes. Every nesting pair claims an average of forty to eighty hectares, either a bay in a large lake or all of a smaller one. Here they mate, nest, and rear their young. While unmated birds may be allowed to pass through, other breeding birds are excluded from part or all of the territory. The area that is actively defended against such incursions reaches its maximum size when the eggs hatch. Hostilities often culminate in frothing, ritualized "foot-races" across the surface of the water and, occasionally, in combat.

These interactions, like much other loon behavior, are performed to the accompaniment of calls, notably the staccato "tremolo" and the prolonged, wailing "yodel," both of which have been subject to numerous human misunderstandings. Is the yodel a love song or a yowl of distress? Does the tremolo signify avian dementia or an oncoming storm? While we are still far from understanding the subtleties of loon communication, biologists suggest that the tremolo is basically an expression of anxiety, with gradations of pitch and volume that convey varying degrees of alarm. The yodel can usually be interpreted as a declaration of territorial possession.

By mid-July, territorial behavior is on the wane, and some of the breeding males have already left their families to join the flocks of nonbreeding birds that gather on neutral areas (those not claimed as territories). Gradually, between late August and freezeup, the birds take off for their wintering grounds along both coasts, and the call of the Common Loon fades from the northern lakes.

Solicitous parents, Common Loons are nonetheless often induced to desert their nests by careless human intrusions.

As a mark of their special regard for loons, the residents of Minnesota have made the Common Loon their state bird.

There is a chilling possibility that these calls will fade permanently from just those places where we want to hear them most. Because of their low reproductive rate and the high, natural mortality of eggs and young (fewer than half survive), Common Loons are vulnerable to human disturbance. Pesticides and acid rain may pose significant threats; so does the continuing expansion of settlement. As a general rule, the more use people make of an area, the fewer young loons are produced. Motorboaters wash out nests with their wakes; canoeists and campers cause birds to flush during incubation, thereby exposing the eggs to gulls and other predators. Too much interference, especially early in the nesting season, will cause the adults to desert their nests altogether. Where do they go? To some still-peaceful hinterland? No, such places already

have their quota of breeding loons. Besides, Common Loons apparently have a strong attachment to their accustomed territories and will return year after year even if their young never survive. Year after year, that is, until they themselves die. If there are too few young in the area to fill all the vacancies, their territory may remain unoccupied.

This result is not inevitable. When shown adequate consideration, Common Loons have been known to rear chicks right beside a public beach, swimming and diving peacefully among the bathers. Public education, and surveillance on a nest-by-nest basis, can be the key to this kind of success. No need to wait on government here: the preservation of the loons' breeding places can best be accomplished by those of us who intrude upon their privacy.

The loons' spectacular dancelike displays, together with their wild, haunting calls, are their ways of communicating with one another. Imperfectly understood by human observers, these behaviors are primarily associated with courtship and territorial defense.

Grebes

- Horned Grebe
- Pied-billed Grebe
- Range Overlap

Before grebes acquired the Latinate distinction of "Podicipediformes," they were known with Anglo-Saxon directness as the "arsefoots." This was a reference to one of their many adaptations to aquatic life, specifically the positioning of their legs, which are far to the rear of the body for maximum thrust while swimming. But they might equally well have been known as "paddle toes," because their feet, on which they rely for propulsion underwater, are not fully webbed but instead are separated into flat, fingerlike lobes, which spread to drive against the water on the power stroke and collapse to minimize resistance on the return. Grebes also have stubby wings and next-to-no tail, features which streamline the body and further increase their swimming efficiency. Thus equipped, the birds can duck below the surface in the twinkling of an eye, creating the now-you-see-them-now-you-don't effect that has earned them the nickname "water witch." Or, like loons, they can lower themselves by degrees, by expelling air from their bodies and plumage.

Grebes and loons are alike in many aspects of their anatomy, behavior, and physiology, so much so that biologists used to place them in the same order. Because of their aquatic specializations, for example, members of both groups are bumble-footed on land. They also have difficulty getting airborne and must sprint along the surface of the water to attain sufficient speed for takeoff. Yet most ornithologists now believe that grebes and loons are not closely related and that their common features arose through convergent evolution—two groups achieving similar adaptations to a shared habitat but by different evolutionary routes.

Many apparently unconnected aspects of grebe behavior relate in some way to their aquatic lifestyle. Take, for example, their habit of swallowing large quantities of feathers. Why is it that a grebe's stomach is sometimes half full of this wadding? Why do the adults feed feathers to their young? One probable explanation is that the feathers protect the digestive tract from cuts and abrasions. Grebes generally eat small fish, crustaceans, and water bugs, most of which are swallowed whole—bones, shells, and all. Some of the ingested feathers serve as a filter, which strains out the hard bits and holds them until they can be digested or brought up as part of a feather-packed pellet.

Another unusual characteristic of grebes is the structure of their nests. These often begin as small, anchored rafts of floating vegetation, perhaps the hollow stems of bulrushes or reeds. In this unfinished state, they may be used as copulation platforms, for grebes never mate on water and seldom on land, preferring to use these little islands that they build for themselves. A female will sometimes even deposit eggs on such a rudimentary structure, only to abandon them when she and her mate move on to their next nest-building project. This may occur as many as six times in one nesting season. The final clutch, which typically includes from two to eight eggs, will be laid on a completed nest. A grebe nest is a buoyant foundation topped with a sodden heap of algae or other rotting vegetation, the very antithesis of coziness. Not only are the eggs surrounded by dankness and decay, they are often right in the water, especially when one of the parents clambers on board to incubate, making the whole mass sink. Nonetheless, the nests are functional, for the eggs are warmed in part by the heat of decomposition.

Grebe eggs are bright when first laid but quickly darken to a chalky, camouflage drab; when not being tended, they are usually covered with vegetation. After about three weeks, the young emerge and almost immediately take to the water, though they are feeble swimmers and easily chilled. The ultimate luxury for a grebe chick, as for a young loon, is to climb onto mom or dad's back and snuggle down under a wing. As many as four young at a time will sometimes share this comfy berth, while the unencumbered parent serves up tidbits to tempt their appetites. Not surprisingly, the youngsters apparently retain their enthusiasm for this arrangement longer than the adults. It is suspected that stab wounds inflicted on would-be hitchhikers by their jaded parents are a significant cause of mortality among grebe chicks. The juvenile death rate among grebes is high and not easily accounted for, though nest losses caused by flooding and waves may be important. Oil spills and pesticides present perils for young and old alike, but grebe populations are thought to be steady.

There are about twenty species of grebes in all, distributed almost worldwide; of these, five regularly occur in Canada and the adjacent states. The one that is most familiar to easterners is the Pied-billed Grebe, *Podilymbus podiceps*. Pied-bills are skulkers, unobtrusive of dress and unsociable of habit. Each breeding pair commands a territory extending some forty or fifty meters in all directions from its nest and defends this area not only against members of its own species but against other grebes, various kinds of ducks, and coots. Fierce in their attacks on other water birds, incubating Pied-bills tend to disappear discretely when a person intrudes, giving few clues to their presence other than a faint splash and the vacant nest. In springtime especially, but at other times of the year as well, they are more readily heard than seen, as their complex calls—a series of hollow "kow's" and "kuk's"

Pied-billed Grebes are so retiring that most of us never get close enough to see the distinctive markings from which they take their name.

Already half-submerged, this Eared Grebe could disappear underwater in an instant.

Facing page: On a half-submerged nest of rotting marsh plants, this Horned Grebe keeps a sharp watch against intruders.

—resonate over the marsh. Since Pied-bills almost invariably nest in dense stands of rushes and reeds, these far-reaching vocalizations are important in maintaining contact between mates and in territorial defense.

Pied-bills will settle on any pond or lake regardless of size, provided there is abundant nesting cover. But their cousins, the Horned Grebes, *Podiceps auritus,* show a preference for sloughs and potholes in the range of one hectare. This species, the most abundant in the West, is generally tame and, in the brilliance of its breeding plumage, conspicuous. As in most diving birds, the colorful markings are concentrated on the neck and head, where they can be prominently displayed during territorial and mating rituals. Unlike the Pied-bills, whose thick-growing habitat offers neither visibility nor space for elaborate behaviors, Horned Grebes require an area of open water on which to enact their stereotyped ceremonies. One example is the "discovery ceremony," which is performed near the nest when a pair is reunited after a temporary separation. It usually begins with a display known as "advertising" (an upright posture associated with a particular call) and proceeds through an invariable sequence of special "bouncy" dives; spread-winged "cat" postures; upright, face-to-face "penguin dances"; and ritualized preening. At every stage, subtle differences in the position of the body and feathers are crucial: the bill may be horizontal, vertical, or intermedi-ate; the "horns" may be partly spread, flared, or compressed; and so on. To add to the complexity, there are two distinct roles in this pas de deux, one for the bird that initiates the behavior and one for its mate. Both roles can be taken by either sex.

Interestingly, there is another species, the Eared Grebe, *Podiceps nigricollis,* that is present through much of the Horned Grebe's range, looks very much like it, and has a similar "discovery ceremony." Yet the rituals are not identical, and it may be that the differences—how widely the wings are spread in the cat display, for example—help the birds to avoid "mixed marriages." The two species are also kept apart by their habitat preferences, since Eared Grebes usually nest on large, open ponds. Horned Grebes generally do not thrive in this environment, because they are highly territorial: the first arrival claims the most sheltered nesting site, and latecomers end up in exposed positions where their nests are likely to be destroyed by wind and waves. Eared Grebes, in contrast, are gregarious and breed in colonies of up to five thousand birds, so that many pairs can share the best nesting location. Sometimes they're packed in so tightly that nests touch each other, with each pair defending only its own boggy pile, a situation that would be intolerable to Horned Grebes. Obviously, behavior, as much as anatomy and physiology, is molded by natural selection as a species adapts to its niche.

16

Order Procellariiformes

Storm–Petrels

Leach's Storm-Petrel

Many a fisherman, in the heel and yaw of a storm-driven sea, has suddenly noticed a flock of dark-colored birds flitting daintily among the heaving waves. Tiny creatures, smaller than robins, they hover and glide amongst the crests, now rising, now turning, now skimming the water, as sure and light as butterflies in a field of flowers. And the fisherman pales, for here are "Mother Carey's Chickens," come to carry off the souls of drowning mariners.

These dreaded apparitions are really inoffensive storm-petrels, the smallest oceanic birds and members of the order Procellariiformes, or Tubenoses, a group that also includes the seafarers par excellence among living birds: albatrosses, fulmars, and shearwaters. They take their collective name from the peculiar form of their nostrils, which really are enclosed in tubes on the tops of their beaks. The function of this structure is not totally clear, though it may be an olfactory organ and certainly plays a role in salt excretion. Since Tubenoses spend almost their whole lives at sea, coming ashore only to breed, they seldom or never get fresh water to drink. But this poses no problem thanks to two large glands near the base of the bill, which extract salt from the bloodstream and excrete it through the tubular nostrils.

There are about ninety species of Tubenoses in the world, but only a few of them occur along our shores. Of this handful, the best known are three species of "Carey's Chicks": Wilson's Storm-Petrel, a southern-hemisphere species that spends its winter (our summer) in the North Atlantic; the Fork-tailed Storm-Petrel, a little-studied bird that breeds off British Columbia; and Leach's Storm-Petrel, which nests on our east and west coasts. As a group, they can immediately be recognized by their erratic, batlike flight, low over the sea. Some species dangle their feet onto the

surface as they feed, giving the impression that they are walking on water. Hence, the name "petrel," or "Little Peter," for the saint who is said to have walked the waves.

Their exceptional skill in flight no doubt contributed to the legend that storm-petrels incubate their eggs in midair, by carrying them underwing. As it turns out, the facts are scarcely less strange. In the case of Leach's Storm-Petrel, *Oceanodroma leucorhoa,* for example, the birds breed on remote, offshore islets, where they congregate in large colonies—from a few hundred to more than one million birds. In suitable terrain, there may be two or three nests for every square meter of ground. Yet if you were to visit one of these avian cities by day, you might never suspect that the birds were there. From before dawn till after dark, they are in one of two places, either far out to sea, where they forage for zooplankton and small fish, or underground. Unlike Fork-tailed Storm-Petrels, which often nest in natural crevices, Leach's Storm-Petrels lay their eggs in burrows that they dig or renovate each spring. Most of this labor falls to the male of the pair. With pick and shovel (beak and feet), he hollows out a tunnel that may reach two meters in length but is usually a third of that or less. Here, in a chamber at the end of the burrow, the female deposits her single egg, safe from the glare of gulls.

Among Leach's Storm-Petrels, eggs are usually laid in June and July. Incubation is extraordinarily long—six or seven weeks—and is shared equally, each parent serving a three- or four-day shift before taking to the sea to feed. (Since their feeding grounds are distant from the colony—often a hundred kilometers or more—the adults have to commute between their food supply and their chick.) The shift-change at the nest always occurs under cover of darkness. Indeed, prime time for birdwatch-

In this rare photograph you can tell at a glance that the Leach's Storm-Petrel is one of the Tubenoses, an order of birds whose acute olfactory sense helps them navigate at sea.

ing in a storm-petrel colony is about two hours after sunset on a foggy or overcast night. It is then the birds are most active, flying over the colony in ritualized pursuit and going to and from their nests. There is a crooning "churr" from thousands of underground nests, a tumult of staccato flight calls, and the occasional thump of small bodies colliding in the dark.

The exact means by which storm-petrels find their nests is still unclear. In this hubbub, in the pitch dark, how do they zero in on one small den among so many, particularly since the entrances are tucked away inconspicuously under grass, stumps, rocks, and shrubs? Some researchers have suggested that storm-petrels might have sonar, like bats and certain cave-nesting birds, but there is no evidence for this. Others postulate that incoming birds orient themselves by exchanging calls with their mates, waiting underground, and this may well occur, though it has not been conclusively shown. But we do know that storm-petrels rely to a considerable extent on their sense of smell,

a sense so acute that some experts think a homing bird may follow the scent of its colony over tens or hundreds of kilometers. Once home, a Leach's Storm-Petrel will hover in the general vicinity of its nest, then circuit and hover again, until it has pinpointed the source of its own domestic odors. Down it plunges, perhaps landing slightly off target and stumbling toward its hole, tripping over obstacles that its nose can't detect.

The scents by which storm-petrels navigate derive from their "stomach oil," a clear, waxy liquid, orange-colored in the case of Leach's Storm-Petrels, with a strong, rancid smell. One function of this substance, which is produced by all the Tubenoses, is self-defense. When harassed, whether by predator or bird-bander, the bird vomits the reeking oil onto its enemy, sometimes causing temporary blindness. One species, the Giant Fulmar, also known as "the Stinker," can hit its victim from several meters away.

Stomach oil is also important in the nutrition of the young. Rich in vitamins A and D, as well as in fat, it is the first food of a hatchling Leach's Storm-Petrel. On an irregular schedule of no more than one or two feedings a night, the youngster grows plump and round, increasing its weight sixteenfold in about five weeks. At that point, it far outweighs its parents and is therefore able to survive the next three or four weeks of its infancy, during which it is seldom fed. (Food supplies at sea decline late in the season.) Reduced to normal adult dimensions, it emerges from its burrow in October or November, exercises its wings on four or five successive nights, and flies out to sea. Already expert on its first flight, it is also innately able to locate the tropical waters on which its species spends the wintertime.

Once out of the nest, young Leach's Storm-Petrels may stay at sea for a year or more before returning to land for a few months of "sweethearting." Still immature, the birds arrive late in the breeding season, participate in aerial displays, dig burrows and even occupy them for a while, but never produce an egg. They don't actually breed until they reach the age of four or five, but once mated, they usually return to the same burrows and the same partners year after year. The oldest known Leach's Storm-Petrel was still breeding at the age of twenty-four. Such long life spans are common among marine birds, an indication that the ocean, for all its violent moods and unmarked distances, is a gentle protector of species that are adapted to its ways.

Gannets, Pelicans, and Cormorants

Wherever you go in the temperate and tropical zones of the world, you can expect to encounter members of this order. There are about fifty-five species in all—large, fish-eating birds such as boobies, gannets, pelicans, cormorants, and anhingas. One interesting feature that they share is the expandable throat pouch, an adaptation that reaches its most spectacular development in the pelicans. Members of the group are also renowned for the size of their breeding colonies: the Northern Gannet rookery at Bonaventure Island, Gulf of Saint Lawrence, is one world-famous example. But the characteristic that seems to be of most interest to taxonomists is the webbing of their feet, since all four toes are connected, instead of the usual three. This explains why they are sometimes called "totipalmate swimmers." Some members of the group use their large webs as heating pads during incubation, warming their eggs by covering them with their feet.

Northern Gannet

After two centuries of trying, biologists still haven't been able to agree on a scientific name for the Northern Gannet. Some experts favor *Morus bassanus,* according to a classification that assigns the birds to a genus of their own, while others prefer *Sula bassana,* thereby grouping them with their warm-water cousins, the boobies. But the ultimate resolution of this and other taxonomic difficulties need scarcely concern us. If we require an unpronounceable name for the species, we might better reach back to Celtic for the lovely and descriptive phrase *Ian Ban an Sgadan*—"white bird of the herring."

Superficially, Northern Gannets resemble gulls, but they can be distinguished by their size (up to a meter in length), their body contours ("pointed at both ends"), and their dazzling plumage. Their whiter-than-white coloration probably serves two functions: it is inconspicuous when seen from below (light against a light background), as a fish would see it; and highly conspicuous when viewed from other angles, making it easy for one gannet to locate another that has found a good place to feed.

The gannet's method of catching prey is nothing short of spectacular. Cruising as much as forty meters above the sea, a bird detects the glint of schooling fish—herring, mackerel, capelin. In an instant it pivots, head downward, wings closed or trailing, and plunges toward the sea, entering the water cleanly but with considerable force. The entry may occur at a hundred kilometers an hour, yet the bird is not injured, thanks to its streamlined shape, reinforced skull, and the cushion of air sacs in its neck and breast. Once underwater, it sweeps downward for a few meters, turns and grasps its prey from below, swallows it whole, and resurfaces, ready to mount for another attack. Add to this simultaneous dives by all the other gannets that have flocked in, and you will have an image of a typical feeding scene—a contin-

Northern Gannet

uous rain of projectiles shooting into the sea.

Because of the position of their legs, gannets waddle awkwardly on land and find it difficult to take off. Accordingly, they usually breed on sea cliffs from which they can leap into the air. Sometimes the ramparts are so sheer and the ledges so slight that the nests—heaps of seaweed and other debris—would tumble into the surf if they weren't held in place by the birds' excrement. For safety from mammalian predators, the birds generally avoid mainland breeding sites in favor of offshore islands and islets. The total North American gannet popu-

lation stands at over 30,000 pairs, a third of which nest along the southeast coast of Newfoundland, at Funk Island, Bacclieu Island, and Cape Saint Mary's. The remainder breed at three colonies in the Gulf of Saint Lawrence: Bonaventure Island (currently the largest gannetry in the western Atlantic), Gullcliff Bay on Anticosti Island, and the Bird Rocks. The last mentioned was once by far the most populous colony in the world, with over 200,000 birds, until a rapacious slaughter by fishermen in the nineteenth century and disturbance associated with the construction of a lighthouse reduced

The rocks of Cape Saint Mary's, Newfoundland, form an ideal nesting site for Northern Gannets—isolated, sea-washed, and sheer.

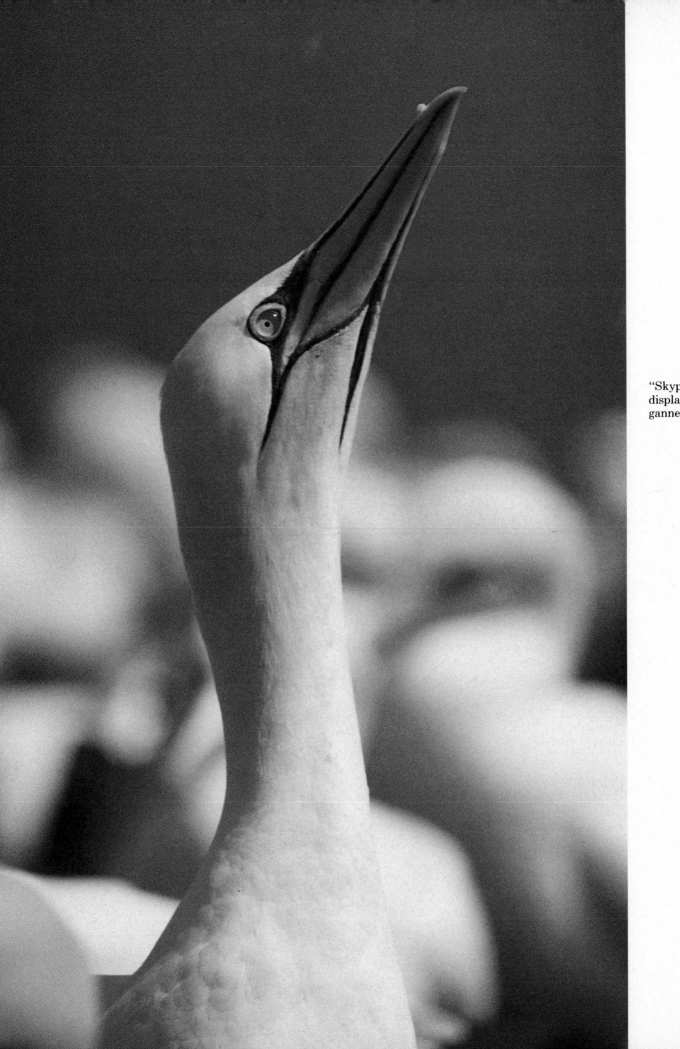

"Skypointing" is one of the displays commonly seen at a gannet colony.

the count to a few hundred pairs. Today, the colony consists of about 5,400 pairs.

When not molested, gannets return year after year to their traditional sites, some of which have probably been occupied for millennia. Above these wave-bashed fortresses, incoming birds circle in revolving flocks, while their mates blanket the rocks in drifts of white. Picturesque, yes, but not as peaceful as this description implies. A gannetry has the atmosphere of an armed camp, with each pair intent on defending its square meter of nesting territory against its neighbors. Repeatedly, tirelessly, from March to October, the birds perform the ritualized bows that proclaim their tenancy and their hostile intentions toward trespassers. Fierce battles are also common, particularly amongst the males, who will sometimes struggle for two hours at a time, until both parties are wounded, caked with mud and dung, and totally worn out.

The aggressive personality that is necessary for territorial defense also finds expression in mate relationships. For example, the male often greets his spouse at the nest by chomping on her neck; he does this the first time they meet and is still doing it when they've nested together for a decade. (Gannets typically live for around sixteen years and only infrequently change nest sites or mates.) Even in the most intimate moments of their pair-maintenance display, there is a raucous muscularity about their interactions, as the birds rear up, chest to chest, and clash bills. This "mutual fencing" is one of the major sources of noise and activity at a gannetry. The birds' other conspicuous display, aptly known as "sky-pointing," also occurs between mates at the nest and probably signals that the displaying partner is about to leave. This helps ensure that both birds don't take off at once: site, nest, egg, and young must be constantly guarded against raids by other gannets.

If there are difficulties associated with living in such dense colonies, there are also advantages. One of these seems to be social stimulation—the sight and sound of bowing, "fencing," and other displays. This advances the birds' hormonal cycles and causes them to breed earlier in the season than they would otherwise, so that more young survive.

Each breeding female produces only one egg a year, which is laid sometime in May or June and incubated by both parents over the next six weeks. The youngster must then be tended and fed for another three months before it embarks on its first, wobbly flight to the sea. So fat that it can't ascend again after landing, it paddles southward for a week or so before managing to get airborne. Its ultimate destination is along the southeastern coast of the United States, where it will remain for a year or two, without touching land the entire time. Supposing that it survives its first year (only one chance in four), it will likely live to breed at the age of five or six, often returning to the same part of the same colony in which it hatched. Mortality rates among adult birds are low, with humans and human garbage—fishing gear, bunker oil, and toxic chemicals—among the most significant causes of death. In recent years, for example, there has been a downward trend in the population and breeding success at the Bonaventure Island colony, which is thought to be the result of human disturbance and pesticide poisoning.

American White Pelican

It's a breathtaking sight: a V of White Pelicans, *Pelecanus erythrorhynchos,* brilliant against the blue of a prairie sky. At adult weights of five to eight kilograms, these are amongst the largest wild birds in the world today. Yet they cruise through the air with buoyancy and ease, borne up on wings that span two and a half meters or more; slow, stately wingbeats alternate with effortless glides.

But if White Pelicans are impressive, they are also somewhat ludicrous. The body seems too heavy for the legs, the bill too long for the head. And oddest of all is the naked, jowl-like pouch that hangs from the bottom jaw. This useful appendage, which turns bright salmon-orange during the breeding season, plays a part in courtship and other social displays. A "heads up" pose, with the bill pointed skyward and the pouch puffed out, apparently functions as a pelican "hello." Under other circumstances, the pouch acts as a cooling organ, operating on the same principle as a dog's wet tongue. When too warm, an American White Pelican sets its pouch to fluttering, so that air moves quickly over its moist surfaces, and heat is lost through evaporation.

The pouch's primary function, of course, is as a dip net. Although White Pelicans have a taste for salamanders, they usually subsist almost entirely on slow-moving fish, taking whatever species are most plentiful. Unlike their southerly cousins, the Brown Pelicans, which plummet into the sea in their quest for food, White Pelicans simply dart their heads under the surface, coming up with scoopfuls of water and fish. The expandable pouch, with its twelve-liter capacity, is capable of holding one or more wriggling prey, including fish half a meter long, but only if the bill is held pointing down. As soon as the head flips up, the fish slides down, and—gulp—dinner is served, headfirst. While it is probably true that the bill will hold more than the "belican," the pouch is not designed for storing or carrying provisions.

Instead, food is packed into the stomach and throat, which are stretchy as well, so that a bird can literally stuff itself right up to the mouth. Overindulgence makes it very difficult to get off the ground, and pelicans sometimes have to throw back part of their catch before freighting home.

White Pelicans seem to have their greatest fishing success when working cooperatively. A flock that happens to swim near a school of fish immediately encloses its prey, forming either a circle or a semicircle facing shore. Advancing in unison, sometimes beating the water with wings and feet, they herd the fish inside an ever-diminishing corral. Then, as if on signal, all begin to feed in a tumult of quick-moving pouches and bills. Although individuals can and do catch fish on their own, food-getting among White Pelicans is usually a communal activity.

In general, American White Pelicans are a gregarious lot, with a sheeplike tendency to imitate and follow one another. This has its benefits: a bird that finds a thermal of upwelling air, suitable for soaring, quickly attracts the attention of other traveling birds, and soon all of them join in an upward spiral, gradually fading to specks and disappearing in the heights. At lower altitudes, they usually fly in formation, with the rhythm of flapping and gliding set by the lead bird. Sometimes the change occurs in near unison; sometimes it passes down the line in precise succession, each bird taking its cue from the one just ahead. No doubt this harmonious behavior serves some prosaic end, such as maximizing lift and minimizing resistance.

The birds' sociability is particularly obvious at their nesting colonies, the largest of which, at Primrose Lake in Saskatchewan, had sixty-eight hundred nests in 1982. White Pelicans always nest on islands and almost always well out in lakes, where they are safe from predatory mammals and as safe as possible from

American White Pelican

human disturbances. Well-established colonies can often be spotted from a considerable distance, even when unoccupied, because the ground is paved with droppings and the trees are stunted or dead. Closer up, the stench of excrement, dead young, and rotting fish is another giveaway. The nests themselves are often obvious as well—masses of soil, twigs, stones, dung, and the like, scraped up on the site, that sometimes reach a meter in width and thirty centimeters in height. Typically, they are just far enough apart so that neighboring birds can't get at each other, but even when they're crowded, there is generally little strife among incubating birds.

The same cannot be said, however, for siblings in the nest. The usual clutch among American White Pelicans is two eggs, laid in May and incubated by both parents over the next month. Of the nestlings, only one, the larger and first-hatched, has much chance to survive. Not only does it demand and get a lion's share of the food, but it also jabs its beak into its nest mate until the smaller bird is bleeding and bruised. This abuse begins before the nestlings can crawl and usually ends in the death of the underling. The parents sometimes

play a part in their offspring's demise, for if they find it out of the nest, seeking respite from attack, they are likely to toss it aside, apparently unable to recognize it as their own. This, from the bird that was once considered an emblem of Christlike charity, credited with feeding its young on the blood of its own breast.

Aside from the murderous conflict that goes on in the nest, relationships among young pelicans are generally cordial. As soon as they can wriggle from the nest, youngsters begin to form bands, or pods, though they still return to the nest at night to be brooded. By the age of one month, flightless but half-grown, they spend almost all their time in the company of their peers, seeing their parents only for feedings. Then, what pandemonium! An approaching adult is often accosted by a hungry mob, who mill around, peck at its feet, reach for its bill, even climb up its body in their eagerness. One or more of them may appear to go berserk, flinging themselves on the ground, flapping wildly, and waving their heads back and forth. Or they may twirl round and round, growling and biting their wings, as if in an agony of starvation. The chick that throws

American White Pelicans are remarkable for their cooperative feeding strategies. Acting in concert, a flock will form a circle around a school of fish; herd their prey into the center; then attack all at once.

Facing page: Capacious, elastic, and versatile, the pelican's pouch serves many functions, including that of lunch bucket for the young.

itself most violently into this display is usually the adult's own offspring, which is the only one that ultimately gets fed. All the other supplicants are driven off with a few strategic passes of the parent's bill.

When newly hatched, a baby pelican feeds weakly from the tip of its parent's bill but not so an older juvenile, which reaches boldly inside the parent's mouth, down the throat, and into the stomach. With its body partly supported on the adult's pouch, it half disappears for two or three minutes at a time to rummage in a paradise of semi-digested fish. When the adult tires of having its innards probed, it tries to leave, but the youngster often refuses to withdraw until it is vigorously shaken out. Sometimes another tantrum of begging follows this expulsion, but usually the young bird settles down on the spot, too heavy with food to move.

In the nine or ten weeks between hatching and first flight, a growing White Pelican devours about seventy kilograms of fish. An older juvenile or an adult consumes nearly two kilograms a day, so a colony of five thousand birds needs around fifteen hundred tonnes of fish to get it through the breeding season (from April to September). These facts have not been overlooked by fisheries interests, who for many years waged an undeclared but nonetheless brutally effective war against their alleged competitors. Well-documented reports that White Pelicans seldom eat species of value to humans apparently did little to restrain the hostilities. Only since 1972, as reports of declining populations have become ever more urgent, has it been illegal to shoot pelicans in Canada and the United States.

Even people who feel no malice toward the birds can cause them great harm, simply by their presence at a colony. White Pelicans are easily induced to desert their nests en masse, leaving hundreds—perhaps thousands—of eggs and young exposed to gulls or to lethal extremes of temperature. Repeated harassment causes the flock to leave permanently. At least twenty-six colonies of American White Pelicans have become extinct in Canada during this century, largely, if not exclusively, because of human disturbances of one sort or another. In contrast to the United States, where most of the pelicans' breeding grounds have been designated as wildlife refuges, Canada has been bewilderingly slow to protect its surviving colonies. New initiatives are being taken by the World Wildlife Fund and others, with encouraging results, but in many cases the regulations are still inadequate.

Strong, buoyant flyers, American White Pelicans can be recognized in the air by their black wing tips and their habit of holding the head back, over the shoulders.

Double-crested Cormorant

Cormorants, or "sea crows," are large diving birds found almost the world around. In the air, they are sometimes mistaken for geese, since both fly with their long, slender necks outstretched. But flocks of geese generally form precise V's and announce their coming with a fanfare of honks. Cormorants, on the other hand, travel in ragged formation or disorganized groups, silent except for the whistling rush of their wings. The iridescent jet of their feathers, their bowling-pin-like shape, and their habit of standing upright when perched are other useful clues. So is the naked patch on the throat, a version, in miniature, of the pelican's famous pouch. The color of this sac, blue, red, or orange, is the key to distinguishing the three species that occur along the Pacific coast (south of Alaska): Brandt's, Pelagic, and Double-crested cormorants, respectively. Unfortunately, this system is less helpful on the east coast, where Great and Double-crested cormorants occur, since both have yellow or orangish pouches. Despite subtle differences in size and coloration, these two confuse even the experts when seen at a distance.

Away from the coasts, identification poses no difficulties, since only one species is present,

Double-crested Cormorant

the widely distributed Double-crested Cormorant, *Phalacrocorax auritus*. A year-round resident on the west coast and in the Atlantic states, it is migratory through most of its breeding range, wintering on southerly coasts in the United States and returning to its rookeries by late April of each year.

The Double-crested Cormorant's first requirement on its breeding grounds is access to food, principally small fish. (Almost any prey species will do, so long as it moves slowly enough to be caught by direct pursuit and occurs at depths of ten meters or less.) An equally important consideration is safety from attack by mammalian predators, including humans. The more remote, precipitous, and storm-lashed a spot, the better the cormorants like it. Accordingly, they choose inaccessible islands, reefs, and cliffs, sometimes nesting in trees but usually on the ground. Here they congregate in close-packed colonies of up to five thousand pairs, often in company with herons, pelicans, or other species of cormorants. More surprisingly but no less frequently, they also share their nesting grounds with large numbers of gulls, allowing these egg-robbers and baby-snatchers to roam unmolested through the colony. It may be that the gulls earn their keep, from the cormorants' point of view, by scaring away other predators, particularly crows. Or, more likely, it may be that neither gulls nor other avian predators are

Double-crested Cormorants are often strangely unconcerned by the presence of gulls around their nesting colonies.

Awkward and somewhat reptilian in appearance, these Double-crested Cormorants remind one of the antiquity of birds. The cormorant on the right is drying its feathers, which are not completely waterproof in this species.

of much concern to the cormorants, which keep their nests under close guard unless distracted by human visitors.

Double-crested Cormorants mount their nest-watch very early in the breeding season, well before any eggs have been laid. Why this vigilance, at a time when the birds have nothing to fear from predators? The answer is that nesting materials—sticks, seaweed, mummified gull remains, and the like—are highly prized by Doubled-crested Cormorants, and thefts are commonplace. One of the very few fights ever observed between two members of this peaceable species broke out over a contested cowparsnip stalk! If a nest is left unattended for any length of time, the neighbors call around and help themselves to anything they fancy, not even hesitating to toss out the eggs if they get in the way. Nests built in previous seasons and not reclaimed in the spring serve as building-supply depots for the colony, so the nest count may go down rather than up as the season proceeds.

Finished nests vary greatly in size and durability. A new nest, the product of one pair and one nesting season, is typically a flimsy affair, no more than a few centimeters high; but a nest that has been occupied and refurbished for a number of years is substantial, perhaps half a meter in both width and height. Sometimes, nests are so close together they touch and support each other; in addition, they are reinforced by a generous layer of cormorant dung on their outside surfaces. In one instance, a large and well-cemented nest came unmoored during a blow and sailed to the opposite shore without losing a stick.

Excrement is a conspicuous feature of a Double-crested Cormorant colony. While the insides of the nests are seldom fouled, the surrounding ground may be covered half a meter deep. There are flies, rotting fish, and a stench that is better imagined than experienced firsthand. But before giving way to spasms of disgust, we might note that cormorant droppings are rich in nutrients, so rich that they burn off all the vegetation at the rookery. In Peru and elsewhere, guano deposited by cormorants is harvested for use as fertilizer.

Like many birds, Double-crested Cormorants seem to have little or no sense of smell, so it probably suits them perfectly to raise their families in these conditions. Incubation of the clutch (usually two to four eggs) begins any time from mid-May to mid-July and is shared by both parents, who seem as dedicated to each other as they are to their eggs. A routine changeover at the nest is often accompanied by what appear to be passionate demonstrations of affection, with much croaking, caressing, bill-rubbing, and amorous snaking of necks. Usually, after being relieved from incubation duties, the male commemorates the occasion by bringing in fresh, nesting materials, which are delivered and accepted with ceremonial bows.

After about twenty-eight days of round-the-clock care, the young pick their way out of the shell. Naked, blind, and too feeble to lift their heads, they are fed on a diet of half-digested fish, which is dribbled into their mouths with great gentleness. The stronger they get, however, the rowdier mealtime becomes. Chicks of three weeks or so often spot the returning parent before it reaches the nest and urge it home with quavering cries and outstretched, weaving necks. As soon as the adult is within reach, they crowd around, waving their heads in its face, and tapping it insistently with their bills. The adult sometimes appears overwhelmed by these frantic appeals but eventually opens its mouth and lets the youngsters cram their heads inside, one at a time. The rule is "gobble your share and hang on tight," lest hungry brothers and sisters pull you out.

Between feedings, the nestlings usually sleep, preen, and exercise their wings, but sometimes they seem to tire of this uneventful life. As a diversion, they may snap playfully at passing insects or pull twigs out of the nest and pass them from bill to bill. Since playfulness often correlates with intelligence, this behavior suggests that Double-crested Cormorants may be fairly clever birds. So does the one recorded instance of tool use, in which an adult cormorant held a feather in its bill and used it as a brush to spread preen oil on its wings. In the Orient, where cormorants, fitted with collars to prevent them from swallowing, were taught to bring in fish for human use, trainers noticed a marked difference in individual ability, with some birds catching on quickly and others headed straight for the soup pot.

Yes, the soup pot. Not only have both the flesh and eggs of Double-crested Cormorants been collected for human food, the meat was once prescribed as a cure for the "Bloody Flux," whatever that was. More significantly, the birds have also been killed because of their alleged competition with commercial fisheries, though all the available data suggests that the charge is rarely true. This persecution, together with the effects of drought in the 1930s, other habitat losses, and human disturbance at rookeries, led to the disappearance of the species over most of its range. In 1972, when the National Audubon Society first published its catalogue of threatened species, the Double-crested Cormorant made the list, as it did consistently for the next eight years. Recently, however, there seems to have been a steadying of the population in most parts of its breeding range, together with heartening increases in many localities. Major declines continue to occur along the Gulf of Saint Lawrence.

Bitterns and Herons

Although the title of this chapter mentions only bitterns and herons, the order Ciconiiformes actually includes an intriguing diversity of species—over a hundred in all—among them storks and spoonbills. In general, they are long-legged, long-necked wading birds, adapted to life in marshes and shallow water, where they make their living by catching fish and other aquatic animals. Twelve members of the order have been known to occur in Canada and the neighboring states, including one—the Cattle Egret—that is native to Africa. This species became established in South America in the 1930s, and has subsequently spread north through the United States to southern Canada; in 1981, it was found nesting at Old Wives Lake, Saskatchewan. The most familiar species, however, are all native-born: Green-backed and Great Blue herons; the Black-crowned Night Heron; and Least and American bitterns. All are members of the family Ardeidae, a group that is characterized, amongst other things, by the development of their "powder-downs." These are a peculiar type of feather that grows continuously from the base and frays continuously at the tip, providing a supply of powder for cleansing the plumage. Although powder-downs are present in certain other birds, they reach their maximum development in bitterns and herons, which also have serrated nails on their middle toes for combing the powder out.

American Bittern

The scene: a reedy patch of wetlands, sometime in May. There's a heart-stopping rush of wings, a series of nasal croaks, and a stocky bird flushes just in front of you, its long legs dangling as it labors into flight. At your feet, on a matted platform of dry marsh plants, lie from two to six eggs, buffy brown in color to match the nest. All is still again, and the adult bird is nowhere to be seen. But chances are that she's nearby, watching surreptitiously from a hiding place in the reeds. In fact, she's probably pretending to be a reed, with her body drawn up long and thin, and her spiky beak aimed at the sky. The streaks on her belly—black, brown, and white—mimic the patterns of light and shadow in the reed bed, and she keeps them turned toward the intruder. If the intruder moves, she pivots; if the wind blows, she sways, keeping time with the plants that surround her. The illusion is impeccable.

This master of concealment is an American Bittern, *Botaurus lentiginosus,* also known as the "look-up" or "sky-gazer." The species breeds in salt and freshwater marshes or, occasionally, in dry meadows, its minimum requirement being a stand of dense vegetation in which to hide the nest. The birds also value solitude and seldom settle in a marsh that already has a resident pair. On their wintering grounds (from southwestern British Columbia to California and across the southern United States), their habitat requirements are much the same—wetlands, with good cover—because their diet and hunting strategies are similar year-round. Bitterns are basically carnivores, subsisting on frogs, fish, crustaceans, and the like. When stalking prey, a bird advances in slow-motion, calculating each footfall with lizardlike deliberation and then darts out its rapier-sharp bill to make the catch.

American Bittern

An American Bittern adopts
its concealment pose, a
behavior so characteristic of
the species that it is called
"bitterning."

Stealth and secrecy are the keys to the American Bittern's character. But there are times when an individual must make its presence known to other members of its species, without revealing its exact location to predators. This accounts for the ventriloquistic "pumping" of the males, those peculiar, gulping sounds that are thought to warn off rival males and attract potential mates. Variously translated into English as "pump-er-lunk," "dunk-a-doo," "oongkiloong," and "plum puddn'n," the calls are usually likened to the sound of an old-fashioned wooden pump or to the squelch of someone hammering stakes into the mud. To account for the hollow, far-away quality of the sound, naturalists used to suggest that the males stuck their heads underground or inside a reed. But we now know that they merely draw air into the esophagus, which becomes thickened during the breeding season to withstand the strain. The throat bulges and the head and neck convulse violently when sounds are produced, as if the bird were wretching or choking to death.

These calls have earned the birds another cluster of nicknames: stake-driver, thunder-pumper, barrel-maker, mire drum, and water belcher. Although the sounds may be heard at any time of the day, they are most common at dawn and dusk, when bitterns are generally most active. The pumping season extends from early spring well into the summer, for the male maintains a fence of sound around his territory during the entire period when the female tends the young.

Among American Bitterns, all parental responsibilities are left to the female. Not only does she locate and build the family home, but she also clears two paths, an entrance, and an exit, using her body weight to bend the stalks and her bill to break them off. These walkways allow her to land and take off at some distance from home and then steal silently along the ground, so she won't expose her nest site with a clatter of rushes or the heavy flapping of her wings. After incubating the eggs for about a month, the female feeds her young in the nest for two weeks and for an unknown length of

Three to five young is a typical brood for American Bitterns.

time after they leave home. At first, she produces half-digested offerings for her chicks, some of which prove too large; these she obligingly swallows and coughs up again, when she senses they might be "done."

There is considerable variation in the tenacity with which mother bitterns guard their nests. One female can easily be flushed, while another stands her ground and menaces intruders with her bill. Not only can this weapon leave nasty stab wounds in a person, a jab in the snout will sometimes repel other meddlesome animals. Nor are the nestlings defenseless. Even before they can fly, they will attack humans or adopt the upright "bitterning" pose that characterizes their kind.

Great Blue Heron

Great Blue Heron

A heron, erect and motionless in the shallows, puts one in mind of an Oriental painting, a pastel form against a wash of water and sky. Indeed, the stately elegance of this family of birds has long been a source of inspiration to humankind. As far back as the tenth century A.D., the Japanese accorded an honorary peerage to the Black-crowned Night Heron (a species that also occurs in Canada and the United States), in grateful recognition of the bird's grace and docility.

In this country, the best-known and most widely distributed member of the heron family is the Great Blue Heron, *Ardea herodias*. A conspicuous bird, measuring a meter or more in height and about two meters in wingspan, it can be identified simply on the basis of its color and size. The only species that might possibly cause confusion is the Sandhill Crane (Great Blues are popularly known as "Blue Cranes" in some parts of the country), but a crane flies with its neck outstretched, while a heron usually travels with its neck folded back in an S and resting on its shoulders.

Within its range, the Great Blue Heron can be found near shorelines and shallows on both salt and fresh water. At northern latitudes, the birds are generally present from April to October, though they linger into winter in the Maritimes and remain year-round in southwestern British Columbia. During the breeding season, the adults, together with some juveniles (birds under two years of age), congregate at nesting colonies, or heronries, each of which typically accommodates two or three dozen pairs. Although the birds are occasionally willing to nest in shrubbery or on heaps of rushes, they prefer the safety of tree tops—twenty, thirty, even forty meters above ground. The nests themselves are unkempt piles of sticks, flimsy in their first year but becoming sturdier and more massive with each year of reuse, until they're a meter or more across. Usually, they are built one to a tree, but not always: a huge spruce in Vancouver's Stanley Park, to cite one extreme example, once supported thirty-nine bristling nests.

Although males and females apparently arrive at the colony at about the same time in the spring, the nest site is chosen by the male. He is immediately faced with two somewhat contradictory challenges: to keep all other herons off his nest and, simultaneously, to persuade a female to share it with him. His first step is to make his presence known, and this he does through a "sign language" of displays. Standing on his nest site, he repeatedly lowers his head and clacks his heavy beak. Or he draws himself up to his full height, with his bill pointed high; then relaxes and goes through the performance again. This apparently conveys the message that he is available to mate and won't attack. But when a female responds to this invitation by approaching the nest, the male is overcome by territorial possessiveness and drives her away. If she's sufficiently impressed by what she's seen of him, she will persist in her approaches, giving him a chance to get used to her. Ultimately, they may reject one another in favor of other possibilities, or they may decide to take one another as mates, on a trial basis, at least.

The first hours of mated life are nerve-wracking for both parties. The female does her best to avoid confrontations with the male by

Patience and stealth are basic to the Great Blue Heron's hunting strategy. This bird waits and watches in the shallows.

Seen here in silhouette, Great Blue Herons tend their eggs and young in an apartment-style rookery. Young are brooded for the first week after they hatch and are guarded around the clock for another two weeks.

When close enough to attack, a Great Blue Heron grabs its prey with a swift and energetic jab.

averting her eyes and keeping her crest sleeked. Should she be so bold as to raise her head, her mate strikes at her with his beak; but the female is on the lookout for attacks and invariably recoils in time to avoid contact. A bout of this ritualized dueling often continues until the female manages to catch her mate's bill in her own and calm him with a "kiss." Such behavior is important because it permits the male to work out his hostilities, at the same time as the female overcomes her tendency to flee. In fairly short order, the pair come to an understanding and are able to get on with nest-building and incubation, tasks they will share over the next four or five weeks.

The aggressive impulses of Great Blue Herons are almost always expressed through ritual. This is not surprising, considering the harm they could do one another if their powers were unleashed: a heron has been known to ram its bill through a solid pine oar. More typically, of course, the bill is employed in the peaceful pursuit of catching fish, the birds' staple food. Great Blues usually take their prey through stealth, either by standing in wait or by inching along with great caution until something edible appears. Then, zap, the neck uncoils with lightning speed and the prey is stabbed or, more commonly, grabbed between the mandibles.

These techniques form the birds' standard food-getting repertoire, no matter where or what they are hunting. But more complex aspects of their behavior—specifically, their social relationships—vary considerably de-

pending on their source of food. When prey can reliably be found in particular locations (voles along a roadside ditch, for example), the birds are solitary, each defending its favorite feeding grounds against all rivals; but when prey is patchy and constantly shifting (minnows in a lake), the herons seem to rely on one another's help in getting enough to eat. While they don't actively cooperate on the hunt, they do take advantage of one another's good luck in foraging. If a hungry bird sees other herons feeding, it rushes over to get in on the feast.

Some researchers believe that this kind of information sharing goes on around heronries and constitutes the primary benefit of colonial nesting in this species: by congregating, the birds probably reduce the risk that any of their number will go without food. This insurance becomes particularly crucial at hatchtime, in late May or early June, when each pair suddenly acquires four or five ravenous young mouths to feed. But in spite of the benefits of communal foraging, only two or three of these nestlings will likely survive to first flight: some starve, while others are killed by storms and by predators such as gulls, crows, and raccoons. The death rate continues high throughout the first year—almost seventy-five percent—in part because juvenile herons are unskilled hunters. Among adults, mortality is much lower, and one hardy individual is known to have lived for twenty-one years. Although victimized by axes, bulldozers, and guns, the birds have proven themselves remarkably resistant to the effects of civilization.

Swans, Geese, and Ducks

Few groups of birds are better known than the waterfowl, yet few are more subject to misconceptions. For example, many of us assume that all birds that look like ducks, be they loons, grebes, or coots, must be ducks or, at least, near relatives. But the fossil record is clear on this point: the connection between waterfowl and other water birds is extremely distant. Judging from their behavior, anatomy, and physiology, the group's closest kin are the screamers, a family of wading birds from South America, which look more like chickens than waterfowl. Taxonomists are so sure of this relationship that they classify screamers and waterfowl as the sole members of the order Anseriformes.

Within the order, waterfowl are placed in their own family, the Anatidae. Membership requirements for this group include a long neck, relatively short legs, and webbed feet; it is also customary to have a broad "duck bill," though the fish-eating mergansers sport slender, serrated beaks. Waterfowl molt their flight feathers once a year, and most species (including all that breed in North America) are flightless for several weeks while their plumage is being renewed. They all lay light-colored, unpatterned eggs and rear downy, precocious young, which are ready to leave the nest at the age of a few hours.

All told, there are 147 living species of swans, geese, and ducks in the world, and getting them sorted into the appropriate subfamilies and tribes continues to trouble biologists. But there is general agreement that the swans and geese belong together, since they share such characteristics as long-lasting pair bonds, slow maturation, care of the young by both parents, and "unisex" coloration. The ducks, by contrast, establish pair bonds each year, mature quickly, and usually entrust care of the young to the females alone. The drakes typically don bright colors for the breeding season. While swans and geese molt just once a year, ducks renew their plumage twice, once in late summer, when the males shed their nuptial finery, and again in fall or winter, when they get it back. As mentioned earlier, the flight feathers are dropped only once, as part of the summer molt.

Canada is the "duck factory" of North America, with about half of the continent's annual hatch of ducklings coming from the prairie provinces alone. Thirty species regularly breed in this country and the neighboring states, including representatives of five tribes: dabbling ducks (American Black Duck, Mallard, Northern Pintail, Northern Shoveler, Gadwall, American Wigeon, and the teals); bay ducks (Canvasback, Redhead, Ring-necked Duck, and the scaups); the so-called sea ducks (eiders, scoters, goldeneyes, mergansers, Harlequin Duck, Oldsquaw, and the Bufflehead); and the perching and stiff-tailed ducks (Wood Duck and Ruddy Duck, respectively). Of these, the dabblers are by far the most numerous and easily observed: any duck that seems to be standing on its head in shallow water, with its tail wagging in the breeze, is almost certainly one of these "puddle ducks." They can also be recognized by their ability to take flight by springing straight up into the air; diving ducks, like those included in the bay and sea-duck tribes, have to sprint across the surface before becoming airborne.

Swans

Among the earliest glimpses we have into the human imagination are Cro-Magnon carvings of what appear to be swans. As the record becomes fuller, we find the birds in myth and legend from Norway to India, as creatures of magic and companions of the gods. There are seven species of these majestic fowl in the world today, three of which breed in Canada and the northern states. One, the Mute Swan, was imported from Europe to ornament public gardens and has since gone wild in a few localities; it can be identified by the black knob at the base of its reddish-orange bill. The other two species, both of which have predominantly black bills, are native to this continent. The Trumpeter Swan, *Cygnus buccinator,* is largest of all North American waterfowl, with wings that span up to two and a half meters and a body weight of around twelve kilograms. The Tundra, or Whistling, Swan, *Cygnus*

columbianus, is generally smaller (about half the weight) and usually has a "teardrop" of yellow just below the eye. But these and other subtle differences in appearance are of little use in the field, where the most reliable clue is their calls—the resonant, brassy blat of the Trumpeter and the softer, more melodious honking of the Tundra Swan. But please note: "Whistling" Swans do not whistle, unless you count an almost inaudible rush of air before every note. Whistlers are the more talkative and companionable of the two, so any time you see a large flock (say, fifty or more), or hear them yelping in the distance, you can be almost certain that you have encountered Tundra Swans.

In fact, the same can be said of most sightings of swans in North America—you can be almost certain that you have encountered Tundra Swans. This is because the Trumpet-

■ Tundra Swan
■ Trumpeter Swan

With grace and ease, this Trumpeter Swan preens its wings and back. Swans have two dozen neck vertebrae, more than any other warm-blooded animal; hence their flexibility. Giraffes, by contrast, have only seven.

Trumpeter Swans prefer to
nest on islets, close to water.
Favorable locations tend to
be used year after year.

Once known as Whistling Swans, this northern-nesting species is now known by the more appropriate name of Tundra Swan.

ers were all but exterminated during the nineteenth century, when fashion took a sudden fancy to swan-down powder puffs and feather boas. In one sixty-year period, the Hudson's Bay Company exported 108,000 swan pelts, most of them from Trumpeters. At present, a few dozen pairs breed in Canada, mainly on small lakes near Grande Prairie, Alberta. The total continental population has more than doubled in the last twenty years and now stands at around nine thousand birds, most of which breed in Alaska and winter along the British Columbia coast. Mankind, having brought the species to disaster, has permitted it a measure of recovery, but who can say what lies ahead? Will we inadvertently find subtler means—through appropriating northern lake shores, draining wetlands, polluting the oceans, and peppering the marshes with lead—to complete the destruction that our ancestors began?

Tundra Swans were also reduced in number and range during the last century, but less drastically, being protected to some extent by the remoteness of their breeding grounds. There are now two populations of about fifty thousand each, one of which nests on the west coast of Alaska and winters on the Pacific slope (primarily in California); the other breeds across the western Arctic and winters on the Atlantic coast (primarily in Chesapeake Bay). Their northward migration follows closely on the retreat of the ice and snow, with stopovers along the way to rest, feed, and wait for the thaw to progress. From late March to mid-April, for example, large flocks congregate in Minnesota, on the Mississippi River, and at Long Point on Lake Erie, before proceeding north to Baffin and the east coast of Hudson Bay. A couple of weeks later, another flight starts moving through Manitoba, bound for Churchill and the Keewatin, while a third group heads across Saskatchewan toward the Athabasca delta and the tundra beyond. Meanwhile, from early April to early May, members of the western population sweep over Alberta or, in smaller numbers, make a beeline across British Columbia. Traveling fast and high, usually at altitudes of .6 to 1.8 kilometers, skeins of migrating birds often pass unseen.

Generally speaking, the swans arrive in the North by the middle of May, just as the marsh plants that they require for food are being unlocked from the ice. The adults disperse widely over the tundra, each pair defending a territory of perhaps two square kilometers, including a small lake. By late May or early June, before the snow has lifted from the countryside, the female is atop a massive nest of sedges and moss, while the male stands guard nearby; the cygnets emerge about a month later, four or five little gray balls with pink feet and bills. Although they still need protection against cold and biting flies, they leave the nest almost immediately and begin foraging for insects; later, they'll join the adults in grubbing for underwater tubers and roots around the margins of the pond. In just seventy days, the youngsters increase in weight almost thirtyfold, so that when the ice closes in again on their nesting pond (around September first), they are usually ready to leave. An early freezeup means widespread hardship and death. Weather, more than any other force, sets the limits on the swans' breeding success, since it not only determines how many young will get away in the fall but, by controlling the food supply, also influences the number of pairs that nest and the average clutch size in a given year.

Assuming that all goes well, a family of Tundra Swans stays together through migration and into the following spring. Then, when the adults go into seclusion on their breeding territories, the juveniles congregate by the hundreds on some of the larger northern lakes, where they spend the summer tipping and grubbing among the reeds. Later, at the age of three or four, they will probably "go steady" for a year, choosing a mate and sometimes even defending a territory, though they may not nest until the following spring. Once well established, pair bonds between Tundra Swans are strong and are thought to last for life.

Canada Goose

Each year, the ragged V's of Canada Geese, *Branta canadensis,* begin coursing northward on the leading edge of spring, awakening us to the season with their stirring calls. By far the best-known wild geese on the continent, they are easily identified by the stocking of black on their heads and necks and the white patches on their cheeks. But other characteristics—size, body proportions, voice—may vary surprisingly from place to place and from flock to flock. One population may include only shrill, short-necked birds, with adult weights as low as a kilogram, while another consists solely of stately, deep-voiced giants, up to ten times heavier. Although the different races, or subspecies, of Canadas have so far defied precise description, there may be twenty or more, each with its traditional wintering area, breeding grounds, and migration routes. Generally speaking, the smallest birds are also quickest at performing such functions as incubation, fledging, and molt and hence can breed farthest north. But in the winter, the situation is reversed as the small fry seek the sun of the southern states and Mexico, while the larger-bodied birds (less vulnerable to cold) tend to remain in midcontinent.

In some respects, the subspecies of Canada Geese are similar to ethnic divisions among people, for both are maintained by social tradition. The population of geese that breeds in a particular area may disperse locally for nesting, each pair seeking out an islet, muskrat lodge, hummock, rarely even a large tree nest built by some other species; but they invariably reassemble to rear their young, choosing places where stands of grass, sedges, and other vegetation promise good grazing. The members of such a "breeding unit" fly south together in the fall, winter in the same region, and return in spring to their common breeding grounds. Since most females and some males nest close to the spot where they themselves hatched, these customs persist from generation to generation, with the result that there is little interbreeding between communities and the subspecies remain distinct.

One advantage of this arrangement is that it permits the development of a stable social order, in which birds recognize one another and know where each fits into the local dominance hierarchy. If every goose knows who it can boss and who it has to give in to, less energy will be wasted on scrapping over food and other resources. Questions of status center on the ganders and are based not on individual size, as is the case in many animals, but on the size of the family. (Clutches range from two to twelve, with an average of four or five.) The larger and more close-knit the brood, the more aggressive the gander and the higher his rank. If a single gosling is experimentally removed from a gander's family, he becomes noticeably less belligerent and more likely to submit, but his status goes up again as soon as the youngster is restored. (Who says birds can't count?) Each additional gosling increases the gander's motivation and makes for noisier and more vigorous threat displays—bobbing, rotating, and extending the head and neck—behavior that is easily recognized and assessed by other geese. Actual fights are only likely between ganders of equal rank that are meeting for the first time.

Dominance relationships are most easily observed in a flock that is feeding under natural conditions. Then, each gander tries to maintain a zone of privacy around his family by menacing any goose that comes too close. This protection is particularly important to the breeding females, who lose so much weight while incubating—a month-long vigil, during which they take only hurried breaks to feed—that they must be free to eat with a minimum of interruption for the rest of the year. The mate of a dominant gander can munch away unperturbed, while her offspring fatten on the choicest berries and greens. The goslings also take courage from their family's high rank and will even bully subordinate adults—so long as father is near. But let a youngster become separated from its kin, and it walks meekly among the flocks of resting geese, head downcast, trying to stay out of trouble until it finds its own.

Family ties are strong and long-lasting in

Canada Goose

A pair of Canada Geese
prepare for flight.

This pair of geese has adopted goslings from other families to form a "gang brood" of twenty-two!

Canada Geese. Young-of-the-year usually stay with their parents until the following spring; then, when their father makes it clear that they're not welcome on the nesting territory, the juveniles, together with other nonbreeding birds, continue northward on a secondary, or molt, migration. The shorter the main migration, the longer this second journey is likely to be: in one subspecies it generally exceeds three thousand kilometers. But regardless of the distance, the yearlings often rejoin their parents later in the summer, after the new brood has attained flight. The next spring, as two year olds, some of the young birds will be ready to breed; but they stand a chance of losing their broods to the care of older, more aggressive pairs—sometimes their own parents. "Gang broods" of ten to twenty goslings have frequently been observed, but it is not known if they have the same integrity as conventional families.

The bond between family members is established and maintained by performance of the so-called "triumph ceremony," which first appears, in imperfect form, among goslings only a few days old. In its mature version, it involves a bout of mutual honking and head-waving, followed by a chorus of companionable snoring sounds. Commonly seen during disturbances, after a separation, and before and after attacks on other geese, it is also important in pair formation. Not surprisingly, given their capacity for abiding relationships, Canada Geese generally mate for life; but contrary to popular belief, they do remate after a partner's death, sometimes within days of the bereavement, and "divorce" also occasionally occurs. After all, as ethologist Helga Fischer once observed, "Geese are only human."

The main cause of death in many subspecies of Canada Geese is hunting; lead poisoning from ingesting shot is also common. Yet the overall effect of human activity in the last two centuries has been beneficial in their case. Not only has the continent been planted to tender shoots and grains on which the birds feed, but sanctuaries have been provided, particularly in the United States, where the birds can winter in peace and plenty. In recent decades, most populations have altered their age-old migration routes to take advantage of these refuges. Between 1954 and 1974, the continental population is thought to have doubled and now stands at two or three million birds.

Mallard

■ Mallard
■ American Black Duck
■ Range Overlap

Ducks (like this female Mallard) need wetlands. It's a simple and obvious point. Yet we seem not really to have grasped it, judging from the rate at which we continue to destroy marshes and sloughs.

Did you know that you have already made a start on learning the birds of Europe, Iran, Tibet, China, and Japan? All these areas provide breeding grounds for the Mallard, *Anas platyrhynchos,* the most numerous and widespread species of waterfowl in the Northern Hemisphere and, incidentally, the ancestor of most strains of domestic ducks. The female is a plain-jane brown bird, easily confused with the equally drab females of such closely related species as pintails and teals; but she can be identified by the markings around her speculum, or "wing window," a patch of iridescent blue, most visible in flight, which is bordered on top and bottom by white bars. The male has a similar adornment which tends to violet, but his most splendid decorations, which he wears from early fall to midsummer, are a metallic green head and white neck band. In season, these characteristics make identification of both the drake and his accompanying mate instant and foolproof. In midsummer, when they're in their "eclipse," or nonbreeding, plumage, males closely resemble females.

As useful as it is to birdwatchers, the males' flashy attire obviously didn't evolve for our benefit: instead, it is directed at female Mallards and helps them pick a mate of their own kind. This task is further simplified by the males' tendency to congregate in all-Mallard flocks around courting time. (In North America, the mating season extends from late fall until spring, with most pairs being formed on the birds' wintering grounds in the central and southern United States.) In spite of the female's unassuming appearance, it is she who makes the first advances, by swimming and quacking through a cluster of males with her head outstretched and low. The drakes respond to this invitation with a furious outburst of displays—rearing out of the water and bending forward to form upsidedown U's; raising both head and tail until their bodies seem compressed; jerking their bills out of the water to shower the female with spray—all the while uttering various grunts, whistles, and "raehb's." Only after she has witnessed several such extravaganzas, each lasting from a few

minutes to an hour, does the female begin to direct her attentions toward a particular drake. She indicates her choice by swimming toward her intended while looking over her shoulder at another male, a gesture that sometimes stimulates her male to attack the other drake. Alternatively, the preferred male will often simply speed up and swim ahead, allowing the female to follow him. When this happens, it is safe to say that the two are becoming paired and that they will travel north together in the spring.

Flocks arrive in their Canadian breeding range about April, and pairs quickly disperse over the countryside, many of them homing on the areas where the females were raised or where they bred the previous year. You can tell when a couple is ready to nest because the female is suddenly overcome by a desire to quack, monotonously, incessantly, at both dawn and dusk; this informs pairs who are still "househunting" that they'll have to look elsewhere. Coincidentally, the drake arouses to his duties as defender of his mate's privacy: now, when the female launches one of her accusing, over-the-shoulder stares at an intruding pair, the male goes into action, directing an airborne attack at the unwelcome female (since she is the one who will choose the nest site), while her mate trails slightly behind, in a "three-bird chase." The area that the resident drake defends may or may not include the nest, but it always includes one or more of the places where he waits for his mate. After the female starts incubating, waiting is one of the drake's main activities; but the female returns to him less and less often, until he loses interest and leaves to join his male cronies. Now a new type of aerial chase can be seen, as bands of drakes harry the lone females, intent on what has been interpreted as rape.

By mid-June to July, the drakes move off to the large bodies of water where they will molt, and at about the same time, the females preside over the hatching of the young. There are nine greenish-buff eggs in a typical clutch, incubated for almost a month in a down-rimmed bowl on the ground. A few days before

His back a blur of motion,
this male Mallard settles his
feathers. Feather care is an
especially important and
time-consuming activity for
water birds.

The American Black Duck is really soot-brown with a light brown head. It can be recognized in flight by the white flash of its underwings and its violet "wing window."

the eggs pip, the mother begins clucking to them—and they begin peeping back. Not only do these prenatal conversations contribute to the "imprinting" process, through which the hatchlings will come to recognize their mother and, ultimately, other members of their species, they also synchronize the hatch, so that the youngsters emerge within a few hours of one another and are ready to leave the nest at the same time. A strong, early bond with the mother is crucial, since she leads her brood to water at the age of one or two days. Usually, the nest is within about three hundred meters of a pond, but in extreme cases, the journey may span two kilometers and take the lives of half the ducklings.

Overall, hunting is the single largest cause of death among Mallards—some four and a half million of these succulent, grain-fed delicacies end up in the oven each year—but the effects of this loss are mediated by management. In nature, the most powerful force acting on Mallard populations is the weather in the richest part of their breeding range, the pothole country of the western plains and parklands. In a good year, the region's ten million sloughs are ringed by luxuriant nesting cover and cereals, and the water teems with tiny invertebrates for the ducklings. But when the prairies shrivel with drought, nine-tenths of the hollows blow dry. Fewer spring ponds on the plains mean fewer Mallards in North America: it's as simple as that. In recent decades, the draining and cultivation of wetlands has caused an alarming decline in the maximum number of Mallards that breed in the West. In the summer of 1984, the population on the prairies reached an all-time low.

In the East, the species' range has enlarged somewhat, as farmers transform woodlands into open country. Unfortunately, each gain for the Mallard has been at the expense of the resident American Black Duck, *Anas rubripes,* a forest-adapted offshoot of the Mallard line. The favorite game bird of the Atlantic region, this wily species is suffering a population decline, which may be due to loss of habitat, overhunting, pesticide poisoning through contamination of the aquatic animals on which it subsists, and/or cross-breeding with Mallards. Hybrids between the two species are now so common that the pure Black Duck strain is thought to be rare in the western part of its range. Mixed-race birds are particularly susceptible to an often-fatal, malaria-like disease which full-blooded Blacks more easily resist.

Goldeneyes

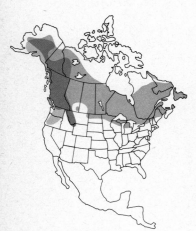

■ Common Goldeneye
■ Barrow's Goldeneye
■ Range Overlap

A goldeneye is a short-necked, heavy-bodied duck with a large, "mumpy"-looking head, somewhat clumsy in overall appearance, though anything but in fact. A supple diver, it can dip beneath the surface of a quiet northern lake with satiny smoothness, reaching depths of up to six meters without raising more than a swell. If the water is clear, you may be able to watch as the bird shifts rocks with its bill or snoops around submerged logs, hunting for crustaceans, insects, mollusks, fish. After a few seconds, up it will come, in sitting position, rising light as a cork.

There are two species of these handsome birds in North America, the Common Goldeneye, *Bucephala clangula,* and Barrow's Goldeneye, *Bucephala islandica.* When the drakes are in their breeding plumage (from fall until the following summer), they are "Pied Ducks," boldly marked with black and white: the head is greenish in Common Goldeneyes, with a round, white mark on the face, and purplish in Barrow's, with a crescent-shaped cheek patch; both drakes and hens show large, white areas on the wings when in flight. The females of both species are like males in "eclipse," or nonbreeding, plumage—gray-bodied birds with brown heads that are difficult to tell apart under most conditions.

A final clue in recognizing goldeneyes (though of no help in distinguishing between the species) is the sibilance of their wings, a sound so characteristic that experienced observers can identify "whistlers" in pitch dark. Some people think that the birds can fly noisily or quietly at will and that the ringing of their wings serves as a means of communication between mates. It has been observed, for example, that a drake that is resting near his incubating mate takes off with a swoosh when alarmed, causing the female to catapult off the nest, cackling in concern.

Goldeneyes, like Wood Ducks, Buffleheads, and Hooded Mergansers, nest in holes in trees or other similar cavities. Common Goldeneyes will accept almost any cavity, provided there's room to squeeze through the opening: even a slit five centimeters wide will suffice, though it's not ideal. Their blueprint for a perfect hideaway calls for a large doorway or, better yet, an open top, together with a roomy compartment, at least twenty centimeters wide by thirty deep; they also prefer to be located near the edge of the woods, since they can then shoot home at top speed, applying the brakes at the last possible moment, an act of derring-do that has certain obvious hazards if there is a wall of tree trunks in the way. Most of their nest sites are created by wood rot, Pileated Woodpeckers, or a combination of the two, but the birds are also attracted to man-made structures, such as chimneys. Unless you fancy having a bird wedged in the flue or starved on the living room floor, it is good policy to fit screens over the chimneys of dwellings in the boreal-forest zone. Nest boxes are often very successful, provided they meet the birds' requirements for size and location; an elliptical doorway about ten to twelve centimeters on a side is best. Barrow's Goldeneyes are even more adaptable than their relatives and often settle in rock crevices, ground burrows, and thickets.

A goldeneye nest typically begins with a layer of wood chips and other debris, which is later topped with a generous quilt of down; puffs of white around the entranceway or on nearby branches are a reliable clue that the hole is occupied. In addition to the current year's eggs (usually ten), the nest may also contain abandoned clutches from previous years and the bones or corpses of adult Buffleheads and goldeneyes. In one exceptional case, a nest tree with a hollow six meters deep held the bodies of twenty-eight Common Goldeneyes, all females and all presumed (perhaps erroneously) to have been killed in fights over the right to use the site. A scarcity of suitable cavities may also result in several females laying in one nest, amassing a "dump clutch" of two or three dozen eggs, which is then abandoned. Good nest sites are a precious resource among goldeneyes and are occupied for season after season by a succession of birds, until the tree deteriorates beyond use.

Shortly after incubation begins (mid-May to

early June), the male goes off to molt, leaving the female to rear the young. Within a month, she has a nest full of fluffy, black-and-white ducklings—but how to get them to the ground, which is from one to twenty meters below? When the brood is a day or two old, the mother stations herself on the ground in front of the tree and clucks to her young inside. Using their sharp claws and stiff tails to advantage, the youngsters eagerly scramble up to the hole and leap pell-mell over the brink, fluttering, tumbling, topsy-turvy, landing in a soft heap. If, as is often the case, the nest is in or over water, they will splash down, collect themselves, and then swim off as a group, with mother at the helm. But if the nest is back in the trees, the young family may have a long and perilous walk to the nearest lake or stream. As with most birds, the death rate among hatchlings is high, and about half the brood is usually lost in the two months it takes them to attain flight. The mother goldeneye is not particularly attentive and often loses her offspring well before they fledge. The young birds, for their part, also lack strong family ties and disperse as soon as they are able, preferring the company of strangers for the annual journey south. Goldeneyes are hardy birds, reluctant to leave their breeding range until the ice closes in and then going only as far as they must to find open water; many thousands winter in the Saint Lawrence-Great Lakes system and along both coasts. In the spring, they're among the first ducks back, often arriving two weeks before breakup. The females from last year's broods, now yearlings, will spend part of the summer "prospecting" for nest sites but have to wait for another year to breed.

The Common Goldeneye is one of four species of North American ducks that nest in holes in trees.

Vultures, Eagles, Hawks, and Falcons

In everyday speech, we often refer to vultures, eagles, hawks, and falcons as "birds of prey," but this is an elastic expression that might logically be applied to all flesh-eating birds, from loons to jays. Hawks and their kin can better be thought of as "raptors," birds characterized by the powerful, grasping feet and piercing claws that they use in subduing prey; they usually have strong, sharply hooked beaks for tearing flesh, as well. Only one other order of birds meets these specifications: the owls, or "nocturnal raptors," as they are often called, a name that distinguishes them from the "diurnal raptors" of the hawk group. Hawks and owls used to be lumped together in one, large order, but we now think that they represent distinct evolutionary lines that have been separate for at least the last sixty to seventy million years. Their common features probably arose through convergent evolution, as each group responded to the challenge of living by tooth and nail or, more properly, by beak and claw.

In addition to their weaponry, the diurnal raptors have a number of other important adaptations to their way of life. Chief amongst these are their phenomenally acute and far-searching eyes, which are without rival in their ability to discern small objects at great distances. Depending on the species (and on who is making the estimate), their vision is said to be from two to eight times sharper than our own. Whereas we have about two hundred thousand visual cells per square millimeter in the most sensitive part of the retina, a typical hawk has around one million. Thus, an eagle really is eagle-eyed and can spot a hare at three kilometers or more. Hawks, eagles, and falcons also have excellent depth perception, since (unlike most birds) their eyes are oriented toward the front rather than the sides of the head. As a result, the left and right fields of vision partially overlap, giving the birds an area of "binocular vision" similar to our own but through a narrower, 35-to-50 degree arc. This permits them to judge distances without error or delay, an ability that is crucial when striking prey. In addition, their eye muscles are designed for rapid refocusing in flight, so they don't lose sight of their quarries or crash into obstacles.

An intriguing characteristic shared by many members of this order is "reverse sexual dimorphism," the tendency for females to be larger than males. This situation, still inadequately explained, continues to provide researchers with great sport, as they gleefully shoot down old theories and advance their own. According to one school of thought, the size differential is important during courtship, when (it is argued) the female needs protection against her mate. But others reject this notion and contend that there must be a link to predation and to the strict sexual division of labor that is practiced by many raptors. You'll find more on this subject in the essays on the Northern Harrier and Sharp-shinned Hawk.

Another adaptation that is widespread in

the order is an ability to travel almost effortlessly, a talent that is of obvious benefit to any hunter. Raptors accomplish this by riding on currents of upwelling air. In some cases, these occur as winds are deflected over an obstacle (a ridge of land along a lakeshore, a sudden rise of hills, a mountain range), forming an invisible wall of air that bears the birds aloft. Elsewhere, the free ride is provided by "thermals," bubbles of warm air that rise from heat-reflective surfaces, such as grain fields and towns. We can detect thermals by looking for cumulus clouds, a clue that is probably used by birds, as well. When ascending, raptors wheel to stay with the circle of updraft; when descending, they coast out, relying on downward momentum to take them at least part way to the next upward flow. Many species rely on both sources of lift—topographical updraft and thermals—to ease the strain of migration, and this helps account for the concentrations of hawks seen each fall around the Great Lakes. Rather than fly out over the water, where there are no strong upward-moving currents of air, the birds soar along the lake shores, following the north edges of Lakes Ontario and Erie and the west shores of Huron, Michigan, and Superior. At Hawk Cliff, near Port Stanley, Ontario, for example, as many as seventy thousand Broad-winged Hawks have been counted in a single day. Heavy flights are also regularly observed along Hawk Ridge at Duluth, Minnesota and the Kittatinny Ridge in the northeastern United States.

Of the eight genera of diurnal raptors that occur in our area, four are built for soaring, with broad, slotted wings and wide, fan-shaped tails. These include the Turkey Vulture; Bald Eagle; Golden Eagle; and the "buteos" (Red-shouldered, Broad-winged, Swainson's, Red-tailed, Ferruginous, and Rough-legged hawks). Of the remaining four groups, each has a distinctive profile and style in flight. The Northern Harrier, for example, has relatively long, slender wings and is typically seen in buoyant, flapping flight near the ground. The Osprey has narrow wings, too, but they're held bent at the wrist; this bird is generally seen above water and is distinguished by its habit of plunging out of the sky to catch fish. The "bird hawks," or "accipiters," including the Sharp-shinned and Cooper's hawks and the Northern Goshawk, all have long tails and rather stubby wings that suit them for darting through forests. The final group, the falcons—Merlin, Peregrine, Gyrfalcon, Prairie Falcon, and American Kestrel—can be recognized by their long, pointed wings and tapered tails. Their specialties are daring and speed, qualities that have made them favorites of falconers throughout the ages.

Of all the diurnal raptors, none is better known today than the Peregrine, for the unhappy reason that one subspecies is almost extinct and another is classified as "threatened." Until the 1930s, the Peregrine, like all its kin, was officially classed as "vermin" and persecuted as such: predators were killers, some of them detrimental to human interests, and did not deserve to live. This mood of righteous indignation was gradually calmed by the new science of ecology, which proposed that raptors were not wanton murderers that killed without reason or bound, but partners in a delicately balanced interplay between predator and prey, which benefitted the "victims" by keeping their populations in check and culling out the infirm and diseased. And so laws were passed to protect raptors from outright harassment—but nothing was done to protect their habitat, and nothing was done to protect them from pesticide poisoning, because no one knew at first that it was happening. Then, in the 1960s and 1970s, DDT was implicated as the major cause of eggshell thinning and reproductive failure in a number of species: the Peregrine, Bald Eagle, Osprey, and others. Although immediately banned in the United States and Canada, DDT is still heavily used in the cotton-growing regions of Mexico and South America, areas which provide wintering grounds for many of our raptors and/or their prey.

Continuing contamination of eagles, hawks, and falcons from this and other unknown sources is deeply troubling, for, if these birds are still being poisoned, so are many other organisms in their food chains.

Turkey Vulture

Turkey Vulture

We usually picture vultures as part of a desert scene: shimmering heat, the bleached skull of a longhorn, and, over all, a wheeling speck in the too-blue sky. But the adaptable Turkey Vulture, *Cathartes aura,* is at home in many other settings as well, from Tierra del Fuego, through the jungles, deserts, forests, and plains of two continents, to southern Canada. A year-round resident in most of this vast region, the species is migratory at our latitude, spending the summer with us and the winter in South America. Though not plentiful in the north, its numbers have been increasing here since the turn of the century: in the lower Great Lakes region, vultures are thought to be relative newcomers, but on the prairies, they may be moving back into areas where they once were common.

The original decline of Turkey Vulture populations in the West probably resulted from the extermination of the buffalo: vultures are scavengers and need a generous supply of carrion if they are to survive in numbers. Although classified as raptors, they lack the strong beaks, grasping talons, and binocular vision that typify the order and hence can kill only if their quarry is helpless—small fish, reptiles, or baby birds. Great Blue Heron nestlings are within their capabilities, but there is one remarkable case in which a vulture chose to thrash the youngsters with its wings instead of killing them, thereby forcing them to regurgitate their last meal; this the vulture gobbled up and took to its own brood.

Turkey Vultures are adapted to their unhygienic diet by having bald heads, which offer no place for scraps to cling, and an extraordinary resistance to disease: even the potent botulism toxin has little effect on them. Consequently, it is of no concern to them whether their food is fresh or slimy with rot; their only care is to be sure that it won't fight back. They approach a large carcass with caution, first circling overhead and landing some distance off, then hopping forward in their ungainly way, snatching a bite, jumping back, and, finally, if there are no signs of life, settling in to gorge.

One of the difficulties of living off death is that you never know when or where it will occur; carcasses may be many days and long distances apart. Accordingly, Turkey Vultures can go for several days without food if they have to. They can also range cross-country with a minimum of effort, by riding on "thermals" of upwelling air. Among land birds, vultures and the closely related condors are the unsurpassed masters of soaring flight. When the weather is right, sunny and still, Turkey Vultures will spiral for hours at heights of a kilometer and more, riding on vortices of warm, rising air. As these currents drift with the wind, the vulture goes with them, circling to stay near the center where the lift is strong. From such a vantage point, the birds can scan three square kilometers at a time, all the while keeping an eye on any other airborne vultures in the vicinity; should one of them suddenly descend, it is a signal to all that a putrid feast is at hand. Alternatively (and more typically at our latitude), they may hunt alone, skimming the tree tops at speeds of around sixty kilometers an hour, searching for small carcasses—skunks, mice, snakes, tadpoles. Unlike most birds (even most other vultures), Turkey Vultures have a well-developed sense of smell, so they can nose out food that is rotting under the plant cover. Usually, however, they rely primarily on their extraordinary eyes: incredible though it seems, they can probably spot and identify the remains of a deer at a distance of six kilometers.

To a human observer on the ground, Turkey Vultures look rather like eagles, those other large, dark, soaring birds. On average, eagles are somewhat bigger, with wingspans of around 200 centimeters as compared to 180 for the vultures, though the differences are too subtle to be useful in the field. A better clue is the color of the underside of the wings—mostly dark in eagles; black fringed with silvery-gray in Turkey Vultures. In addition, eagles soar with their wings more-or-less flat, while vultures hold theirs above the horizontal, in a shallow V, a configuration that gives them greater stability. At a distance, vultures can

Turkey Vultures are important members of the ecosystem—Nature's own sanitation crew. Regrettably, the overall population of the species has declined in the last two or three decades, perhaps because of pesticides.

also be distinguished by their smallish heads, but their warty, turkeylike faces (red in adults, black in juveniles) can only be properly appreciated at close range.

At our latitude, young Turkey Vultures attain flight about September, at eight or ten weeks of age. A typical breeding pair rears two young a year, choosing some dark, bare cavity as their nesting site—a hollow log, a crevice between rocks, a burrow on a steep bank. The parents share the six-week task of incubation and also cooperate on feeding the nestlings, which flourish on a diet of semidigested putrescence. Young Turkey Vultures are bright-eyed, alert creatures, and it is said that they make friendly pets, who enjoy being handled and follow their keeper like dogs. (It is, of course, illegal to confine wild birds, except under special permit.)

Young Turkey Vultures are precocious, alert, and surprisingly friendly to humans.

Bald Eagle

It was no less a personage than Benjamin Franklin who declared Bald Eagles to be birds of "bad moral character." For all their soldierly bearing, he complained, these creatures were guttersnipes, who lived on what they could scavenge or steal instead of by acts of predation. But there was another school of thought that accused the birds of being too predatory and charged them with taking waterfowl, fish, and livestock that should have ended up in human hands. Whatever the truth (and, as we will see, more of it lay on Franklin's side), one thing was obvious: the Bald Eagle had few champions. And so it was that *Haliaeetus leucocephalus* became the object of an officially condoned campaign of extermination. In Alaska, for example, where the birds remained under bounty until the 1950s, more than 100,000 are known to have been shot. Today, killing or molesting Bald Eagles is illegal throughout North America, but still the war goes on, for the birds have as much to fear from the hammer as the gun: every cottage that goes up on the shores of a wild lake destroys another piece of potential nesting habitat. Then too, there are the pesticides and other contaminants that have found their way into the eagles' food supply, with the all-too-familiar results of eggshell thinning and failure to reproduce.

It comes as little surprise, then, to learn that Bald Eagle populations in eastern Canada and the United States have suffered a calamitous decline, much of it in the years since World War II; the species is now considered endangered throughout the conterminous states. What is surprising is the survival of a flourishing population along the Pacific coast, from Puget Sound north and west through the Alaska panhandle. Here, in the rain-drenched land of the eagle totem and eagle clan, Bald Eagles are the most abundant of the large birds of prey, with numbers approaching those of primitive times. And what is even more surprising is the discovery of another substantial population in the boreal forests of central Canada—perhaps fourteen thousand in Saskatchewan alone—whose presence was scarcely suspected before 1960. Although there is concern about the effects of future human incursions into this wilderness and about pesticide poisoning in some localities, the majority of these birds appear to be thriving.

Generally speaking, Bald Eagles are found in association with large trees and large bodies of water, though neither is an absolute requirement: even a desert will suffice, if road-kills or other foods are available. In most areas, however, Bald Eagles subsist largely on dead and dying fish. During salmon runs in Alaska, for example, the air is alive with their soaring, as two or three thousand converge along a ten-kilometer stretch of riverbank. Here they gorge on spent salmon and on scraps left behind by the Brown Bears that come to join in the feast. When they have to, Bald Eagles can take healthy fish as well, sometimes wading belly-deep in the water and plunging their heads under to catch prey with the beak. More typically, they sight their quarry from above (either from a tree or atop an updraft of air) and then swoop down in a long, flat curve, talons dangling, ready to make the grab. If the catch is too heavy to lift, the bird may tow it to shore by settling in the water and paddling with an "overhand" stroke of the wings, rather like a human swimmer doing the butterfly. This technique is sometimes used to bring in waterfowl, as well. Diving ducks are the most frequently caught, since their underwater escape-routes are easy to trace from the eagle's vantage point; each time the duck comes up for air those fierce black talons are in place to force it down again, a process that continues until the prey can no longer resist. Sometimes several eagles gang up on one victim and take turns harassing it, though it is by no means certain that this represents cooperation. In all probability, each individual is intent on seizing the prize for itself or on stealing it from whoever makes the successful strike. Bald Eagles are well known for their piracy on other carnivores—Turkey Vultures, Ospreys, Red-tails, Peregrines, Gyrfalcons, Common Mergansers, even seals—and are certainly not averse to thieving from one another when they

Bald Eagle

In the words of Roger Tory Peterson, an adult Bald Eagle, with its large size, white head and tail, and heavy yellow bill is "all field mark." Immature birds may be more difficult to identify.

have the chance.

If their diet ties them to water, their nesting behavior explains the link with large trees. Consider these nest specifications: height above ground—from 3 to 45 meters; exterior dimensions—up to 3 meters in diameter and 3.5 meters in height; weight—as much as 2 tonnes; age—up to 30 or 40 years. Though there are exceptions—pairs that scrape together a few strands of seaweed on bare rocks—most Bald Eagles construct nests of this type, which are amongst the largest built anywhere by a single pair of birds. A pair may have several of these mansions on its territory, which are used in successive years; nests located within a kilometer of one another are usually assumed to belong to the same birds.

Bald Eagles mate for life and renew their bond each year in a courtship ritual that may include maneuvers of breathtaking daring and grace. Suspended in midair, the two great birds will sometimes lock feet and then, with their wings outstretched, cartwheel toward earth, breaking their fall just in time to avoid a crash. More often, courtship involves calling, soaring, and undulating display-flights, either singly or in pairs. The issue of these sexual adventures is usually two athletic youngsters, who use the broad expanse of the nest for their practice flights. At the latitude of Puget Sound, the young have fledged by June, but on the Mackenzie Delta, they seldom reach this stage until mid-August. What happens next also depends on latitude, with eagles from British Columbia migrating north along the coast for their annual salmon orgy, while the inland population heads south in search of open water for the winter. Coastal birds are often back on their territories by fall, but the others delay their return until spring, when thawing temperatures signal the arrival of March, the Eagle Moon.

If you know that a Bald Eagle's wings span around two meters, it will give you an idea of the size of this nest, which is not exceptionally large for the species. The adult in the picture is bringing fish to its mate and young.

Northern Harrier

Northern Harrier

For a raptor, the Northern Harrier has large broods—about five young, on average. This is probably related to the insecurity of nesting on the ground. Only about one-third of the eggs laid yield fledglings.

This species has been badly served when it comes to names. Known in North America as the Marsh Hawk, it might better have been called the "open-country hawk," because it hunts over fields, foothills, sagebrush deserts, and tundra, as well as wetlands. Known in Europe as the Hen Harrier, it might more accurately be described as the "mouse harrier," since it subsists on ground squirrels and other small mammals, with side orders of frogs, injured waterfowl, nestling songbirds, and other animal food; the habit of taking chickens is only acquired by an occasional pair. Known to science as *Circus cyaneus,* it might better be known as almost anything else, since it does not generally enscribe circles in the air, as its generic name implies; nor is it *cyaneus,* which is to say "dark blue"!

Fortunately, its new name, Northern Harrier, suits it perfectly, reflecting both its distribution and its affinities. This species is the only North American representative of the harrier group, a genus of slender, long-limbed hawks that have evolved a distinctive hunting strategy. Rather than spiraling up the sky, like many other hawks, harriers usually fly within ten meters of the ground; and, instead of soaring, they alternately flap and glide. A Northern Harrier can cover 150 kilometers a day with this easy, graceful flight, though its travels are confined within the 2 or 3 square kilometers of its hunting range. This it crisscrosses tirelessly, sometimes tilting as it turns to reveal the white patch on the top of the rump, which is one of its trademarks.

Another unique characteristic of the species is the ruff of feathers on the sides of the face, which gives it its wide-faced, owl-like look. As in owls, this structure acts as a funnel, which directs sound toward the ears and helps account for the bird's exceptional hearing: guided by sound alone, a Northern Harrier can detect prey at a distance of five or six meters and, from closer in, can pinpoint its location to the last millimeter. Interestingly, this combination of facial ruff, ultra-sensitive ears, and low, quartering flight is also found in the Short-eared Owl, an unrelated species but one

which is adapted to a very similar niche and which takes over the night watch from the Northern Harrier in many localities.

Among the aspects of this harrier's ecology that intrigue biologists are the differences between the sexes. In size and coloration, adult males resemble gulls, while the females are heavier and a rich, streaky brown. Accordingly, therefore, the females are thought to be more powerful and capable of taking larger prey, while the agile, well-camouflaged males should theoretically be more versatile and reliable in their food-getting. If true, this would help explain why males are able to linger here after their mates head south in the fall and return a week or two earlier in spring. There is also the question of those few hardy individuals that spend the winter here: does one or the other sex predominate among them? So far, we don't know, though it would seem a relatively simple matter to investigate.

In any case, the males are mostly back on their breeding grounds by April, full of exuberant sexuality. This is the season for "skydancing," a display of steep dives and ambitious ascents, strung together like a series of capital U's. When the females arrive, the performance intensifies, with up to seventy repetitions in a sequence and both partners sometimes involved. Through these behaviors, the birds form and advertise their attachment to the mates and territories with which they will be linked for the remainder of the breeding season. They are evidently fairly flexible in their sexual relationships since bigamy and even trigamy occasionally occur; alternatively, several monogamous pairs may settle close together (within one or two kilometers) and assist one another with nest defense.

Northern Harriers nest on the ground, usually in a moist hollow that offers a dense and obscuring thicket of growth. Though the male helps carry in lengths of grass and reeds, the female does most of the building and also tends the eggs during the five weeks before they hatch. In addition to being brawnier than the male, the female is usually the more aggressive in repelling intruders, as well. The

male's role is to feed his mate during incubation and then to hunt for the entire family during the next two weeks; yet he seldom, if ever, delivers prey directly to the nest. Instead, he calls to the female, who rises to meet him in midair and deftly catches the morsel with her talons when he releases it; or she may snatch it right from his claws. These aerial "food passes," which are typical of the harriers, may occur fifteen or twenty times a day. By watching the female land (bearing in mind that she may pause to pluck the prey before carrying it home), a careful observer can quickly build up a notion of where to look for the nest. But before blundering in, it is important to reflect on the effects of such an intrusion.

By laying a scent trail straight to the nest and by trampling protective plants, the visitor invites in all the predatory mammals in the vicinity—dogs, coyotes, skunks, mink—for a meal of eggs or young hawks.

Sharp-shinned Hawk

Sharp-shinned Hawk

It's the stuff murder mysteries are made of: a dark shape speeding beneath the branches of a shadowy, woodland path, skimming the undergrowth, veering around trees. Suddenly, in front of this darting shadow, a small bird flushes in alarm. There's a lightning chase, and both pursued and pursuer are lost to view as they streak through the underwood. Unseen, the victim cries out in distress—then silence; later, perhaps, a wing or pile of feathers litters the forest floor.

The aggressor in this avian suspense story is a Sharp-shinned Hawk, *Accipiter striatus,* one of the most numerous but least well known of our predatory birds. Although falconlike in its speed and energy, it is actually a "bird hawk," or accipiter, and is marked as such by its long tail; short, rounded wings; and characteristic five-flaps-and-a-glide pattern of flight. The only species with which the Sharp-shin is likely to be confused is another, lookalike accipiter, the Cooper's Hawk; but Sharp-shins usually nest in conifers, while Cooper's Hawks tend to seek out deciduous woods. Another clue is the tip of the tail, which is rounded in Cooper's Hawk, with a white border, and forked or square-cut in the Sharp-shin, with little or no white trim. There is also a difference in overall size: if the bird is very small (around twenty-five centimeters long), you can be sure it is a male Sharp-shin; if it's fairly large (up to fifty centimeters), it's a female Cooper's. Midsized birds—female Sharp-shins and male Cooper's—are often difficult to tell apart.

More interesting than size difference between the two species are the size differences found among Sharp-shins themselves. Hawks in general tend to exhibit "reverse sexual dimorphism," which simply means that females are larger than males, and Sharp-shins hold the record for this trait: at a lusty 180 grams, an adult female is almost twice as heavy as her mate. Why go to such extremes? No one knows for sure, but researchers agree that the answers are to be found in the birds' reproductive behavior.

Sharp-shins are on their breeding grounds by about May each year, arriving alongside the sparrows, warblers, and other small birds on which they feed. Here, in a dense grove of evergreens surrounded by meadows or leafy woods (sometimes the same grove that was used in previous years), they build a sturdy platform of sticks, about sixty centimeters across, which is supported by strong branches and concealed by thick growth. Although they generally build anew each year, we know very little about their behavior during this period. Does the male assist with construction? Does he do all the hunting for the pair? We do know that he will support his mate throughout the five weeks of incubation and then feed both her and their family for another two weeks. A typical brood consists of four or five ravenous youngsters, each of which requires two Song Sparrows, or the equivalent, in food every day. But the male Sharp-shin is adapted to meet their needs by his slender build, which grants him the agility to catch small, quick-moving

prey that might elude the more cumbersome female. This is a rich niche, with all the plenitude that one expects from the lower levels of the pyramid of life. Thus, the male is usually able to keep his household well and regularly fed through much of the breeding season, and at no great cost to himself.

Meanwhile, the female has been attending to her specialties. Because of her heavier build, she is well equipped for warming eggs, brooding young, and for defending the nest, which she may do with considerable ferocity. She is also able to take on fairly large prey—birds bigger than House Sparrows—which might be daunting to her dainty mate. Her hunting skills are usually called on about the time her offspring enter their third week, just as one of her mate's principal resources—nestling songbirds—is literally taking flight. Through their Mutt-and-Jeff partnership, the parent birds are able to take a greater range of prey than would be the case if both were the same size. And because she can deliver more meat per kill, the female is still free to keep watch around the nest, in case she is needed to ward off predators.

With the exception of a few eccentrics that remain in southern Canada throughout the year, most of our Sharp-shins winter farther south; a few reach Central America. The newly fledged young are the first to go, beginning as early as August, with the adults following through September and October. In many parts of the country, Sharp-shins are best known as migrants—at Point Pelee, Ontario, for example, where the birds are temporarily stopped by the prospect of crossing Lake Erie. Curiously, of the many thousand Sharp-shins that pause here (to the terror of songbirds traveling the same route), almost all are young-of-the-year; where the adults from this area migrate no one knows. Large numbers of Sharp-shins are also seen at Duluth's Hawk Ridge in September and October each year. West of the Great Lakes, there are no such build-ups during the fall migration. In the spring, the Sharp-shins' arrival is always clandestine. Their secrecy makes it difficult to assess their population with any accuracy, but current data suggests they are not in any serious trouble.

The Sharp-shinned Hawk was a principal victim in the "great hawk shoots" of the 1920s and 1930s, partly because it was conspicuous during migration and partly because people, in their ignorance, disapproved of predators. Shooting Sharp-shins and other hawks is now an offense.

Red-tailed Hawk

Red-tailed Hawk

In theory (and sometimes in fact), Red-tailed Hawks, *Buteo jamaicensis,* are amongst the easiest of birds to identify. As their name implies, they typically have brick-red tails, a characteristic that sets them apart from all other raptors. But, as is usual in such matters, there are variations and complexities: for instance, the red coloration occurs only on the upper surface of the tail and is missing entirely from juveniles (birds under two years of age). What's more, in the western grasslands and Arctic, there are races of very light and very dark colored birds in which even the adults generally lack this "tell-tail" marking. Are they Red-tails or some other buteo—Broad-winged Hawks, perhaps, or Swainson's or Rough-legs? It takes an experienced hawk-watcher, with an eye for subtleties in body size and contours, to be certain. But whatever the difficulties, our rule of thumb holds true: any hawk with a deep chestnut tail is a Red-tailed Hawk. Simple and sure.

Of all the large hawks on the continent, the Red-tail is the most numerous and most often observed. Frequently, an individual draws attention to itself with a piercing, drawn-out scream—"tsee-eeeee-arrr"—somewhat like the shriek of a high-powered saw. If you follow the sound with your eyes, its author can usually be found spread-eagled against the sky, soaring, wheeling, twenty or thirty meters above ground; alternatively, it may be perched atop a telephone pole or in the crown of a lofty tree. But in spite of its elevation, its attention is focused closely on the grasses at your feet. The rustle of a mouse, the flick of a gopher tail, or the sheen of a snake are all it takes to send the hunter, silent now, swooping down on set wings. More often than not the strike is unsuccessful, but the birds are persistent and so versatile in their feeding habits that they are usually able to kill more than they need. While rodents and rabbits are their staple foods in most areas, they have been known to feed on

The Red-tailed Hawk has been called the most successful hawk in North America, because of its versatility and its ability to survive on little food.

earthworms and rattlesnakes, shrews and weasels, chickens and woodpeckers, a gastronomic Noah's Ark of small and medium-sized animals.

There is one circumstance in which certain populations of Red-tails do suffer a food shortage, and that is during a Snowshoe Hare population crash. For reasons that are still not wholly understood, hare numbers are cyclic, with an oscillation between high and low that recurs about every ten years; from peak to trough, the population drops by ninety-five percent. For Red-tails, this dramatic reduction in the food supply means that fewer nestlings are likely to survive, though it does not cause a decline in the adult, breeding population or the number of nests. But among Great Horned Owls, which hunt the same fields and woodlands as the Red-tails and seek much the same prey, the adults' reproductive effort is directly tied to the hare cycle: few hares means few owl nests. The difference between the two predators appears to be that the owls winter here, with little to eat but Snowshoe Hares, while the hawks generally migrate toward the Gulf

Coast and Central America, where they can feast on Meadow Voles and other dainties.

The Red-tails are back on their breeding grounds in early April, and it is then that courtship is most likely to be observed: lazy, looping flights punctuated by lightning-quick dives and mock fights in midair. Their nest is a flat-topped dish of twigs, up to a meter wide, lined with shredded bark and other fine materials, and furnished with sprigs of green. Curiously, the Snowshoe Hare cycle has an indirect effect on the Red-tails' nest-building activities, for the more hares—and Great Horned Owls—there are, the more new nests the hawks have to build. From the owl's point of view, a large hawk nest is prime real estate: fully three-quarters of the nests used by Great Horned Owls are built by Red-tails. Since the owls lay early in the season (before the hawks return), they get their pick of last year's housing stock. Given the chance, Red-tails will often occupy the same site for a couple of years in succession and if displaced by owls usually settle in the same woodlot, sometimes within fifty meters of the intruders; by contrast,

The hunger cries of young
Red-tailed Hawks have been
likened to the squalling of
baby pigs.

neighboring pairs of Red-tails allow an average of 1.5 kilometers between nests. Yet the owls can scarcely be considered good companions or grateful guests, since they prey on their bene-factors' young. When Red-tails live in close proximity to Great Horned Owls, they have only a one-in-three chance of successfully rearing their young.

Among Red-tails, a typical clutch contains two or three eggs. Although incubation is shared by both parents, the female spends more time on the nest, where she is fed for the entire month by her mate. At least, that is what usually happens, but if food is short, the female may leave briefly to hunt for herself, leaving the eggs exposed to jays, raccoons, and other marauders. Assuming that the eggs survive to hatch, the infants are in peril of predation, bad weather, blood-sucking insects, falling from the nest, and, in hungry years,

being eaten by their siblings. People add to the losses by stealing hawklets from the nest: in recent years, Red-tails have become much sought after for falconry, because of their strength and biddability.

After the young leave the nest site, around the middle of July, they make themselves conspicuous with their persistent hunger cries. Although intended to catch the attention of the adults, on whom the fledglings are still dependent for food, these cries may also draw the notice of gun-toting humans, on the look-out for "chicken hawks." A significant number of Red-tails are still being shot in North America each year, in spite of the fact that it is illegal and that, overall, the birds are beneficial to agriculture. These killings are indefensible, especially at a time when Red-tail populations are thought to be slipping in many parts of the continent.

American Kestrel

The American Kestrel, *Falco sparverius*, is the smallest diurnal raptor in North America —and one of the most beautiful. Do its striking markings serve a function? Some experts think so. They suggest that the dark patches on the back of the head (a line reminiscent of a beak and two spots that suggest eyes) form a "second face," which may repel predators or mobbing songbirds.

How might this work? Imagine, for a mo-ment, that you are a bird of prey, a Red-tailed Hawk perhaps or an accipiter, hunting over a meadow. On the ground below, you spot a russet-backed hawk, no bigger than a jay, which is feeding in the grass, unaware of your menacing approach. This should be an easy kill, made easier still by surprise. Down you swoop, prepare to strike, but no—what's this? a bobbing, owl-like face scowls up from what should have been the back of your victim's head! Disconcerted, your advantage lost, you have no choice but retreat. (Or so the theory goes.)

In addition to the markings on the back of the head, the kestrel also has patterns on the face, which possibly provide camouflage of a

different sort—a vertical black line running up through the cheek may mask the position of the bird's real eye, to the confusion of both its enemies and victims. Whatever their function, these features distinguish the kestrel from its cousin, the Merlin (Pigeon Hawk), which is similar in size and in the swallowlike cut of the wings but which lacks facial markings. The kestrel can also be identified by the color of its back and tail, which are reddish-brown in females and reddish-brown crossed with a shawl of blue-gray wings in males.

Even at a distance, an American Kestrel makes itself easy to identify and observe. A noisy, high-strung creature, it meets any dis-turbance—a mob of aggressive songbirds, a large raptor, or a human intruder—with a clangor of shrill, scolding "klees." It is even conspicuous when sitting quietly, since it generally chooses a high, exposed perch—a powerline crossing an open field is one favor-ite—and fidgets its tail up and down, as if incapable of keeping still. If something edible shows itself in the grass below, the little falcon speeds to the spot and plunges straight down to make the kill. Alternatively, these lightning-

American Kestrel

bolt attacks can be made directly from the sky instead of from a lookout, since the kestrel has perfected the art of hovering and can "perch" lightly in the middle of the air for short periods of time. In either case, a headlong dive toward the quarry signifies the capture of a mouse or small bird, while a feet-first approach is used on grasshoppers and other large insects. Mammals and birds are grabbed in the talons and stabbed at the base of the skull with the two toothlike points near the tip of the falcon's notched bill. Carcasses may be stored in a tree or clump of grass and literally saved for a rainy day, as much as a week later; the birds remember their cache sites with great accuracy, even when using several at the same time.

American Kestrels are extraordinarily efficient hunters—successful on about seventy percent of their strikes—and this no doubt helps explain why they have developed the ability to stockpile surplus food.

The kestrels' hunting prowess is taxed to its limits when they are raising their broods. An average pair tends four or five eggs, which are normally laid in a natural cavity or flicker hole in a tree, though an old magpie nest, a bank burrow, or a crevice on a big-city highrise will serve as well; they also take readily to birdhouses, provided the boxes are about thirty centimeters on a side, have an entrance width of eight centimeters, and are placed within easy access of hunting fields. The female is

The American Kestrel is abundant and familiar over much of the continent.

Facing page: The American Kestrel was formerly known as the Sparrow Hawk, a name that did not accurately reflect the species' varied diet.

largely responsible for incubation, which usually occupies the month of June, give or take a couple of weeks. The male, meanwhile, takes on the entire task of feeding himself, his mate, and later, their pink-skinned, potbellied hatchlings.

Within about ten days, the youngsters are already approaching adult size and more than adult appetites, so their father is required to bring in about 150 grams of food per day, or one and a half times his own body weight. By this point, however, the nestlings no longer require brooding by day, so the female is free to hunt and is soon contributing more than her mate to the family's support. The fledglings leave the nest after about a month but remain with their parents for another two to four weeks. During this period, the family can sometimes be seen cruising over fields or sharing a perch, and they can certainly be heard, in unanimous complaint, if a person wanders into their territory.

Then, by mid-September or October, the family breaks up, as most of the Canadian population heads to wintering grounds in the southern United States and Mexico. Interestingly, it has recently been discovered that males and females go on "separate holidays," with the females, which are slightly larger, commandeering the wide open spaces where hunting is easiest, while the males make do with cramped clearings and vacant city lots. Why should these poor, put-upon males, who feed their mates through most of the breeding season, have to cede the most favorable winter habitat, as well? The answer is that both behaviors assist the birds in raising the maximum number of healthy progeny, and that, after all, is the Meaning of Life, from an evolutionary point of view.

Grouse

According to the textbooks, the members of this order are fowllike, or "gallinaceous," birds with short, stout beaks and four toes; they feed mainly on plants and spend most of their lives on the ground. But such a definition, though accurate as far as it goes, leaves out at least one of the group's salient characteristics—their exceptional edibility. It was no doubt this trait that led to the domestication of the Red Jungle Fowl of southeast Asia, perhaps as early as 4,000 B.C. Just think of it: six thousand years of chicken dinners! Other species, no less succulent, have been transported across continents and around the world: the Wild Turkey, a native of North and Central America and first domesticated here, was taken to Europe by the conquistadores; sometime later, two Old World species, the Chukar and the Gray, or Hungarian, Partridge made the return voyage; on a smaller scale, quail from the United States have been successfully transplanted in southern British Columbia. But the most remarkable story is that of the Ring-necked Pheasant, a bird that originated in Asia, reached North America in the late 1800s, and is now securely established as a game bird in southern Canada and the northern United States.

Canada also has its native species, of course, ten in number. One, the Northern Bobwhite, is a warm-weather creature whose range just barely extends into the extreme south of Ontario. The other nine are grouse, cold-adapted birds that apparently evolved in the Northern Hemisphere and are year-round residents at our latitude. The hardiest of all are the ptarmigans (Willow, Rock, and White-tailed, by name), which are found at high latitudes and high elevations. There are also several woodland species (the Blue, Spruce, and Ruffed grouse) and a number of prairie types (the Sharp-tailed and Sage grouse and the Greater Prairie Chicken).

Apart from their gastronomic appeal, these birds are well known for the booming, hooting, drumming, and exuberant gyrations with which the males draw attention to themselves during the breeding season. Their mating systems fall quite neatly into three categories. Among ptarmigans, for example, every male attempts to defend a large territory within which his mate (or, less commonly, mates) builds her nest; both parents assist in rearing the young. In the woodland species, the cocks also claim spacious domains, but the hens come and go as they please, mating in one male's territory, perhaps nesting in another, and generally making their own way in life; the males are polygamous, given the chance, and take no part in raising their offspring. Out on the grasslands, the cocks congregate on "arenas," or "leks," where each defends a tiny territory that is used for nothing but mating. Lekking probably evolved in response to the openness of prairie habitats, which offers little shelter from predators. Under these circumstances, a cock does well to surround himself with his plump and juicy kin, who hopefully will divert attention from himself.

Although Arctic and woodland grouse seem to be holding their own, grassland species have suffered severe population declines in the last century. The culprit is habitat loss—the continuing destruction of native prairie by commercial agriculture. Already, the Greater Prairie Chicken is endangered in Canada and its cousin, the Lesser Prairie Chicken, is in trouble in the United States. Sage Grouse numbers are dwindling in both countries, and it is possible that the species will not survive into the twenty-first century. But this grim trend need not continue if we conserve the few remaining islands of prairie-grouse habitat.

Ruffed Grouse

Ruffed Grouse

Here is an experiment for you to try some morning in spring—the hour before sunrise is best. First, choose a patch of woodlands where there are aspen poplars in stands about thirty feet tall. The canopy should be dense enough to screen the ground, yet lacey, so that a Goshawk or Great Horned Owl would show up against the sky. The understory should be leafy but not opaque, so a lynx or fox couldn't slink in unseen. Now, thump the ground with your fist, first slowly four times, then as fast as you can for about ten seconds; and listen. You may be rewarded by a muffled response from the surrounding woods—"Whump, whump, whump, whump, whir-r-r-r-r." If this happens, you can take it as a sign that you have been accepted as an apprentice Ruffed Grouse, *Bonasa umbellus.*

By pounding the ground in that way you were making an announcement: "I am a male Ruffed Grouse on my territory. Other breeding males should keep away, but females who want to mate will be cordially received." Perhaps you also gave some clue as to your individual identity or social standing; we really don't know how much information is conveyed through drumming. A male grouse sends out his messages by beating the air with his wings as he stands erect on some elevated surface such as a snowdrift, a boulder, or, most commonly, a fallen log. Each male has up to six such stages on which to perform, all within an area of about four hectares. One of these sites usually serves as his main venue, though later in the season or the following year—should he live so long—he may shift to another location. Since he chooses the same spot and faces the same direction each time he uses a log, you can tell which one is his favorite by comparing the volume of droppings that accumulate "backstage."

Ruffed Grouse drumming territories often seem to be arranged in loose clusters, though scientists aren't sure why; it may be because suitable habitat occurs in patches or because the birds are attracted to each other and participate in some kind of expanded lek. At the very least, we know that they stimulate each other to drum and thereby presumably attract more females to the area than if each were on his own. Fights between cocks are almost unheard of, though neighbors sometimes indulge in so-called "drumming duels" in which the challenger moves to a log near a territorial boundary and beats out his threatening tattoo. Usually, the sound of drumming is itself enough to repel rivals, but should another cock intrude, the resident may bring out a second line of defense, a display known as "strutting." With his tail fanned to its full magnificence and his dark ruff spread, he stalks toward the trespasser, hissing like a locomotive and shaking his head in a blur of motion. Then, extending his wingtips to the ground for even greater effect, he rushes the intruder with another prolonged hiss. In early spring, this behavior sometimes leaves a characteristic sign in the snow—a closely trampled footpath flanked by marks from the trailing wings. Close examination might even reveal the tracks of the trespasser as he fled.

Interestingly, the same display is given when a breeding female approaches a cock, but with more titillating effect. A hen may treat herself to several such performances on different territories before mating and choosing a sheltered spot (perhaps at the base of an aspen) for her leaf-lined, cup-shaped nest. Here, in late April or May, she lays about a dozen eggs, which she defends with great devotion. Her first stratagem is to sit tight until the last possible moment, and then to flush with an alarming roar of wings. Or she may launch into a broken-wing act. In June, when the chicks hatch, she is more likely to front danger directly with her own version of the strutting display. Not until her offspring attain flight at the age of ten days will she seek a measure of safety for herself. If she is killed, her orphaned chicks may attach themselves to another hen; but ordinarily, the mother and her family stay together for about three months, as the youngsters graduate from their infant diet of insects to their adult fare of leaves, seeds, and fruits.

Then suddenly, explosively, in the fall, the

The drumming displays of male Ruffed Grouse are a means of repelling rival males and attracting mates. These are the same functions that are served by singing among songbirds.

Female Ruffed Grouse rely on their mottled, woods-brown markings for protection when tending their nests.

young birds disperse, each along its own unique, unidirectional course. These journeys, which are accomplished mostly on foot, take the birds an average of three kilometers, farther than they'll ever travel in their adult lives. In all likelihood, these compulsive movements are responsible for the so-called "crazy flights" in which grouse crash into buildings and through plate glass, though this explanation is disappointingly drab when compared to some of the wild-eyed theories that have been put forth: for example, that the birds have been eating "magic" mushrooms. Along their route, young males attempt (sometimes successfully) to get established on vacant territories, and their ambitious incursions may account for a second, lesser peak in drumming in the fall.

Those juveniles that fail to establish themselves in adequate habitat have little chance of surviving till the following spring, for Ruffed Grouse are not known to migrate. Their minimum requirement for overwintering is a stand of mature, flower-producing male aspens in which to feed: the buds are their staple food during the snowy months. Accordingly, you can expect to find them treading the tree tops, often in small flocks that cast lumpish silhouettes against the twilit sky. Their toes are equipped for winter with a horny, comblike

fringe, which may either give them a better grip on slender branches or, as has more often been supposed, function as snowshoes. Ruffed Grouse not only walk on snow, they also burrow in it and thereby insulate themselves from extreme cold. But in spite of these adaptations, the death rate is high: it is not uncommon for half the population to succumb before spring, mostly to raptors.

Predation has also been suggested as the motive force behind the perplexing oscillations in Ruffed Grouse numbers that occur in rough synchrony from Alberta to Ontario and south to the Great Lakes states. On average, the population cycles from high to low about every ten years, with an eight-fold decline from peak to trough. One explanation that has often been advanced links the grouses' fortunes with those of the Snowshoe Hares, which have a similar and equally mysterious ten-year cycle. When Snowshoes are in decline, the theory goes, predators switch to grouse and cause the birds' numbers to drop; when hares are plentiful, the pressure comes off the grouse and their populations recover. If this is true, then the grouse cycle will always lag behind that of the hares. So how to explain the instances in which the grouse declined first? Science has, as yet, no clear answer for this.

Ruffed Grouse stay with
us all year round, relying on
the snow for insulation and
on speed to protect them
from raptors and other
predators.

Sharp-tailed Grouse

Sharp-tailed Grouse

There was a time, not so long ago, when two species of grouse commonly performed their exotic mating rites on the grasslands of western Canada—the Greater Prairie Chicken, and the Sharp-tailed Grouse, *Tympanuchus phasianellus*. To the pioneers, both were simply "chickens," and there are still many people who confuse the two, though the diagnostic differences are quite obvious: a Prairie Chicken has a dark, rounded tail, while a Sharp-tail really does have a pointed rear end, which is dark in the center and white on the sides. In Granddad's time, prairie grouse were so plentiful that the bag limit was set at twenty birds a day, but today, the Greater Prairie Chicken is extremely rare in Canada, an endangered member of an endangered ecosystem, the tall-grass prairie. Sharp-tails have also lost range to modern, intensive farming but, being more versatile, are still relatively plentiful. All they require is some combination of brush and open space, whether in a forest clearing, a muskeg, or a partly wooded farm. Even a railway right-of-way may serve them well, for they are thought to have entered western Ontario by following the cuttings made for the Canadian Pacific Railway.

The most celebrated aspect of the Sharp-tails' existence is the lekking behavior, or "dancing," of the males. While these displays have been observed in every season except midsummer, the most regular and vigorous bouts occur in April and May, stimulated by the rising libido of spring. A typical performance involves about a dozen cocks and centers on a sparsely vegetated area, or "arena," some twenty to forty meters in diameter; this may be an airport runway, a rocky outcropping, or, more often, an open knoll that has been trampled smooth by generations of dancing feet. At the height of the season, the cocks often perform twice daily, at dawn and dusk, but the morning show, which begins in the hour before sunrise, is best attended by both birds and birdwatchers.

When approaching a lek, you are likely to be guided in by the dancers' calls: throaty coos and weird gobbles, which carry for about a kilometer, and shrill "chilks," which travel twice as far. The first two denote aggression, since what we choose to call dancing is really a struggle for power; the last, by contrast, is a sexual invitation to nearby hens. As you drive closer, you may see one or more males take low, fluttering leaps off the ground, a behavior that advertises the location of the arena. Inch closer still, and the birds will likely flush, only to return a few minutes later, even if the arena is ringed with cars. By working with marked birds, biologists have proven that the cocks always return to the same relative positions on the dancing grounds, each in his own territory. Indeed, this is true whether their behavior is recorded from day to day, from season to season, or—remarkably—from year to year, unless a death in the group prompts a reassessment of their relationships.

In spring, the territorial boundaries are particularly well defined and rigidly maintained. Thus, you can expect to see pairs of neighboring cocks running parallel to one another or crouched down beak to beak, each on his own side of the imaginary line; or, more rarely, there may be violence. When females are present, aggression is usually expressed through a "dancing duel." With wings outspread and rumps held high, rival cocks rush at each other in a whir of stamping feet and rattling tail feathers. In a split second, the mania spreads to other males on the lek; then just as suddenly dies out, probably on cue from a lead bird. Silent and still, the cocks catch their breath and take stock of their surroundings before losing themselves in another ardent outburst.

Often, the object of this passionate excess is not another cock but one of the females that has come to mate. The hens' response—wary disinterest. This attitude makes the females easy to pick out, as they wander among the dancers, apparently unimpressed by the cocks' machismo. When ready to mate, a hen usually makes her way toward the male or males who hold territories near the center of the lek. These are the older, dominant cocks and the ones that perform the great majority of copu-

lations. Once bred, the hen retires to nearby shrubs or grass where, over the next five weeks, she will lay and incubate around a dozen eggs.

Sharp-tail chicks leave the nest within hours of hatching, under the watchful care of the mother hen, whose one priority is keeping her young alive. Though precocious, the chicks require brooding, protection from predators, and help in finding food (first insects, then seeds, leaves, flowers, and fruits). But the chicks already have another preoccupation beyond simple survival: their dominance hierarchies. Preliminary evidence suggests that two peck orders are established within the brood, one for each sex, and that the rank a bird attains in infancy may carry over into its adult relationships, ultimately affecting its

reproductive success.

Young males get a chance to test their mettle in the adult world at the age of two or three months, when dancing resumes for the fall and most vacancies on the lek are filled. With the onset of winter, display activity becomes more sporadic. Coveys combine to form large flocks, flocks coalesce into even larger "packs" (up to four hundred birds), and the whole population shifts to the birch and aspen woods. Here they feed on berries, buds, and catkins and take shelter in snowdrifts. Through all these changes, the dancing-ground males generally stay close to one another and to their lek. By March, with late-winter snows still on the ground, they are already appearing with increasing regularity on their dancing grounds.

To the accompaniment of eerie gobbles and squawks, this male Sharp-tailed Grouse performs an early-morning "dance." The yellow comb and violet air sac are expanded during displays.

Rails and Cranes

The cranes and their relatives comprise a group of about two hundred species worldwide, the only living representatives of a sixty-million-year-old marshland lineage. Of the sixteen species that occur in North America, the majority are long-legged waders known as "rails," birds so secretive that they are seldom closely observed. Slim as shadows ("thin as rails"), these henlike creatures can slip through jungles of crisp marsh plants with scarcely a sound. Much better known and much more conspicuous where they occur are the Gallinule, or Common Moorhen, and the Mudhen, or American Coot. Both are squawky swimming birds that paddle about like ducks and pump their heads like chickens but are nonetheless linked to cranes through their anatomy.

The "glamor birds" of this order are the cranes themselves. Two species are native to our continent, the slate-gray Sandhill Crane, *Grus canadensis,* and its larger cousin, the white Whooping Crane, *Grus americana,* one of the rarest birds in the world. Whooping Cranes occur only in North America and now nest only in Canada. Though they may never have been particularly numerous, there were probably about fifteen hundred in 1850; within a century, the population had plunged to twenty-one. This calamitous decline correlates with the settlement of the interior plain of North America, the vast wilderness in which Whooping Cranes once bred. Today, the only natural relict of these privacy-seeking birds nests within a restricted area of Wood Buffalo National Park and winters in eighty square

Whooping Crane
■ Present range
■ Approximate former range

On the Aransas National Wildlife Refuge in Texas, two of the endangered Whooping Cranes indulge in a gangly dance. Similar displays are also performed by Sandhill Cranes.

You can tell a Sandhill Crane by its size (about a meter in height), red crown, and "bustle" of feathers. Birds often are stained reddish-brown by digging in dirt and then transferring ferric oxide to the plumage when preening.

Sandhill Crane

81

In the air, Sandhill Cranes
can be identified by their
body profile: feet and neck
are both outstretched. This
distinguishes them from
Great Blue Herons, which
fly with their necks crooked.

kilometers on the Texas coast. Under rigorous protection, the population of this flock has crept up to about eighty birds, half of which are breeders; each year sees an increase, at most, of four or five nesting pairs.

In order to augment and protect this fragile recovery, wildlife biologists have launched an extraordinary program of jet-age midwifery. One of the first things they noticed in studying the birds, both Whoopers and Sandhills, was that a breeding pair typically lays two eggs but produces only one young. (Among Sandhills, twins are reared about twenty percent of the time.) For the most part, the second chick seems to serve as a backup, which doesn't become important unless the first egg is lost. In 1967, biologists with the Canadian Wildlife Service began removing some of these "surplus" eggs from Whooping Crane nests in the Northwest Territories and airlifting them to a research station in Maryland for artificial incubation. Since then, the wild birds have actually produced more chicks than before, while the scientists have been able to raise an additional thirty cranes. Eggs from Wood Buffalo, together with a few from the captive flock, are also being taken to the mountains of Idaho, where they are slipped into the nests of selected Sandhill Cranes, in place of the Sandhills' own eggs. Through this foster-parent experiment, a small migratory population is being established, in the hope of safeguarding the Whoopers if some disaster occurs in the Wood Buffalo flock.

Like Whooping Cranes, Sandhills have lost much of their range to people in the last few hundred years, with the result that three subspecies in the southern states and Cuba are now on the verge of extinction. Until quite recently, the midcontinent race was endangered as well, but it has undergone a heartening resurgence and appears to be expanding into southern Ontario. By far the majority of the population (some 300,000 birds) breed in the North, from the boreal forest to the Arctic archipelago and Siberia. Obviously, the future impact of northern development—highways, oil rigs, low-flying aircraft—is of vital concern.

And with more people in the area, will hunting be allowed to increase? Already, sportsmen take over 15,000 Sandhills a year, mostly on their fall migration, though no one knows if the population can afford the toll. A final and more pressing worry is the destruction of habitat along the Platte River in Nebraska, where the cranes' feeding and resting areas are being lost to agriculture and to various water diversion schemes. This area is crucial because it serves as a major spring staging ground for Sandhills that migrate east of the Rockies.

The Sandhills return to Canada around late April each year, cheering themselves along with a chorus of brassy "garoo-a-a-a" calls. Indeed, their high-flying formations might pass by unseen if it weren't for these resonant sounds, which are amplified by the trumpetlike coils of the trachea and penetrate down through four kilometers of sky. This call is also heard during the excitement of "dancing," a socio-sexual display in which the gangly giants bounce repeatedly into the air, light as moon walkers, reaching heights of two meters. Such performances occur in large flocks, like those that stop over at Last Mountain Lake, Saskatchewan and Big Grass Marsh, Manitoba, as well as in the seclusion of the nesting ground.

A typical pair arrives on its territory with last year's young in tow: for an entire year, the adults have stood guard while junior ate and ate. Now independent of its parents, the yearling joins a flock of underage birds, which congregate in remote marshes to feed and loaf and choose the mates with which they will likely breed for life. Over the next couple of years, these "newlyweds" establish themselves on territories of up to four hundred hectares, each with safe marshes for nesting and uplands for feeding. (Sandhills forage for roots, seeds, berries, insects, and small animals.) Only as four year olds will they be ready to breed. Cranes have a long reproductive life—up to seventeen years in the wild and thirty in captivity. But their delayed maturity and slow reproduction hinder their recovery from population declines. Hence, the extreme importance of protection for these stately birds.

Shorebirds, Gulls, and Auks

Judging strictly by appearances, one would never suspect that the clown-faced puffins, with their stalky bodies and parrotlike bills, were closely related to the slender avocet, or that the shy, bumble-winged woodcock was first cousin to the gulls and terns. Yet science assures us that these species, and about two hundred others as well, all derived from a common ancestor within the last seventy-five million years. Together they comprise the Charadriiformes, a group that has now diverged to occupy the shores, marshes, beaches, and meadows of the seven continents. Of the one hundred odd species that occur in Canada and the northern states, the majority are waders, or shorebirds: the plovers, sandpipers, curlews, woodcocks, and snipes, et alia, with their stiltlike legs and variously contorted bills. A second grouping includes the well-known gulls and terns, plus the less-familiar skuas, jaegers, and skimmers. The third subdivision encompasses the auk family: the auks, auklets, murres, murrelets, guillemots, and puffins.

The most renowned of all the auks may be the flightless Great Auk that once nested by the millions along the North Atlantic coasts. But in the seventeenth and eighteenth centuries, those millions were reduced to thousands, as the birds were slaughtered for food and fish bait. Then even those thousands were killed, so their feathers could be used to stuff mattresses. The species has been extinct since 1844. Another Canadian species whose numbers declined for similar reasons is the Eskimo Curlew, a pigeon-sized shorebird that was a favorite of nineteenth-century hunters. Although the Eskimo Curlew was once presumed to be extinct, there have been a few confirmed sightings in recent years. Is the species doomed, or might it stabilize and recover? No one can say. Nor can we predict the fate of the Piping Plover, a shorebird that is disappearing from parts of its breeding range, particularly in Ontario and Quebec. The problem seems to be increasing human use of the sand and pebble beaches on which these little birds breed. Today, the total North American population is about one thousand pairs, all in Canada.

Killdeer

Shorebirds sometimes seem more like wraiths —mysterious condensations of mist and spray—than they do like flesh-and-blood birds, for they are often only vaguely discernible from their surroundings. The reason is protective coloration (hues and markings that permit a species to merge with its surroundings), an essential attribute for creatures like these, which occupy barren and exposed habitats. The Killdeer, *Charadrius vociferus,* is a case in point, for its somber tones blend well with the sand beaches, close-cropped pastures, ploughed fields, and gravel pits that it inhabits during the breeding season. Surprisingly, its brilliant white belly provides camouflage as well, by brightening the shadows on the

Of all the shorebirds in
North America, none is
better known than that
"noisy plover," the Killdeer.

Killdeer

underside of the body so that the bird looks flat and formless when seen from above. Even the stripes on the head and the two black bands across the breast are helpful, since they divide the body into meaningless shapes, none of which looks like part of a bird. These illusions help protect the Killdeer from predators.

Its impressive "cloak of invisibility" is not the Killdeer's only adaptation for evading its enemies: with its strong, falconlike wings and long legs, it is also a master of the quick escape. Thus equipped, a Killdeer can afford to take the risk of announcing its whereabouts to the world. By day, by night, on the ground, in flight; spring, summer, and fall, they draw attention to themselves by shouting out variations on their name—"k-dee," "kill-dee," "kill-deah," "deah," "dee-kidee," "kit-a-dee-year"— and other strident calls. The first cry of the season can usually be heard by mid-March, as birds begin to filter in from their wintering grounds in southern North America and beyond. (Small populations also winter in southwestern British Columbia and a few other scattered locations in Canada and the northern states.) As soon as the snow begins to

clear, a vociferous controversy breaks out, mostly amongst the males, as each chooses a territory, often the same three or four hundred square meters that he held in previous years. This he claims by perching in some conspicuous spot and shrieking "di-yeet" every few seconds for hours on end. Not yet satisfied that his occupancy has been registered, he may also fly broad circuits overhead, using slow, showy, butterflylike wingbeats and screaming "kill-deer." If another male dares to intrude on this domain, he is usually repelled with a chase and a tongue-lashing; but a visiting female arouses no such hostility. Instead, she is invited in for an enthusiastic display of the male's domestic skills—specifically, his nest-making ability—and a serenade of stuttering trills.

A Killdeer nest is a simple hollow on some soft or pebbly surface (even a graveled roof!), sometimes lined with smooth stones or bits of grass. As a warm-up to copulation, the male makes a number of these scrapes, one of which is ultimately used by the female for her four mottled, clay-colored eggs. Laying begins by about late April, just as the ground vegetation is beginning to emerge, so the nest is almost

The chief means of protection for young Killdeer is obvious from this photograph—camouflage.

The Killdeer has one of the most elaborate "distraction" displays of any North American bird. The rufous patch on the rump is thought to be of particular importance in attracting the attention of enemies.

totally exposed. But try to find it! Like the birds themselves, the eggs meld perfectly with their surroundings. In addition, the adults have a number of active defenses, each appropriate to a particular circumstance. Thus, if a cow or some other grazing animal approaches, the incubating bird sits tight until the last minute and then explodes in its enemy's face, thereby deflecting the course of those lumbering, egg-smashing hooves. But if the intruder is a potential predator (such as a human), the Killdeer turns secretive: as soon as danger appears, the bird sneaks well away from the nest and only then raises the alarm. This lets you know that a nest is somewhere within thirty meters or so of the displaying bird, but in which direction? And what do you make of the bird's mate and all the neighbors that arrive to join in the uproar? If, despite these distractions, you blunder close to the nest, at least one of the parents is likely to meet you with its final ruse: a highly polished broken-wing display. With wings beating spastically on the ground or twitching above the back, tail dragging, and body listing to one side, the bird twitters in evident anguish and runs in tortured spurts, sometimes pausing to crouch for a moment as if it had stumbled onto its nest.

But this is all deceit, for the bird magically recovers its health and returns to its clutch as soon as it feels that you're well off course. Such injury-feigning displays become even more common about the middle of May, when the chicks hatch and leave the nest.

Interestingly, the fathers are more likely than the mothers to launch this arduous defense. Indeed, if male Killdeers could somehow be transformed into human form, they would no doubt be in great demand as mates! Not only do they bear most of the responsibility for territorial defense and nest-building, they take on about three-quarters of the incubation, including most of the dangerous night duty. If, as sometimes happens, the female deserts before the chicks attain flight and independence at about a month of age, the father will raise them by himself. But the male has one fault from his mate's point of view—an interest in other females that persists well into the incubation period. His female therefore takes special pains to keep possible rivals out of their territory. In her spare time, she feeds on grasshoppers, beetles, dragonflies, and other invertebrates. Thus fortified, she has the resources to lay as many as eight replacement eggs and sometimes to rear a second brood.

Spotted Sandpiper

Spotted Sandpiper

Learning to distinguish amongst the sandpipers, with their sparrow-brown uniforms, long beaks, and long legs, may seem a daunting task. But take heart, for there is a bird that is at once common, easy to identify, and fascinating. The Spotted Sandpiper, *Actitis macularia,* is a versatile species, probably as numerous and widespread now as it was two hundred years ago. During the nesting season, it can be found from coast to coast and from sea level to the mountain timberline, usually near streams, small lakes, and temporary ponds, where it hunts flying insects and other invertebrates. Seldom still, it works both the shallows and the shore, pecking bugs off the surface, nabbing them in midair, sometimes stalking them with catlike stealth; occasionally, it swims in deeper water to take floating prey. As its name implies, this is the only sandpiper that acquires freckles on its breast prior to breeding time, markings that, interestingly, are more pronounced in the females than the males. (Females are larger, as well, a fact that will take on significance as we proceed.) An even more striking characteristic of the Spottie and one that is common to both sexes and all ages is its habit of wagging its rear end up and down while walking, as if in perpetual danger of overbalancing. When alarmed, it springs into the air with a staccato "peet-weet"; and in flight, it can be recognized by the stiff, downward curve of its wings as it scales out over the water and settles again a little farther along the shore. Even when flushed, it doesn't go far, for the Spottie is, by nature, a rather tame and trusting bird.

The Spotted Sandpiper is one of a small number of species in which the usual avian sex roles are reversed. The males care for the young, while the females defend territories.

Spotted Sandpipers winter across the continent, from southern British Columbia to South Carolina, and south to Central and South America. They move north unobtrusively, often traveling singly and by night, and begin arriving on their nesting grounds in May. Then something unusual occurs: the females, not the males, establish themselves on territories and initiate courtship. There's a confusing tangle of chases—female-female, female-male, male-male—and a clamor of excited calls; and sometimes the female struts, with her tail spread and head held high, in front of her intended mate. As a rule, the female chooses a male with which she bred in the previous year. If she takes on a new partner early in the season, she is likely to drop him cold if her old mate reappears before egg-laying begins. The males are readily wooed, and pair bonds are often formed in a matter of minutes.

The first order of business for the newly formed pair is to scrape out a simple, saucer-shaped nest in some protected spot—in grass, under logs, near bushes, among rocks—usually close to water and almost invariably on or near the site that the male used the year before. For this is really the male's nest. The female stays around long enough to lay the eggs (normally four to a clutch), but even before she finishes, her attention is wandering to other corners of her territory. It's early in the season yet—only a week has elapsed—and unmated males are still trickling in from the south. With the laying of her third egg, the female's aggressive and sexual urges suddenly revive, and in little more than a week, she may have completed a second clutch with a new mate. Ten days later, she

may have a third. All told, counting the replacement of eggs lost to predators, she can lay five clutches in a season. Her mates squabble amongst themselves, but for the most part they're preoccupied with incubation, which lasts three weeks, and taking care of the young, which occupies another two; the female usually only assists with the last clutch of the year. Such a breeding system, in which the female takes a number of mates in turn, is known as "serial polyandry" and is also found amongst the phalaropes and several other shorebirds.

It is interesting to speculate on why and how this arrangement evolved among Spotted Sandpipers. In the first place, biologists note that Spotties are one of the few members of their order to breed in the temperate zone; most of their relatives nest in the Arctic where there is not time to rear successive broods. Another pertinent fact may be the high rate of nest predation that Spotties suffer: a fifty percent loss seems to be typical. Thus, multiple clutches are not only possible in this species, they may also be essential. This creates at least one problem: the strain placed on the female by the constant egg-laying. One obvious solution is to reassign some of the other reproductive tasks, such as incubation and brooding, to the male. This, in turn, leaves the female free to seek new mates. But now the male is at a disadvantage, because the female's later broods will compete with his offspring for survival. Unable to repel her new mate, he settles down to his nest-duty, evidently better served by tending his clutch than by warring with rival males.

American Woodcock

The American Woodcock, *Scolopax minor,* (otherwise known as the timberdoodle, bog-sucker, and siphon snipe) must surely take first place for oddity among North American birds. For one thing, it spends much of its life with its beak hilt-deep in the dirt, hunting for earthworms. You can tell a woodcock has been around by the pencil-like bore holes it leaves, usually in alder thickets and other moist

woods. Its prey is apparently located by touch, since the tip of the bill is ultra-sensitive and is thought to function as an underground antenna, able to detect the movements of an earthworm several centimeters away. Sometimes, a bird will jab its beak into the soil, hold it there for a few seconds, and then scurry to a nearby spot, where it immediately comes up with a snack; or it may stamp its feet sharply

first, as if to set the worms a-wriggling so they'll be easy to find. Prey is not stabbed but grasped neatly in the beak, which can be opened underground; the upper bill is flexible and equipped with serrations for a better grip. A woodcock can and will pick insects off the ground or snatch them out of the air, but juicy, squirmy earthworms are its staple and delight. On average, a bird eats about 150 grams of worms every day, or the equivalent of its own body weight.

Another, related peculiarity of the woodcock is the structure of its head. The bill is exceptionally long; at six or seven centimeters, it constitutes a fifth to a quarter of the bird's overall length. Yet this unwieldy protuberance is of obvious advantage in reaching low-lying worms. The extra-large eyes are easy to account for as well, since the woodcock feeds all day long, even in twilight. But why are the eyes placed so far back on the skull? The answer is that this arrangement permits the woodcock to see over a full 360 degrees, with a narrow arc of binocular vision in the front, a wide sweep of monocular vision on each side, and another band of binocular vision directly behind the head! Thus, the woodcock can keep watch for owls and other predators even when it has its face to the ground. But with the eyes in their new position, the ears have had to shift

A mother woodcock and her three chicks await the emergence of a fourth hatchling. The adult's long bill is one of several adaptations in this species for hunting earthworms.

91

American Woodcock

forward and down, onto the lower cheeks. The brain, meanwhile, has swung backwards and now lies tilted downwards, toward the base of the skull!

Yet another fascinating aspect of the woodcock's existence is its courtship behavior. The birds winter in the southeastern states, mostly along the Gulf Coast, but are drawn north early in spring, arriving as soon as the first patches of ground are soft enough to be probed. By April, the males are already establishing themselves on "singing grounds," sparsely vegetated clearings (usually less than a hectare in size), which are bordered by trees and shrubs. During daylight, a territory holder takes shelter in the surrounding woods, all but invisible in his coat of leaf-litter browns; but twice daily, at dawn and dusk, he flutters into his field, bent on making his presence known to the world. "Peent, peent, peent": he beeps out his insectlike calls, then suddenly spirals into the sky, climbing fifty, eighty, a hundred meters in ever-diminishing rings. The only sound on the ascent is the whistling trill of his three outer primaries, which are specially designed to "sing." At the summit, the bird seems to pause in midair—a vague, batlike form in the half-light—and begins to pour out his true song, a sequence of burbling chirps. Down he floats, still singing and zigzagging back and forth like a falling leaf. Once on the ground, it's "peent, peent, pent," and the performance begins again. He may make a dozen or more flights in a session, with time-outs to ward off rival males and to mate with any females that have been attracted by his display. Singing grounds are in short supply, and the turnover among incumbents seems to be rapid. The males begin to lose interest in maintaining territories around the end of May, and later in the season, from midsummer on, the singing grounds are taken over by the whole population (male and female alike), who use them at night as communal roost sites.

The females, meanwhile, have been rearing their families. The nest is a shallow cup in the underbrush, and here each hen lays four brown-splattered eggs. Exceptionally well camouflaged, the mother woodcock protects her clutch by sitting tight and may actually permit herself to be stroked on the nest. But when the chicks hatch and follow her into the world (around the middle of May), she adopts a more active defense: a labored decoy-flight, with her legs dangling and her tail tucked between them, close to her body. Or could that be a chick, grasped between her thighs? Naturalists used to believe that a mother woodcock carried her young to safety in this unusual manner, but the claim has been largely discredited.

Despite the female's protection, the death rate is high during the youngsters' first months of life, and half or fewer will return to breed the following spring. But then, no woodcock is likely to survive for very long: the average life expectancy is less than two years. Major causes of death are thought to be severe winter weather and hunting. Approximately 1,500,000 of these delectable morsels are bagged in North America each year (over 100,000 of them in Canada); yet the long-term effects of this kill are thought to be negligible. The crucial factor in determining the woodcock's fortunes is the preservation of its habitat. Without young woodlands, interspersed with clearings, there can be no American Woodcock. Intensive agriculture has dealt a heavy blow to the species, as has the suppression of forest fires and tree-killing insects. Surprising as it may seem, the lumberman and his bulldozer are about the only friends that the woodcock has left.

Herring Gull

When a dryland farmer pauses in his work to watch the flurry of white birds following his plow, what he sees are not just "gulls" but "sea gulls." For even here, gulls seem to bring with them the tang of salt air and a rumor of the surf. The fact is, however, that most gulls are primarily coastal rather than ocean-going birds. Indeed, there are many species that leave the ocean entirely for five months or more at a time—sometimes virtually for life—to breed in the interior of the continent. The black-headed Bonaparte's Gull, for example, nests in conifers in the boreal forest zone; its cousin, Franklin's Gull, makes floating platforms in prairie marshes; and the large, white-headed Ring-billed Gull settles on is-

lands in inland rivers and lakes, as well as along the east coast. Since the Ring-bill is plentiful both on the prairies and in southern Ontario and Quebec, it may be the gull that Canadians most often see. But the most widely distributed gull on the continent is the Ring-bill's lookalike relative, the Herring Gull, *Larus argentatus.*

Herring Gulls may well be the best understood birds in the world, thanks mainly to the penetrating investigations of Nobel Prize-winning ethologist Niko Tinbergen. When pressed to explain why he had spent the better part of his adult life in a gullery, Tinbergen said simply, "Blood is thicker than water." And it is true that Herring Gulls and people are surpris-

The Herring Gull is the most widely distributed member of the so-called "Herring Gull group"—four closely related species of large, white-headed gulls with gray mantles—which also includes California, Ring-billed, and Thayer's gulls. These species are similar in appearance, behavior, and habits.

Herring Gull

ingly alike, for both can seem sociable, cooperative, and loyal; fractious, thieving, and murderous. All these qualities find full outlet at the Herring Gulls' colonies, those clamorous cities of breeding birds that re-form each spring on certain islands and, less commonly, shoreside cliffs. To the hurried visitor, the scene is a chaos of bird droppings, half-digested food, and milling gulls; but patient observation of marked birds reveals an orderly system of social relationships. The colony is not a collective holding in which a bird can come and go at will, but a mosaic of individual territories, from five to fifty meters in diameter, each defended by a resident pair. Birds return to the same colonies and the same territories year after year; they are also thought to nest with the same mates for life.

The constancy of Herring Gull mate relationships may be an indication of their powers of memory and personal recognition. "Mates recognise each other instantly, in various positions, and from great distances," Tinbergen wrote; "in fact they were infinitely better at it than we." On one memorable occasion, Tinbergen and his associates were watching a newly formed pair in a "club," a part of the colony in which gulls gather to squabble, loaf, and court. After a while, the female of this pairing flew off, out of sight, and almost simultaneously, a fight broke out on the club. By the time she returned, many of the remaining birds had taken up new positions, and her mate, who had been a ring leader in the commotion, was a good twenty meters from where she'd left him. Yet she swooped down without hesitation and settled at his side.

Sometimes Herring Gulls show signs of reacting to one another's "personalities." If a particular bird is jumpy, easily panicked, its associates learn to ignore its alarm calls, though they continue to heed the warnings of other gulls. Similarly, a territory holder may have different relationships with its various neighbors, allowing one an unusual liberty to trespass, while subjecting another to repeated attacks. Often, these differences seem to come down to nothing more tangible than personal compatability.

Interestingly, Herring Gulls never learn to recognize their own eggs, though they tend them loyally for four weeks (usually mid-May

to June). But each pair does know its nest site, and that's enough since the eggs can be counted on to stay put. Chicks are a different matter entirely. Immediately after hatching, while the infants are still too weak to get about, the parents are blandly tolerant and will accept any youngster that is put in their care; but four or five days later, that same "foster child" would be pecked to death. In the interim, the adults have learned to recognize their offspring by markings and voice and henceforth respond to young intruders with ferocity. The chicks become freely mobile within about ten days, and many lose their lives by wandering across the invisible lines that bound their territories.

The death rate among young Herring Gulls is extreme: from a normal clutch of three, only one will likely survive to leave the colony at the age of six to nine weeks. Besides territorial aggression, cannibalism by adults and adolescents (birds under three or four) is often a significant cause of death among the very young. Usually this occurs during a momentary lapse in the parents' attention, but in one fascinating case (Tinbergen again), marauding gulls were able to snatch infants from under the parents' bodies. No defense was possible, because the kidnappers did not adopt a threatening pose. Without this specific stimulus, the parents' defensive behavior was not "turned on," and they could not attack.

The die-off of young gulls continues during their first month of independence, this time because of starvation. The youngsters are not as skillful at food-getting as their elders. When an adult gets a clam, for example, it will likely fly to land, locate a rocky shore or stretch of pavement, mount to just the right height, and take aim. Whack, crack, the shell breaks, and the gull swoops down to feed. But an inexperienced juvenile often drops shells in water, on sand, or from the wrong height. Young-of-the-year seem desperate for food and are given to pirating other gulls.

Herring Gulls are scavengers that will eat virtually anything, from bread crumbs and fresh-caught fish to carrion, offal, and vomit. They also have a decided taste for sewage, garbage, and fishery refuse, and therein lies a problem. With their food supply augmented from twenty to forty percent by human activities, Herring Gulls are experiencing a popula-

The world of the Herring
Gull includes not only the
sea but also rivers, lakes,
and urban settings across
northern North America and
Eurasia.

tion explosion throughout their range; in some areas, their numbers have been doubling every ten to fifteen years. This presents a hazard to us, particularly when the colonies are near major airports: jet engines don't work so well when they've sucked in a flock of gulls. But it's an even greater threat to highly specialized coastal birds, such as puffins and terns, which may be displaced from prime breeding areas or have their eggs and young devoured by Herring Gulls. Attempts to find an answer with poisons and predators have not been successful, and the ultimate solution lies with us and the way we handle our wastes.

Puffins

■ Atlantic Puffin
■ Tufted Puffin

The large, brightly colored bill of the Atlantic Puffin, so useful for handling fish, also carries the bird's breeding colors. At the end of the breeding season, the outer layers of the bill are shed, leaving it smaller and duller in color.

The North Atlantic in winter is grim and tormented by storms, with waves that surge thirty meters high and cold that can kill a person in five minutes or less. Yet here Atlantic Puffins, *Fratercula arctica,* make themselves at home for seven or eight months each year, from about September to March. Nobody knows exactly what they do or where they go, but they probably live alone, widely dispersed across the ocean, and never come ashore. Then, in early April, their existence is revolutionized, as the adults are suddenly and simultaneously drawn toward each other and land. What motivates this change? Folklore finds the answer in the call of a puffin king, but science points to a scarcely-less-mysterious interaction between day length, hormones, individual experience, and genetic programming. Be that as it may, the puffins congregate in dense rafts around the bases of certain rocky, coastal islands, where they will subsequently nest. (Each individual seeks out the colony at which it bred in previous years.) The birds' final destination is, at most, a few hundred meters above, on the grassy slopes at the top of the cliffs, but it takes them the better part of a month to settle in. Apparently shy of land, they alight for a while, then inexplicably disappear, only to return a few days later for more reconnaissance.

One day, finally, they take up residence, "sea parrots" by the dozens; by the thousands; even, in some colonies, by the millions. Each is recognizable as a puffin by its beak, that remarkable appendage with which it catches fish, wards off enemies, and communicates with its kin. If the bill is pointed upwards, it's like a hand outstretched in friendship; pointed down, it's a clenched fist. When two birds—a male and a female—stand head to head and press the sides of their bills together, they are indulging in a puffin hug and kiss.

The beak also serves as a pickax, for puffins nest in burrows that they dig and maintain themselves, most of this labor falling to the males. Though they normally work into turf, they can, in time, make progress through hard earth or fractured rock. Scientists, showing a reckless disregard for their fingertips (puffins bite!), have discovered that these hideaways are usually about a meter or two in length and may be connected underground. But each pair has a private entrance, which is defended in the early weeks of the season by the male, and a private nesting chamber at the dark end of the passageway. Some other species of seabird—a pair of razorbills or guillemots—will sometimes nest in the daylit "vestibule."

One of the consuming interests of an Atlantic Puffin's life is nest-lining material. At least, it looks like nest-lining material—great facefuls of grass, seaweed, feathers, roots, and dirt, which the bird gathers with its bill. But there's often something giddy, disconnected, about this passion. A bird will pluck grass furiously, as if nothing else mattered in life, amassing a burden larger than its head and will then defend its treasure against all the covetous neighbors that come crowding around. But later, this same material may be carelessly dropped, perhaps at a distance from its burrow, or in the entranceway, or halfway down the corridor. A few sprigs may actually make it to the nesting chamber, but it doesn't seem to matter, since the eggs often do perfectly well without. Is this a behavioral relic from a time when ancestral puffins built substantial, surface nests?

96

Puffins have two brood patches, one of which may be vestigial as well, since the birds normally lay a single egg. The incubation period is long—about six weeks—and the parents serve by turns, with the mother doing by far the larger share. Many evenings, when the wind conditions are right, the nesting adults and nonbreeding birds declare a general time-out, take to the air, and socialize. Some of them join in the whirring, whirling flocks that fly circuits over the colony, while others loiter about their burrows, watching their neighbors and looking for excitement. Any activity—a fight, a pair rubbing bills—is taken as a general invitation to rush up and get involved.

Around the first of July, the chicks hatch, and a new element is added to the life of the colony. Many of the adults coming in from sea now sport "muttonchops" of sardine-sized fish, primarily capelin, which they carry to the infants waiting below ground. These meals, like all the puffins' food, are caught by direct, underwater pursuit: puffins are expert divers and "fly" at least as well in water as they do in air; their feet are used for steerage, not propulsion. Prey is killed with the pincerlike tip of the bill and transferred, with a jerk of the head, toward the back of the gape; here it is secured by spiky serrations on the roof of the mouth and by the muscular, fingerlike tongue. As many as thirty small fish can be loaded in at once, and cargoes of ten are not unusual.

It is dangerous even for puffins to carry their wealth so publicly, and incoming birds are often beset by pirates as they near the colony. Gulls in particular will patrol the air approaches or lie in ambush on the ground, ready to badger the puffins into giving up their catch. If an egg is accidentally rolled toward the mouth of the burrow, if a hungry chick wanders up to check for its parents, it will be snatched, as well. This no doubt accounts for the fact that when puffins fledge, at around forty or forty-five days of age, they leave their burrows at night, tumble over the cliff, and paddle out to sea. They will not return for two years and will not breed until they are five years old.

Predation and parasitism by gulls have probably been a factor in the severe population decline that Atlantic Puffins have suffered recently. Yet this is not the gulls' fault, but ours; for we provide the garbage, sewage, and fishery waste on which the gulls' ever-growing numbers are sustained. Direct human interference is another probable cause, particularly at colonies along the north shore of the Gulf of Saint Lawrence. On the Atlantic coast, the ill-considered fishery policies of the Canadian government have recently led to the near exhaustion of the capelin stock, thereby jeopardizing the survival of the most populous puffin colonies on this continent—225,000 pairs that nest in Witless Bay, Newfoundland. Oil slicks on the ocean are already a life-threatening hazard, and the development of offshore oil and mineral deposits is a virtual guarantee of further calamities. Scientists close to the problem unhappily conclude that the future of Atlantic Puffins and other seabirds is imperilled, as long as we continue on our present course.

The Tufted Puffin is a west-coast counterpart of the Atlantic Puffin. Although much less studied, it is basically similar in habits. Horned Puffins and Rhinoceros Auklets are other closely related species that may be seen on the west coast.

Pigeons and Doves

Mourning Dove

It may be true, as the poet claims, that "a rose by any other name would smell as sweet." But in that case, it must also be true that the birds we know as "pigeons" can croon as gently as those we call "doves"; for there is no basis in science for distinguishing between the two. Pigeons are simply largish doves; doves, small-ish pigeons. In fact, the roughly three hundred species of pigeons and doves that occur in the world today are so closely related that they are customarily placed in the same taxonomic family. Some species, such as the crowned pigeons of New Guinea, are as big as turkeys, while others, like Australia's Diamond Dove, are sparrow-sized; yet most can be instantly recognized as "some kind of pigeon," thanks to their small heads and jerky, nodding walk. In Canada and the northern states, we have only three species: the introduced Rock Dove, or common pigeon, which came to us from Eurasia and now fills the niche of sidewalk-bomber-and-statue-defiler in most of our cities and towns; the native Band-tailed Pigeon, which breeds from the Rocky Mountains west to the Pacific coast; and the adaptable Mourning Dove, *Zenaida macroura,* which graces farmlands and broken woods from here to the Caribbean.

We used to have another species as well, the fabled Passenger Pigeon, which occurred from central Saskatchewan east to the Atlantic and south to the Gulf of Mexico. Almost unimaginably numerous, it bred in colonies that sometimes extended over several thousand hectares, and on migration its flocks literally darkened the skies. But numbers alone are no defense against human self-interest, and the Passenger Pigeon is now extinct—has been since 1914—a victim of both the shotgun and the plow.

Any thinking person looks back on these facts with chagrin. But at the same time, it is well to remember that extinction (like death) is a natural event, which natural systems can accommodate: the demise of one species often creates opportunities for the next. In this case, one of the beneficiaries may have been the Mourning Dove, which seems to have followed the farmer into parts of the Passenger Pigeon's former range, as well as other areas. Even in recent decades, the species has expanded in both Canada and the adjoining states. In the interior of British Columbia, for example, the breeding population has increased to the point that hunting is regularly permitted for several weeks in the fall.

Elsewhere in Canada, Mourning Doves are completely protected by law, but in many parts of the United States, they are a traditional game bird. Every year, American hunters take three or four times as many Mourning Doves as they do all species of waterfowl combined. While there are indications of slight and persistent declines in certain areas, dove populations have generally held remarkably well against this pressure, and the continental population is thought to stand at around 500 million. One reason for this success lies in the birds' full-blooded libidos, which can only be totally quenched, it seems, by subarctic cold. In the south, the breeding season may extend over nine or ten months of the year, and a typical pair will rear five broods. Even at our latitude, active nests can be found from March or April until September, and two broods per season is the average.

When Mourning Doves are amorous, they really do "bill and coo"; or, to be more precise about the sequence, they "coo and bill." The males are active with the first light of day, sighing out their hollow, plaintive tunes: "oh-oh coo coo coo." These calls are usually given from a high vantage point, such as a telephone wire, and may be one of the means by which an unwed male attracts a mate. Listen closely and you may also hear another, quieter call, a sort of short, staccato yodel. This sound, together with various soft gestures, is used by the male to lure his mate to the nest site. Once united, the birds caress each other on the head and neck, and murmur soft nest calls.

The birds often turn "lovey-dovey" during nest-building as well, since every straw that the male brings to his mate may stimulate a new round of endearments. The finished nest is what you'd expect from a pair of love-blurred minds—a scanty shell of grass and twigs that is often too frail to withstand summer storms, so that a substantial fraction of nests and eggs is lost. This inadequate construction is actually a result of the birds' inheritance, of course, and one wonders what it was that kept their ancestors from attaining greater proficiency: a need for speed and secrecy during nest-building? One skill that the species has acquired is the ability to usurp the nests of other birds, notably robins and thrashers; and this often markedly increases their success in rearing young.

A normal clutch for a pair of Mourning Doves consists of two pure white eggs. Barring mishap, these are incubated for about fifteen days, with father taking the day shift (roughly nine to five) and mother working nights. After the squabs hatch, the parents take turns brooding them for another two weeks and continue to feed them for several days after they leave the nest. Unlike the young of most seed-eating birds, which are fed on a pablum of insects, baby doves are raised on a substance called "pigeons' milk," a rich, cheesy liquid that is produced in the adults' crops. The young are also fed small amounts of grain and weed seeds, plus quantities of snails, which serve as a calcium supplement for young and old alike.

Even before the first brood is fully independent, the adults are busy with preparations for their second family. As in many birds, first-year mortality is quite high (about sixty percent), yet over a few seasons, the parents are likely to replace themselves and even achieve a surplus, enough so that the species can continue to withstand both natural and manmade adversity.

Mourning Doves seem to prefer conifers as nesting sites but they will accept deciduous growth—or cacti—or whatever's available, even using the ground if necessary. Despite their delicate appearance, they are hardy birds, capable of wintering in southern Ontario where food is available.

Cuckoos

Black-billed Cuckoo

Black-billed Cuckoos have a remarkable taste for caterpillars, even the hairy varieties that most birds refuse to eat. The peculiar "sucking pads" that occur in the young of this species can be seen in the mouth of one of the nestlings.

There is no point in looking for cuckoos in March, when the killdeers and bluebirds arrive; they've barely begun on their journey north from Ecuador and Peru. Nor will you find them in April, when the robins are singing and the ducks are back on their ponds. Even the great influx of songbirds that moves through in the first weeks of May is generally too early for them. But check again toward the end of the month, and there's a chance you will glimpse a lean, lissome, brown-backed bird gliding among the shadows of the underbrush. If it's about the size of a Mourning Dove, with a downcurved bill and a long tail that streams out behind, you can be sure that you have found a cuckoo. Composed but wary, it will likely take temporary refuge in the tree tops, then pause—silent, still—to fix you with a cool, over-the-shoulder stare. Its showy white breast is turned away for better camouflage, and no matter how you maneuver around its perch, it will pivot to compensate. The watchword among our cuckoos is "secrecy."

Only two species of these elusive birds breed at our latitude. The Yellow-billed Cuckoo, which can be identified in part by the white polka dots on the underside of its tail, is the common species throughout much of the United States. But it usually only ventures into Canada in southwestern British Columbia and southern Ontario, two areas where the climate is un-Canadian in its docility. The characteristic species in our area is the Black-billed Cuckoo, *Coccyzus erythropthalmus,* and even it is far from plentiful here. It can be distinguished by the narrow white bands on its tail, its red eye-ring, and, of course, its all-black bill.

Taken as a whole, the cuckoo family is best known for its tendency toward "brood parasitism": no longer inclined to build their own nests, such "parasites" rely on other species to incubate and rear their young. Of the eighty-seven hundred species of birds in the world, only seventy-five have evolved this remarkable habit, and more than half of them are cuckoos. So well adapted that one almost suspects them of cunning, these birds often lay eggs that look like those of their hosts, and their young may be programmed to push out any other eggs or chicks that they find in the nest. But interestingly, these specializations have not spread to the North American members of the cuckoo family. Certainly, North American cuckoos do occasionally lay their eggs in other birds' nests, and there have even been reports that their hatchlings will toss other youngsters out, but this is not the birds' usual strategy. Instead, they lay in frail, saucerlike nests of grass and twigs that they make themselves. In the case of Black-billed Cuckoos, these are usually placed in hedgerows, orchards, and thickets or near the edges of woods, well-concealed by greenery, and within a meter or two of the ground. Since the nests are probably not very stormworthy, it may be that Black-bills sometimes use other birds' homes when their own blow down. Accidental loss of nests, if followed by renesting, may also contribute to the wide range of egg dates reported for this species—from May to September in the northern states and southern Ontario.

Black-billed Cuckoos normally produce between two and four eggs, which are tended by both parents, beginning with the first laid. The incubation period for each egg is an amazingly short time—only ten or twelve days—but the eggs hatch at intervals, so the total time involved is somewhat longer. The chicks are odd little creatures at first, with black, greasy-looking skin and a sparse, hairlike down that never unfurls. This unfluffy down is quickly

replaced by an unfeathery plumage, for the emerging feathers are encased in hard tubes, or sheaths, so that the birds' tiny bodies seem to bristle with bluish quills. These can be erected whenever the nestlings want to look formidable, a defense they maintain until their sixth or seventh day. Then the feathers suddenly bloom, and the nestlings are transformed into dapper brown-and-white birds. If they're threatened now, the youngsters may adopt an upright, bitternlike pose, or even play dead. In the one recorded instance of this latter behavior, the bird was so limp that it could be draped over a branch, yet it revived instantly and scurried to safety when it slipped onto the ground.

From the start, Black-billed Cuckoos are overwhelmingly hungry. The rustle of leaves, a parent's footstep on the nest branch, or the adults' special mewing call may all elicit the chick's begging display: flapping wings, outstretched neck, open mouth, and a hunger cry that sounds like the buzzing of bees. "Feed me! Feed me!" Inside the gaping mouth, the nestlings show a group of curious, snow-white disks with roughened surfaces. Are these "sucking pads" that permit the baby to grip its parent's bill; targets for the adults, so the food gets in the right spot; or devices that permit the infant to grasp live food? No one knows.

The consistent staple in the diet of North American cuckoos is caterpillars, including the spiny ones like tent caterpillars that most birds won't touch. A Black-billed Cuckoo can devour a whole ball of writhing larvae in five minutes flat and will stand and eat until it's literally bulging with food. Sometimes it shears the hairs off by working the insects with its bill, though this is by no means necessary. A cuckoo's digestive tract may become completely studded with spines, yet the bird appears unharmed by its internal hair shirt.

On average, baby Black-bills are probably fed about three times an hour all day and receive not only caterpillars but grasshoppers, beetles, and the other large insects that are relished by their kind. It is not altogether surprising, therefore, that they grow up rapidly and are ready to leave the nest when scarcely a week old. Not yet able to fly, they spend another two weeks as "branchers" in their home tree. Then they and their parents virtually disappear for another year. Do some start south straightaway? This and many other questions about North American cuckoos remain unanswered, and much of what we think we know rests on a shaky foundation of too few observations. If you have a chance to watch them, be sure to take notes; chances are that you'll learn something new.

Order Strigiformes

Owls

Imagine the dark of night. Turn out the streetlights, let the moon wane, and blanket the stars with cloud: impenetrable dark. Or so it seems from a human point of view. But to most species of owls, these conditions are not impenetrable at all. Creatures of the night and "owl light," they fly and hunt with confidence where we could only jitter and stumble about. How do they do it?

One advantage that owls have is exceptional eyesight, both by day and night. Their pupil is unusually responsive, capable of "stopping down" to a mere pin prick in sunlight or opening to a wide disk after dark; each eye can adjust independently to its own circumstance of light or shade. As in all vertebrates, the retina is composed of two types of visual cells, "rods" for low light and "cones" for day; but whereas cones predominate in the human eye, the owl has mostly rods. This helps explain how it is that one species of owl (possibly others as well) can hunt successfully in light equal to that thrown by a candle three-quarters of a kilometer away. But relying on rods poses problems, as well, particularly a loss of resolution. In a cone retina, every visual cell fires its own neuron, so that each detail is registered separately by the brain; but rods work in clusters, several of them feeding impulses to the same nerve cell, so that fine points may be merged and lost. As a result, owls' eyes have become elongated, roughly tubular, with a long "throw" between the lens and the retinal screen. Thus, the image is large and is cast over many rod clusters, so that the details are perceived.

The sheer size of owls' eyes is another of their remarkable characteristics. The eyeballs of a Snowy Owl, for example, may be as big as your own, though the bird stands only half a meter tall. There's scarcely room for them in the skull, certainly not enough for them to go in end to end, angling outwards, like the eyes of most birds. Instead, they sit side by side, looking frontwards, with the result that the left and right fields of vision partially overlap. This gives the birds a broad band of two-eyed, or binocular, vision, which greatly increases their ability to judge distances. But, again, there are disadvantages. Because the eyes are focused straight ahead and are too large to move in their sockets, owls have "tunnel vision." Their glance encompasses only about 110 degrees, compared to 180 for people and 340 for pigeons. In order to see behind them or to the side, owls must swivel their whole head. Accordingly, their necks are limber enough to permit a quick half turn in either direction.

Another key to the owls' ability to defeat darkness lies in their ultra-sensitive hearing. The ears are large and are located on the sides of the head, just at the edge of the facial disk. As in other birds, there are no protruding ears to offer wind resistance in flight. (The earlike tufts, or "horns," seen on some species of owls are thought to play a part in communication, species recognition, or in disrupting the contours of the head for better camouflage.) Sound is probably funneled into the ears by the dished-in contours of the facial disk and by the specialized feathers and flaps around the ear openings. An owl's ears are very sensitive to high frequencies—the squeak of a mouse, rustling grass—and are so keen that certain species (notably the Barn Owl) can hunt blind, in the total absence of light. In some species, the positioning and structure of the ears is asymmetrical, and this unusual feature is thought to assist the birds in pinpointing sounds through triangulation.

Owls are also renowned for the silence of their flight, an attribute that is related, in part, to their reliance on hearing. Their aural refinements would be of little value if their ears were filled with the roaring of their own wings. An owl's plumage is soft, and the flight feathers are finely fringed along the leading edge, so as to deflect the air smoothly rather than cut it percussively. Most species also have a low "wing loading" (comparatively large wings in relation to body mass), which also helps account for their easy, noiseless flight.

Obviously, the ability to move about in secrecy is of great value to a predator. An owl's prey must often have no inkling of an impending attack until the hunter's talons pierce its flesh. Perhaps this explains why smaller birds instinctively create an uproar whenever they encounter a roosting owl, thereby depriving it of the element of surprise.

Owls have probably existed since about the end of the dinosaurian age but may not have been abundant until more recent eras, when seed-bearing plants and seed-eating animals, particularly rodents, became well established. Today there are about 134 species in all (16 in Canada and the neighboring states), which are customarily divided into two families, the Barn and Bay owls, or Tytonidae, and the "typical owls," or Strigidae. In terms of behavior, these two groups are very similar. For example, in almost all species, females tend to be larger than males; no nest is built; only the female incubates; incubation begins with the first egg laid; and the male provides for his mate and family during incubation and early development of the young. Many of these characteristics are also shared by vultures, eagles, hawks, and falcons of the "diurnal raptor" group, but this is probably the result of convergent evolution, not kinship. The owls' closest relatives are thought to be the oilbirds, frogmouths, potoos, and nighthawks of the nightjar group, an order with which owls share their mastery of the night.

Great Horned Owl

This is the "cat owl," *Bubo virginianus,* one of the largest and most widespread owls in the Western Hemisphere. Not only does it nest in almost all the wooded and partly wooded regions of North and Central America—wild northern forests, deserts, jungles, mountains, suburban parks—it is also adapted to the life zones and upside-down seasons on the other side of the equator: its range extends to land's end in South America. Although there are regional variations in coloration (birds from dense coastal forests are dark, for example, while those from the snowy subarctic tend to be pale), the species can always be distinguished by its feather-tuft "ears" and its size. With a wing span that approaches 1.5 meters and body weights of around 1.5 kilograms, the Horned Owl far outclasses the other "eared" owls that occur on our continent.

For a bird of such impressive dimensions, this "king of the owls" can make itself surprisingly inconspicuous. By day, it often slips in beside the trunk of a thick-growing conifer and draws itself up tall and sleek, like a person hiding behind a post. Crows or jays will sometimes give it away with an outburst of loud complaints, for they object to having a large owl in the neighborhood and will harry it into flight; but otherwise the owl slumbers on in privacy. We only become aware of its presence at nightfall, when its mellow song stirs through the darkening woods: Whoo, hoo-hoo-hoo, hoo-oo, hoo-oo. Each utterance consists of from three to eight hoots, grouped into phrases to form a pattern. The bird may be as far off as a kilometer or more when we hear its voice, yet we can identify it positively as a Great Horned Owl, by its insistent hooting.

Horned Owls are generally nonmigratory—they winter wherever they breed, throughout their vast range—so their calls can be heard in every month of the year. At our latitude, the birds are noisiest in midwinter, when their reproductive season opens with bouts of "competitive hooting" amongst the males. The issue seems to be territory, with each individual reasserting his claim to the eight or ten square kilometers of habitat in which he and his mate will nest and hunt for themselves and their young. This area is their

Great Horned Owl

This Great Horned Owl has caught a Meadow Vole. The owl's ear tufts are the long, dark feathers at the side of the head, which are smoothed back in this photograph. They can also be held erect.

permanent home, and the boundaries are thought to change little from year to year. Mate relationships are believed to be stable, as well, and are renewed annually in an intimate winter ritual that has only rarely been observed. Standing side by side on a branch, the lovers bow low and hoot, then face each other and rub bills gently, bow again, caress, and bow once more, dancing to the staccato beat of their calls and clacking beaks.

The birds are on their nests by March, give or take a couple of weeks. They have been known to breed in almost every conceivable situation, from hay barns to cathedrals and cliff faces to cacti, but they usually choose large stick nests built by crows, herons, or hawks; in our region, the nests of Red-tailed Hawks are particularly favored. Horned Owls display no aptitude for home-building or renovations, and such improvements as they occasionally make—the addition of a feather lining, for example—are probably accidental. Sometimes, the structure becomes so dilapidated that it literally falls apart, dumping the

eggs or owlets on the ground. By the end of the season, even the best of nests is unfit for further use, unless its original occupants return to fix it up.

Great Horned Owls usually lay two or three eggs, which take a month to hatch; the female does most of the incubation, while the male stands guard in a nearby tree. Since the weather in March is harsh, the eggs must be tended almost constantly. If you flush the adult by climbing to the nest, the embryos may be chilled to death. It is also distinctly possible that you will be seriously hurt, since the owls sometimes launch a blitzkrieg of body blows and slashing talons in defense of their young. The likelihood of this happening depends, in part, on the mood and temperament of the pair in question, so unless you have a gift for mindreading owls, you'd be wise to stay on the ground.

In general, the parents' concern seems to peak when the young are ready to leave the nest. This may happen as early as a month of age, two or three weeks before the owlets

Facing page: Hissing and clacking its bill, this fledgling Great Horned Owl has expanded itself to maximum possible size as a defense against intruders.

Great Horned Owls develop slowly and do not usually become fully independent until late summer.

attempt their first flight. A fledgling Horned Owl is an inept, backward creature that can make hard work out of landing on a branch and is totally incapable of feeding itself. Consider the case of one typical young novice, two months out of the nest, which made three unsuccessful strikes at a rabbit and then proceeded to crash into the ground on its final attempt. The rabbit, needless to say, got away. So slowly do the juveniles gain proficiency that their parents have to feed them until late summer, almost to the time when the youngsters disperse.

A seasoned adult, on the other hand, is a master hunter, capable of taking a wide range of prey, from shrews and songbirds to skunks and geese, including animals that exceed it in weight. "Winged tigers" they're sometimes called; but it would be more accurate to think of them as the "lynx of the air." Like lynx, Great Horned Owls specialize in killing mid-sized birds and mammals, such as hares, rabbits, and grouse. In Canada, Snowshoe Hares and a few grouse may be almost the only food during the six hardest months of the year, when the songbirds have fled and the rodents are under the snow. It follows, then, that when the hare population crashes, as it does about every ten years, the owls inevitably suffer a corresponding decline. While some may starve, most respond to a wintertime food shortage by shifting southward; and nesting may also be curtailed. In one Alberta study, for example, an area that supported sixteen breeding pairs when the hares were at the crest of their cycle was found to carry only a single nest through the trough. Clutches also tend to be smaller in a low-hare year, with the result that the local population stays more or less within the limits of its food supply.

Great Horned Owls are the top predators in their food chains and have no significant enemies except people. Although one strains to think of a legitimate reason for killing these creatures (except perhaps for the occasional individual that persistently takes poultry), many of them meet their end through shooting. In the wild, their maximum life expectancy is about seventeen years, though few survive so long.

Snowy Owl

There is only one "great white owl," *Nyctea scandiaca,* a creature supremely adapted to the tyrannical climate of the far North. For six or eight months of the year, its homeland falls under the subjugation of darkness and snow, with temperatures as low as –50° C and driving, cutting winds. Yet the Snowy Owl survives by putting its belly to the ground and facing into the storms. One adaptation that helps it accomplish this feat is its compact and relatively massive build. Though the Snowy is the heaviest owl on the continent, with females that sometimes reach two kilograms, it is not the largest overall. Thus (like most Arctic animals), it has a comparatively large body mass with which to generate heat and a comparatively small surface area through which heat can be lost. What's more, the entire body, from the top of the head to the tip of the toes, is insulated with a dense layer of feathers and down; only the eyeballs and the tips of the beak and talons are exposed.

But if these birds are so well equipped to withstand Arctic conditions, why do some of them winter far to the south? And why do these visitations not occur in equal numbers every year? The answers to these questions are thought to lie in the curious biology of two species of northern rodents, the lemmings. These plump little creatures, which are the year-round staple of Snowy Owls and a number of other predators, are subject to violent oscillations in their populations and suffer calamitous die-offs about once in four or five years. Severe weather, food shortage, psychological stress, and genetic deterioration have all been suggested as contributing factors in the lemmings' ups and downs; but whatever the causes, the effects are spectacular. One spring, there are lemmings by the thousands, nipping in and out of burrows, scurrying across frozen lakes, and nesting in every conceivable

Snowy Owl

recess: a person can easily see fifty at a glance. A year later, in the same place, you'd be hard pressed to find a single one.

The booms and busts of the lemming cycle are echoed in the reproductive behavior of Snowy Owls. When lemmings are superabundant, the entire owl population turns out to nest. By May, the males are already hooting aggressively across the frozen tundra, as each stakes out a few square kilometers of habitat on which to hunt and rear his family. His mate, meanwhile, prepares a shallow, cuplike scrape on a hillock or mossy rock, and here she lays the eggs—occasionally as many as fourteen, though eight is about average for a good year— Incubation, by the female alone, begins with the first egg and lasts for about thirty-three days per chick, or seven weeks in all. By the time the last little "ookpik" cuts its way out of the shell, its siblings embody all the ages and stages of infancy, with some still in their white natal down and others working their way through darkening shades of gray. Soot-black by the age of two weeks, the chicks leave the nest in turn and go into hiding on the tundra, within a few hundred meters of home. Although their faces start turning white again almost immediately, it will be another six weeks before they look like Snowy Owls and only then, when their plumage is almost complete, will they be able to fly. All told, from the day the first egg is laid until the last chick has fledged, the owlets are dependent on their parents for nearly fifteen weeks.

Throughout this period, the youngsters' two urgent needs are protection and food. The father in particular is on constant alert, ready to launch his "crippled bird" routine or a plunging, feet-first attack; he will even go into action against humans and wolves. During the months when the female is busy at the nest (she stays in attendance until the last chick

With its compact body and thick feathers, this Snowy Owl is well equipped to protect both eggs and hatchlings from the uncertainties of an arctic spring. In general, females (like this bird) are more heavily marked with black than the males.

leaves), the male is also responsible for feeding the entire family. The youngsters gain forty times their original weight in as many weeks, and each requires about 140 full-grown lemmings, or the equivalent, during its dependency; that's eleven kilograms apiece! Yet, when lemmings are plentiful, the father can feed himself, his mate, and a dozen or more chicks by hunting for less than five hours a day. Under these conditions, almost all the chicks will survive.

But every year of surplus is inevitably followed by a great famine, during which few pairs nest and infant mortality soars. The owls are forced to rely on alternate prey such as ptarmigan, songbirds, and waterfowl. One individual was seen catching fish, by lying prone beside a hole in the ice; another regularly patrolled along an antennae wire on which phalaropes were often hurt or killed. Versatile and resourceful, the owls take advantage of almost any opportunity that presents itself. Though predominantly diurnal, they will prey on murrelets and storm-petrels in the dead of night; though they prefer to hunt from perches,

they can strike from midair like a kestrel or work over rodent burrows from the ground like a fox. Nonetheless, when lemmings are scarce, food must often run short.

Though a certain number of Snowy Owls come south each October, dramatic "irruptions" are thought to occur whenever there is a widespread lemming crash. A few wayward emigrants end up far out to sea, but most of the travelers move south toward central Europe, southern Siberia, Mongolia, southern Canada, and the northern states. In North America, the flights are heaviest over the prairies and Great Lakes. As one might expect of tundra-adapted birds, the owls avoid forests in favor of open country and show a particular preference for stubble fields, where Meadow Voles (the southern equivalent of lemmings) are plentiful and easily caught. Such prime habitat is often taken over by adult females, which may claim territories for two or three months; juvenile females get second pick of the hunting range, while the males are generally nomadic. Assuming that no one shoots them, the birds are usually on their way north by March.

Not having the advantage of a tree-perch, young Snowy Owls learn to fly by springing from the ground, beating their wings furiously, and falling back to earth. Then one day, finally, they're airborne.

Burrowing Owl

The people at the *Guinness Book of World Records* might want to consider establishing a new category, one for "the most Burrowing Owls, *Athene cunicularia*, seen in a single year." If they did, the laurels would no doubt go to Jim and Shirley Wedgwood of Saskatoon, Saskatchewan, who made a summer-long project of locating these rare and rarely seen birds. Every Saturday morning, it was up, pack a picnic, and away, to cruise along another few hundred kilometers of back roads and dirt trails. The object of the search was, first, to find an area of close-cropped natural grassland and then to scan the ground for a lanky, feathered sentinel, standing abruptly upright on a gopher mound. By the end of the season, the Wedgwoods had sighted 276 of these little "prairie owls" in an area where only 6 had been reported in the preceding ten years, and in the process, they counted themselves richly entertained.

Field biology is one of the few sciences in which a dedicated amateur, motivated solely by the joy of discovery, can still make important contributions. The Wedgwoods, for example, learned that Burrowing Owls at our latitude seem less adaptable than their counterparts farther south. When the Great Plains of the central United States were planted to cereals and tame grasses, the owls there were able to adjust to the changed conditions, though probably in reduced numbers. In California, there are now prosperous Burrowing Owl populations around golf courses and airports. But in Saskatchewan, the birds generally restrict themselves to the remaining patches of native vegetation, such as the farmyard pastures that were set aside in the era when every family had its own milk cows. As farming becomes increasingly specialized, this and other short-grass habitat gradually disappears and so do the Burrowing Owls. Other factors

Burrowing Owl
(Southern boundary
uncertain)

must also be at work, as well—road kills, shooting, pesticide poisoning, problems along migration routes or on the wintering grounds—for in recent years, the Saskatchewan population seems to have declined faster than the rate of habitat loss. There is every reason to believe that this is also true in the neighboring provinces and states. In Canada as a whole, there are probably about two thousand pairs, and the species is now officially listed as "threatened."

Burrowing Owls are appealing creatures, with a number of surprising characteristics. For one thing, they can be sociable—a rare quality in predatory birds. In the old days, they are said to have gathered by the hundreds to breed; today, with their habitat fractured, they are more solitary. Another peculiarity, this one well known, is their habit of nesting below ground, usually in dens abandoned by badgers, prairie dogs, or ground squirrels, which the owls remodel to suit their needs. (The rarity or virtual disappearance of burrowing mammals in certain areas—notably British Columbia—may be responsible for the owls' decline there.) An occupied burrow can be identified by the feathers, pellets, and food scraps that accumulate on its doorstep and, early in the

The staple diet of Burrowing Owls is insects—this one has a grasshopper—and rodents. Unlike most owls, Burrowers may be active at any hour of the day.

With an adult (probably the mother) standing guard on the right, two young Burrowing Owls come out—or halfway out—of their nest hole.

season, by the lining material that pokes out of the hole. The owls furnish their homes with whatever is at hand—dried grass, divots from a golf course, newspaper, bird wings, bits of trash—but they prefer to use dry, shredded cow and horse manure. This is placed along the entire length of the tunnel: down the sloping entranceway, around all the curves and bends, right to the chamber at the end, two or three meters in all. No other species of owls goes to so much trouble over its nests. Perhaps the Burrower has a special need for insulation (the eggs may be almost a meter down, where frost lingers in spring) or for protection from predators such as housecats, badgers, and skunks. Who'd expect to find a meal of tasty birds or eggs in what smells like a dung heap?

The female owl goes underground in May, and there, in the dark, amid swarms of fleas, she lays and incubates six to eleven eggs. Except for brief daily airings, she remains in confinement for about five weeks, while her mate does the hunting and stands by to defend the nest. If a person or predator approaches the nest, he responds with a lavish welcome—his "howdydo" display—in which he bobs and bows so deeply that his breast almost hits the ground. The real purpose of this behavior is to lure the enemy away, as becomes obvious when the bird swoops to another, more-distant mound and goes through the performance again.

The first indications we get that the young have hatched are the reappearance of the female and the disappearance of the nest lining, which she inexplicably removes. Nothing is seen of the infants themselves for another two weeks, until one day in late June, there they are, standing in a tight cluster on the entrance mound. At the slightest hint of danger, the nestlings vanish down the hole. If really frightened, they utter an alarm call that sounds almost exactly like a rattlesnake, thereby scaring off intruders and, incidentally, giving rise to the legend that rattlers and Burrowing Owls live in the same dens. As an extra measure of protection, the mother attends the youngsters closely for the first three or four weeks, so that the male bears full responsibility for keeping everyone fed—no easy task. Burrowing Owls are voracious: adults routinely stuff themselves with forty to sixty grasshoppers in succession, and a brood of growing young can devour several dozen insects, plus an assortment of reptiles, amphibians, and rodents in an hour or two. Most hunting is done in the twilight, before sunrise and after sunset, but the owls also work by day, particularly in midsummer when the young are hungriest.

By mid-August, the new generation of Burrowing Owls is on the wing. Some of them immediately head off, but most move into private burrows near the nest site and stay for another month or six weeks. No one knows where our owls winter—probably Oklahoma and Texas—but we do know they require burrows for shelter throughout the year. Assuming that their habitat is not disrupted while they're gone, at least one of the adults will likely return to the nest den in the spring.

Great Gray Owl

Great Gray Owl

The Great Gray Owl is a rare and impressive bird, agile and efficient in flight, beautiful when perched. Once considered a strictly north-woods species, its known range has expanded greatly in recent years.

No matter how much you've read or how many pictures you've seen, the sighting of a Great Gray Owl in the wild is thrilling. The chance is most likely to come toward dusk on a winter day, as you travel through broken forest or bushy fields near the southern edge of the species' range. You stop the car, scan a few meters up in the aspen and spruce along the road, and there's your bird, *Strix nebulosa,* perched on a stout side branch. The first thing that impresses you is its size, for this species is the biggest of all North American owls. A large individual stands as tall as a two-year-old child, and the circumference of its head almost equals that of a grown woman. Its wings, when it unfurls them, seem immense—broad, like a heron's, and almost as long as a woman's arm span. (These characteristics, together with the absence of "ear" tufts, make the Great Gray unmistakable, even at a distance.) Yet its imposing dimensions are little more than illusory, for the bird consists primarily of feathers and air. An average specimen weighs about a kilogram, slightly less for a male, slightly more for a hen, making it lighter than a frying chicken! As a taxidermist once put it after examining a carcass, the Great Gray offers "the most bird for the least substance" of any he'd seen.

Few North Americans ever have the privilege of seeing these creatures alive. Apart from irregular wintertime incursions into southern Canada and the adjacent states, Great Grays are generally associated with northern coniferous forests, where the seasonal progression from muskeg and mosquitoes to impassable snowdrifts discourages most human visitors. Even those who make the trek are often disappointed, for the birds are so inconspicuous that they used to be known as "spectral owls." Their dark, vaguely patterned plumage blends with the lichens and shadows around them, and their behavior is usually not flamboyant. To make matters even more difficult, the species is rare in most localities. The best recent estimate puts the North American population at about fifty thousand, though some would argue that this is far too high.

As recently as the mid-1950s, Alberta biologist Al Oeming traveled fifty thousand kilometers searching for active nests; yet only two could be found. His conclusion: that the birds were near extinction, largely because so many had been shot by trappers. Since then, however, there have been signs of a recovery. In the late 1970s and early 1980s, researchers in Manitoba have often been able to band several dozen Great Grays in a winter, mostly within a few hours drive of Winnipeg. (They have also documented the existence of a substantial summertime, nesting population in southeastern Manitoba and central Minnesota.) In general, there seems to be a trend for the birds' southward "migrations" to occur more frequently and to involve greater numbers than in the past. The winter of 1978-79 saw what may have been the influx of the century, with thousands of sightings from Manitoba to the east coast. On Amherst Island, near Kingston, Ontario, where forty Great Grays were noted, it was possible to see eighteen in a day and once, remarkably, nine in the same tree!

In addition to the birds themselves, winter owl-watchers can also hope to see their sign. Great Grays have two methods of hunting. They can locate their prey by sight—a vole on the snow two hundred meters away—swoop down, and snatch it in their claws, in which case they leave little trace. Or they can rely on their discerning and sensitive ears to find food under the snow. As the owl moves from perch to perch, watching, listening, the incoming sound waves are caught and focused by the specialized feathers of the facial disks. Nothing is missed: the tiny, snow-muffled grating of a vole chewing on a seed instantly catches the hunter's attention. Absolutely intent, the owl may permit you to walk right up to it rather than break its concentration on the spot from which the sound is issuing. Finally, it swings into the air, hovers briefly to perfect its aim, and crashes through the snow with its feet, making a crater about twenty-five centimeters deep. But what if the snow is deeper than this, as is often the case in the northern woods? Then the bird hovers, tilts in midair, and plunges face first into the drifts, sometimes hitting with such force that snow is compacted in a thick cone underneath. By drawing its feet to the bottom of the hole and reaching down, a Great Gray can grab for mice through half a meter of snow. As far as is known, no other species regularly uses these techniques, so the presence of owl-sized craters, flanked by the imprint of wings, is strong evidence that Great Gray Owls are around.

From January on, as the owls begin to court, plunge-diving may sometimes take on sexual overtones: up to thirty-three holes have been found near a nest. Courtship feeding also occurs, and the pair bond is sealed when the female begins to accept her suitor's nuptial offerings of fresh-caught voles. The male goes on to provide for his mate and young through the spring and summer. The female, meanwhile, is at the nest (one built in a previous year by a hawk, raven, or crow), first incubating her clutch of two to five small eggs, then shielding the chicks from rain storms and hot sun. For two or two and a half months, she stays at her post almost twenty-four hours a day, with occasional brief breaks to bathe, stretch, or cough up a pellet of fur and bone. An owl-watcher should approach the nest with caution, since the bird is unpredictable and may attack. Often, though, she will seem gentle and placid, willing to tolerate considerable human disturbance without sign of alarm, perhaps even sitting quietly on the side of the nest while the young are being weighed. In general, Great Grays seem to trust us not to cause them harm, and we must hope their faith becomes increasingly well placed.

Northern Saw-whet Owl

After reading this, you may never again pass a woodpecker tree at nesting time without giving the base a sharp rap. For sooner or later, if you persist, a small, round head will pop out of one of the holes, and you will have found a Northern Saw-whet Owl, *Aegolius acadicus,* on its nest. The species can be recognized, first, by size, since it only grows to be twenty centimeters tall, or about the height of an adult person's hand. Other distinguishing characteristics are its black bill, chunky build, and lack of "ear" tufts. The best place to look for a nest is in a dense stand of trees—a wooded coulee, a river valley, or an extensive tract of forest; the birds usually settle near water, within ten meters of the ground, and almost always in cavities made by Northern Flickers. The best time to look is early spring, about April, when the birds have just begun incubating, since that's when they're most likely to flush. Later in the season, many Saw-whets will sit calmly inside the hole, no matter how you thump and clatter around. Indeed, some particularly nervy individuals will permit

Northern Saw-whet Owls often spend the day roosting in the shadowy shelter of dense growth.

118

Young Saw-whet Owls bear
so little resemblance to the
adults that they were once
officially considered a
separate species, under the
name of Kirtland's Owl. By
fall, parents and offspring
are almost indistinguishable.

themselves to be lifted off the nest by hand, rather than give themselves away by showing alarm.

Any adult Saw-whet found on a nest is likely to be a female, since the mother bird is thought to do all the incubating. The male spends his days sleeping in a tree, usually perched quite close to the ground and in a spot where he is protected from view by thick foliage. If you hear a ruckus created by warblers or other small birds, it's worth investigating, for they may lead you to one of these Saw-whet hideaways. Here, as at the nest, your bird is likely to seem quite unperturbed by a close approach and may permit himself to be held and stroked. Although it helps to have another person or a dog along to create a diversion, a Saw-whet can be beguiled simply by tossing a glove on a nearby branch or wriggling your fingers in front of his face. These maneuvers so hold his attention that he fails to detect the hand sneaking up from behind to capture him. But beware: touching the sensitive bristles at the base of the owl's bill is irritating and may provoke him to attack. Treat him gently, and he will probably seem quite unmoved by his encounter with humanity. When you put him on his roost, he will likely go right back to sleep. Better yet, you might enjoy knowing that the bird would let you touch him but choose to leave him in peace.

Unless disturbed, a male Saw-whet usually rouses just before sunset to go hunting mice, other small mammals, and, occasionally, song-birds. His visits to the nest site are generally brief—just long enough to drop a carcass down the hole—but he sometimes pauses for a few seconds to reassert his claim to the area with a shrill territorial call. (In late winter and spring, when the birds are establishing their territories, they can often be attracted by an imitation of their whistling.) The male supports his mate and his family of four to seven young for about six weeks, through the egg and early nestling stages; then, when the young are well feathered, the female begins to help with the food-getting. The chicks leave the nest in June or July, when just over a month of age.

What the birds do in the winter is still not totally clear. In some areas, Saw-whets may be permanent residents within their breeding range, except for years of famine when they winter farther south. But elsewhere—particularly around the Great Lakes—there are regularly timed spring and fall migrations. Between early October and mid-November, Saw-whets travel by the hundreds along the north shores of Lakes Ontario, Erie, and Superior with special concentrations at places like Long Point, Toronto Island, and Point Pelee, in Ontario and Hawk Ridge in Minnesota, where they lay over for a while before attempting the long water crossing. Less secretive than in the summer but just as docile, they are easily caught and banded at their daytime roosts. The return voyage is made in April or May, but the route and concentration points are less well known.

Northern Saw-whet Owl

Order Caprimulgiformes

Nightjars

Common Nighthawk

Although hawks by name, Common Nighthawks bear little resemblance to raptors. (Note the tiny beak and small, weak feet.) Because of their "booming" displays, Nighthawks are sometimes known as "bull bats."

In many ways, the nightjars can be considered the avian equivalent of bats. Of the ninety-odd species of birds that belong to this order, all are active by night or twilight, and at least one, the South American Oilbird, has gone so far as to develop sonar, a power that enables it to navigate through the utter blackness of its nesting caves. Like many bats, most nightjars are insect-eaters and take their prey in flight. They are aided in this by an unusual adaptation—enormous mouths. Nightjars typically have tiny beaks but tremendous gapes, which literally stretch from ear to ear. On the basis of this characteristic, the ancients called them "goatsuckers," believing that they fed by suckling goats. In many species, the corners of the mouth are furnished with long bristles, which help to prevent insects from escaping sideways. Thus, functionally, most nightjars can be thought of as flying insect-traps.

Only four members of the order occur in Canada and the neighboring states: the Chuck-will's Widow, Poor-will, Whip-poor-will, and Common Nighthawk. Of these, none is better known nor more widely distributed than the nighthawk, *Chordeiles minor*. A medium-sized bird (about as big as a robin), it usually spends its days dozing right out in the open—on the ground, a fence post, or a tree branch—yet is seldom noticed because it looks like dry leaves or loose bark. Curiously, nighthawks generally perch lengthwise on a branch, rather than at right angles to it, a habit that may be related to their need for camouflage or, more probably, to the structure of their feet, which are small, weak, and ill-suited for balancing. Although able to walk quite nimbly for short distances, Common Nighthawks are at their best in the air, and that is where they are most often observed, darting, turning, and wheeling against a darkening sky. With few

exceptions, their active period begins just before sunset and ends just after sunrise. You can expect to see them over open countryside (marshes, meadows, and pastures), but look for them in cities as well, especially in the haze of bugs around streetlights. Nighthawks have been known to vacuum up five hundred mosquitoes in one feeding, or twenty-two hundred flying ants; termites, beetles, and grasshoppers are other important foods.

In flight, Common Nighthawks are often recognized by the bar of white that decorates each of their long, pointed wings. But another and much more spectacular clue is the so-called "booming" of the males, a behavior that is most commonly (though not exclusively) observed at mating time. Fifty or sixty meters up, a tiny speck in the sky, the bird circles and calls: "peent, peent." Then, suddenly, he plunges earthward, down and down, closer and closer to the ground, until, at last, he breaks his fall and swoops up again, perhaps to prepare for another dive. At his turning point, he twists his wings in such a way that air is forced through his flight feathers, producing a loud, dull "woof." Booming seems to be associated primarily with courtship and territorial defense and is the nighthawk's equivalent to song.

A male's booming flights tend to be clustered over his nest or, to be more precise, over the area in which the female tends the eggs. Strictly speaking, Common Nighthawks do not build nests. The two spotted eggs are laid directly on unprepared ground, usually sand, pebbles, leaf litter, or recent burns; the graveled tops of flat-roofed buildings are particular favorites. Here, as on their day-roosts, the birds rely on camouflage for protection, with the mother masquerading as a pile of leaves or stones and the eggs as pebbles. This latter

illusion is so convincing that the female herself sometimes seems to be taken in and will settle on a cluster of egglike rocks for a few seconds when she's trying to find her clutch. Another reason for her confusion is that the eggs are often moved frequently during the three weeks of incubation, either accidentally, when the adult settles on them, or deliberately, when they're shifted out of puddles or into shade. Although it would be fun to imagine the mother bird carrying eggs in her mouth or under her wings, as has sometimes been supposed, she actually trundles them along in front of her with her legs.

The hatchlings, of course, are easier to move, since they're physically precocious and come when mother calls. The female broods them against cold, heat, and rain; defends them against predators; and, with the help of their father, feeds them for about three weeks—longer, if the chicks have their way. Like some human children, young nighthawks sometimes seem to assume that mom and dad are willing to wait on them forever. Even when three-quarters grown, they may try to squirm under their mother for shelter, knocking her off her feet; or they may hang around home for an extra week or two, quite content to depend on their parents for food.

Ultimately, the adults may have to tease their "spoiled babies" into flight by offering feedings and then withholding them. But by late August, all the youngsters have cut the apron strings, and the entire population is free to move southward, toward South America. Unlike their remarkable cousins, the Poorwills, which sometimes crawl into crevices in canyon walls and go dormant during the winter, Common Nighthawks apparently do not hibernate.

Looking more like bedroom slippers than living birds, these Nighthawk fledglings doze on a log.

Order Apodiformes

Hummingbirds

Think of it, if you like, as an explosion of life: hummingbirds, bright as sparks, radiating from their origins in the American tropics. Near the equator, particularly in the mountains of Ecuador and Columbia, the birds exist in dazzling variety—163 species within ten degrees of latitude, and there may well be more that we haven't seen yet. North and south of this zone, the numbers gradually decline, to fifty or sixty each in Mexico and Bolivia; then to twenty or so in the United States and Argentina. At our latitude, eight species have been known to occur, all quite similar in habits and ecology. Seven of them (the Anna's, Allen's, Black-chinned, Broad-tailed Calliope, Costa, and Rufous hummingbirds) are confined to British Columbia and the Pacific states, on the lush downslopes of the mountain barrier. From the mountains east, in both Canada and the United States, only one species breeds, the Ruby-throated Hummingbird, *Archilochus colubris,* a bird that shares fully in the splendor and vitality of its family.

One of the most delightful characteristics of the Ruby-throat is the shimmering brilliance of its plumage. Indeed, hummingbirds have sometimes been referred to as "living prisms," a description that (while not wholly accurate) is less farfetched than it may at first seem. Except for certain dull hues, such as cinnamon, brown, and purplish-black, a Ruby-throat's feathers are not pigmented. Instead, its iridescent hues—the metallic green on the back, the ever-changing red-to-orange-to-black of the male's gorget—are produced by a process known as "interference." Because of peculiarities in the ultrastructure of the feathers, incoming light is refracted and reflected in such a way that some wavelengths are cancelled out: the crest of an incoming wave coincides with the trough of an outgoing one, and vice versa, so that the wave cannot be perceived. But other colors are not so affected, and these are the ones we see. On the male's throat, the microscopic reflecting surfaces are flat, and light is sent out unidirectionally; whether or not you receive it depends on the angle between you and the bird. This explains why the color shifts as the hummer turns. But on the back, the "mirrors" are concave and reflect light in many directions, so the color is constant, though more diffuse than on the throat.

Another reason for our fascination with hummingbirds is their size. This family includes the smallest of all warm-blooded animals, the Bee Hummingbird of Cuba, which attains a weight of less than 2 grams, about the same as a dime. Our own Ruby-throat is only slightly heavier, 2.5 to 4.5 grams, so light that it can be pinned down by a dragonfly or held by a spiderweb. Like all very small animals, the Ruby-throat has great difficulty in maintaining its body temperature: the smaller the diameter of a cylinder (or hummingbird), the higher the ratio between its volume (the mass of tissue with which it generates heat) and its surface area (the layer of skin through which heat is lost). Thus, hummingbirds have to feed almost constantly, from dawn to dusk, just to maintain their physiological status quo. If people consumed energy at an equivalent rate, an eighty-kilogram man would need double his weight in potatoes or one and a half times his weight in meat every day. What's that in Big Macs?

Ruby-throats sustain themselves on insects and, more importantly, on sugary nectars and saps, which are high in calories. Since an individual may have to find and empty a thousand or more blossoms a day, the emphasis in hummingbird evolution has been on

Ruby-throated Hummingbird

125

Hummingbirds are a uniquely American phenomenon, unknown to Europeans before Columbus. Their closest relatives are those high-flying acrobats, the swifts, which also belong to the order Apodiformes. The bird shown here is a female Ruby-throated Hummingbird.

126

feeding efficiently. Thus, the tongue is long, extensible, forked at the tip, and folded over on each side to form a tube-like groove into which nectar can flow. The darning needle of a bill not only helps guide the tongue deep into the flower's honeywell but also increases the bird's feeding speed, since the tongue need be drawn back only a short distance after each lick. Even split-second savings count in the hummer's energy regime.

Hummingbirds also have the advantage of mental attainments such as long-term memory (they can recall the position of feeders or flowering bushes from year to year) and at least a minimal ability to learn. Throughout the Americas, there are certain plants, such as jewelweed and columbine, which have evolved with hummingbirds and rely preferentially on them for pollination; insects do not serve them so well. From the hummers' point of view, these flowers are especially worthwhile because the nectar is unusually sweet. Curiously, such hummingbird flowers tend to be orange or red, probably because hummers are highly sensitive to the long-wavelength end of the spectrum, while most insects are not. Although hummingbirds seem not to have any inborn liking for red, they learn to associate it with rich sources of food. This explains their occasional interest in such things as red paper, red shoelaces, and sunburned noses! A touch of red on a newly installed feeder is a good idea, since it may help the birds to locate it.

But what if neither learning ability, nor memory, nor physical adaptations are enough? What if the hummingbird simply cannot get enough to eat? Then it is able to conserve energy and save itself by going dormant overnight. All its body processes slow down until the bird approaches insensibility, and it enters a state akin to mammalian hibernation or the daytime torpor of a bat.

Hummingbirds live their lives in a constant energy bind, and all because they are approaching the biological minimum for size in a warm-blooded animal. Why has it been useful for them to go to such extremes? One reason may be that only a very small bird can afford the energetic costs of the hummers' mode of flight. Suspended between twin halos of green (its motion-blurred wings), a Ruby-throat seems in perfect equilibrium with the air, as free as a fish in the sea. Straight up it darts, straight down, backwards, to the side. Often, especially when feeding, it hangs motionless, as if resting on the sky.

But there is actually nothing restful about hummingbird flight. The wings of a Ruby-throat beat three or four thousand times a minute (no wonder they hum!), but this is equivalent to six or eight thousand strokes in another bird. Because of a unique configuration of joints and muscles, a hummingbird is able to do work—create power and lift—on both forward and backward phases of its wing stroke. In hovering, for example, the wings first sweep forward, then swivel at the shoulder, "palms up," so that the front of the wing leads again on the return; there is no waste effort, no resting or recovery phase. Not surprisingly, it takes extra fuel to maintain this double-powered flight, and the cost goes up with each additional gram of body weight. A really large hummingbird could not eat enough to keep itself in the air.

Hummingbirds truly are creatures of the sky: they eat, drink, fight, flee, and court on the wing. At mating time, the males fly arcs over unmated females, their wings buzzing loudly as they oscillate back and forth like the bob on a pendulum. The liaison between the sexes is brief, with each male mating as often as he can. The female chooses a sheltered branch, where she builds a dainty nest, about the size of a walnut shell, out of plant down, lichens, and cobwebs. Often, nests are located within commuting distance of a tree in which Yellow-bellied Sapsuckers have been drilling, because the oozing sap provides a reliable source of food for both the mother Ruby-throat and her offspring. No bigger than honeybees when they hatch, the two youngsters are usually ready to leave the nest by mid-July or August, at the age of three weeks. By the end of September, both they and their parents will have left on a sixteen-hundred-kilometer journey to Central America. Incredibly, their route may take them across the Great Lakes and even over the eight-hundred-kilometer expanse of the Gulf of Mexico. (It's almost easier to believe the old legend that they hitch rides on eagles and geese!) The return trip is no less heroic, and they arrive on their northernmost nesting grounds by mid- to late May.

Order Coraciiformes

Kingfishers

Belted Kingfisher

There are more than seven dozen species in the kingfisher family, most of them tropical and subtropical. The only North American member of the group is the Belted Kingfisher, shown here delivering a fish to young in a bankside nest.

Throughout most of North America, "kingfisher" is synonymous with Belted Kingfisher, *Ceryle alcyon.* You can expect to find it along shorelines where there are dead trees for perching; clear, shallow water; and plenty of small fish. Or to be more precise, that's where it will find you, for chances are the bird will see you first. Uttering a harsh rattle of displeasure, it will likely swoop along the water's edge, giving you a chance to notice its distinctive white collar and heavy-headed, tousled silhouette. Or it may follow you as you proceed along the bank, still shouting out its machine-gun rat-a-tat-tat of protest. Then suddenly the barrage will cease, as the kingfisher doubles back to its lookout tree; evidently, you have moved out of its territory and are of no further concern. But you may simultaneously have entered the realm of another bird, which now takes up the challenge of drumming you off its property. And so it goes, in densely populated terrain.

During the nesting season, each pair of Belted Kingfishers commands a strip of shoreline on a stream, pond, lake, or ocean, from 250 to 5,000 meters in length. This is defended with vigor and persistence by both the male and female. In late April and May, when territorial lines are being established, the birds may make eighty or ninety circuits a day around the perimeter of their domain, calling to assert their claim; and later in the season, marking the boundaries remains one of the first orders of business in the male's daily routine. When another kingfisher intrudes, it is immediately challenged with staccato outbursts of calls and routed in a reckless, darting chase—two speeding streaks of blue, pursuer and pursued.

Why do Belted Kingfishers put so much energy into defending territories? For one thing, they are protecting their feeding grounds. Kingfishers might be described as "perch and pounce" fishermen; their basic strategy is to wait on a pier or bare branch until they pick up the silvery glint of a minnow or fingerling swimming near the surface and then to plunge headlong into the water in a sharply angled dive. Sometimes an individual will hover over its quarry for a moment before shooting down, as if to perfect its aim, and will continue supplely to adjust its course as it descends, following the movements of the fish. Entering the water with a splash and a whack, the bird may submerge completely yet seldom, if ever, goes deeper than about fifty centimeters. Prey is caught with a pincerlike grab of the bill and is carried back to the perch, to be pounded and swallowed whole. Crustaceans (particularly crayfish), amphibians, reptiles, and insects are also taken at times and are handled in a similar way.

Kingfishers find their best hunting in the riffling waters of shallow streambeds or in the calm of protected bays, and each territory encompasses some such foraging grounds. But perhaps even more crucial is the inclusion of one or more nest sites. Ideally, the female lays her eggs underground, in a burrow that extends a meter or two into the face of a steep earthen bank; most nests are located at or near the water's edge. Both parents take part in the excavation, hacking out the soil with their beaks and spraying it out the doorway with their feet, a labor that occupies anywhere from three days to three weeks, depending on soil conditions. Ordinarily, the tunnel is near the top of the cliff, for protection from mammalian predators such as skunks, weasels, and mink. But perfect nest sites are in short supply, so

kingfishers frequently have to accept substandard accommodations: gravel pits, road cuts, hollow stumps, and the like, where they are close to the ground and far from shore. The scarcity of suitable nesting sites is probably one of the major factors limiting the population of Belted Kingfishers. Human disturbance may be another, since the birds desert their clutches if bothered too often by our comings and goings.

A typical kingfisher nest contains about half a dozen eggs, which are incubated, mostly by the mother, for twenty-four days; after hatching, the young are fed in the nest for as long again or longer. Over this period, one might expect their living conditions to deteriorate considerably. How would you like to spend three or four weeks in an underground cell with a large group of fish-eating birds that have no outdoor latrines? But, while the floor of the nest chamber does become layered with indigestible food remains, mainly fish bones and scales that the adults regurgitate, the space is otherwise often surprisingly tidy. The nestlings spray liquid excrement in all directions, but they instinctively clean up after themselves by rapping at the dirt walls until the soiled surface falls to the floor and, in time, is buried. As the floor rises, the space may become so squat that there is scarcely room for the youngsters to shuffle about!

Whatever the discomforts of their home life, the nestlings are at least relatively safe. Not so once they fledge and enter the outside world. Fat, listless, and unaccomplished in flight, the young birds are easy prey for large falcons and bird-eating hawks. The adults, by contrast, have little to fear and often go out of their way to provoke attack, not just once but a dozen or more times in a row. Although this may look like thrill-seeking—a high for an avian adrenalin addict—it is more likely a form of distraction display: by drawing attention to itself, the adult kingfisher protects the more helpless members of its family. The surviving young disperse to individual territories in late summer and generally head for the southern states and South America by mid-October. A few birds successfully overwinter in extreme southern Ontario and in British Columbia, but those that linger in the Atlantic provinces usually die before spring.

Woodpeckers

From a human point of view, the woodpeckers' lot in life seems unenviable. Think of the hours they spend relentlessly dashing their heads against tree trunks, as they peck for food and excavate their homes. But woodpeckers are well equipped for their arduous way of life. Not only are their skulls heavily reinforced with bone, their brains are enclosed in a thin cushion of air, which acts as a shock absorber. Their neck muscles are massive, for power and stability, and their beaks are sharp and hard. The tongue is specialized, too—long, extensible, hard-tipped, sticky with saliva, and fringed at the end with barbs—so it can be used to spear wood-boring grubs, trap ants, or brush up sap. Even the nostrils have been modified by the addition of a ring of bristlelike feathers that help keep sawdust out. To permit the birds to maintain the upright posture that is best for hammering, their tail feathers are pointed, stiff, and serve as a prop, while the toes (two of which point front, with one or two to the rear) are provided with sharp claws for a good grip.

Woodpeckers are an ancient and successful order, with over two hundred species in the world today. Of these, thirteen regularly breed in our area: the Northern Flicker; Yellow-bellied, Red-breasted, and Williamson's Sapsuckers; and White-headed, Lewis's, Red-headed, Red-bellied, Downy, Hairy, Three-toed, Black-backed, and Pileated woodpeckers. Of these, the Northern Flicker and Downy Woodpecker are best known in most localities.

Downy Woodpecker

Have you ever fed a woodpecker? While you won't likely persuade one to eat out of your hand, you can hope to attract members of at least two species to a winter bird-feeder. The best location is along the edge of a patch of open woods (city park, woodlot, or wilderness), and the best lure is high-energy food such as cornbread, peanut butter, and, especially, suet. The latter may be spread on a tree trunk or packed in a string bag and hung; but never offer it in a metal cup to which the birds' eyes might adhere in extreme cold. Although nuthatches and chickadees often arrive in numbers to accept such handouts, woodpeckers appear one or two at a time: largish Hairy Woodpeckers, with their long, stiletto-like bills, and smaller Downy Woodpeckers, with beaks that are shorter than their heads.

Except for the populations that live on the Pacific coast and in Newfoundland, these species can also be distinguished by their outer tail feathers, which are pure white in Hairies and white with black bars in Downies. Of the two species, the Downy Woodpecker, *Picoides pubescens,* is more numerous by far. Female Downies are particularly common at feeders, since they are more mobile than males in winter and hence more likely to locate the free lunch. The occasional male that does show up can be recognized by the swatch of red on the nape of his neck.

One of the unusual activities that has been noted at feeders is "nut cracking." When presented with a sunflower seed, a Downy Woodpecker will sometimes wedge the shell into a crevice in the back of a tree, as if placing

Downy Woodpecker

The Downy Woodpecker is the smallest and one of the best known of North American woodpeckers. Its long, sticky tongue, so useful in catching wood-boring insects, can be seen here.

it in a vice, and hammer at it until it breaks. An oat seed may be anchored in much the same way, so that the husk can be peeled away from the kernel. This behavior has been reported so rarely that some people think it must be learned rather than innate. Perhaps a few unusually observant birds got the idea by watching other species at the feeder, particularly nuthatches, which commonly use a similar nut-cracking technique.

Although many Downies shift slightly southward for winter, the species is represented at our latitude throughout the year. From December until March, the birds' overwhelming preoccupation is getting enough to eat. When they aren't huddled in their roost holes, resting, they are out foraging. Under natural conditions, Downies subsist on berries, seeds, and, most importantly, small insects, which they find by poking and peering into cracks in the bark or by striking the tree sharply with the bill and listening for the squirming of a grub or the hollow reverberations of an insect tunnel. Interestingly, the two sexes follow different feeding strategies, with the males concentrating on the upper branches, where the bark is thin and easily drilled, while the females work on the main trunks, where the rough surface provides many hiding places for spiders, aphids, and the like. Some researchers think this is a peaceable arrangement, with each sex seeking out the conditions in which it can forage most efficiently (males tend to have longer tongues, perhaps as an adaptation to their feeding niche); but others conclude that it is achieved through male dominance. However it comes about, the partitioning of the food supply no doubt reduces competition amongst the birds and helps them to survive hard times.

The Downies' cycle of sexual activities usually commences as soon as the weather begins to ease, often as early as February or March. Both males and females locate resonant sounding boards—dry twigs, dead trees,

metal pipes, and the like—which they batter with their beaks to produce long, muted drum rolls. Through these energetic, head-blurring tattoos, each pair asserts its dominance within the ten or fifteen hectares of its summer territory. Once established, both territorial boundaries and mate relationships tend to be stable from year to year.

As the season progresses, drumming takes on other moods and other functions, as well. For unpaired birds, it is the means of finding a partner; for those with mates, it is a way of making contact with a spouse that has not yet returned from a night roost or a foraging trip. Sometimes it seems to be an expression of "intimacy," as in the soft duets of a closely bonded pair or the brasher tones of an invitation to copulate. Or, by contrast, it may be the vehicle for an "argument," as when the members of a pair have different ideas on the selection of a nesting tree and each drums and taps to draw attention to its chosen spot.

In the end, the female generally takes precedence in such disputes but leaves the male with primary responsibility for excavating the hole. Hacking out a suitable cavity—up to fifteen centimeters wide by thirty deep—will occupy at least half his waking hours for two or three weeks, usually in April and May. Most nest holes are located on the east or south sides of dying trees or stubs, between three and fifteen meters off the ground. An average clutch consists of four or five pure-white eggs and is incubated by both parents (mostly the male) for twelve days. After a hectic three weeks, during which the nestlings are fed as often as twenty times an hour, the youngsters fledge, but they remain partially dependent on their parents for perhaps three more weeks. Then, finally, the young birds disperse and, as far as we know, never again see their parents, siblings, or natal woods. Downy Woodpeckers have few natural enemies and have been known to live to an age of ten years.

Northern Flicker

Northern Flicker

As any picnicker can attest, North America is inhabited by millions upon millions of ants, all of which seem to have a taste for fried chicken and a reckless propensity for drowning themselves in the margarine. So why don't we also have anteaters, like the aardvarks and echidnas that occupy other parts of the world? The fact is, of course, that we do have anteating creatures, foremost among them being the Northern Flicker, or "antbird," *Colaptes auratus.* A bird of open woodlands, farmyards, and suburbs, the flicker is a woodpecker that feeds mostly on the ground and, accordingly, lacks some of the heavy-duty skeletal structure of its close relatives, which chisel their food out of trees. The flicker's tongue, on the other hand, is second to none: powerfully muscled and anchored by bones that sweep over the back of the head, it has a barbed, spearlike tip and a coating of sticky saliva. Thus equipped, a flicker can take beetles, wasps, grasshoppers, caterpillars, worms, and berries; but ants, ant eggs, and ant larvae are its meat and potatoes; as many as five thousand may be consumed in a single meal. Ants, regurgitated by the parents, are also fed to nestlings, in such quantities that a line of black from gullet to paunch is sometimes visible through the youngsters' translucent skin.

There are three varieties of Northern Flicker in North America, all similar in habits but so strikingly different in coloration that they used to be classified as separate species. The "gilded flicker," a desert-dwelling race from the southern United States, sports a yellow lining on its wings and tail and, in the males, a red mustache. The "red-shafted flicker," the form most commonly found west of the Rockies, also has a red mustache, but the undersides of its wings and tail flash are a bright orange-red. The "yellow-shafted flicker," which occurs primarily from the mountains east, has a black mustache, yellow linings, and a red crescent on the back of the head. Isolated from each other for thousands of years during the Ice Age, the three subspecies are now in contact again and interbreed freely wherever their ranges overlap. In British Co-

lumbia and along the western edge of the Great Plains, crossbred birds, with orange-yellow wing linings and speckled or mix-and-match mustaches, are commonplace.

The flickers' markings—including the spotted breast and the black crescent on the throat, which are present in all races—provide the birds with one of their modes of communication. Their major display is a face-to-face dance, usually performed on a branch or tree trunk, in which all their conspicuous features are highlighted: the wings are spread, the tail is twisted forward and fanned; the breast bobs and sways; and the upturned bill describes smooth circles and figure 8's, as if in time to music that only flickers hear. Exactly what this "means" and how the birds "understand" it is inscrutable; the display seems to be both aggressive and sexual and is a central component of both courtship and territorial defense. Perhaps the ritual permits the participants to confirm that they belong to the same species and, at the same time, lets them express the excitement they feel at being so near to a potential rival or mate. The precise significance of the behavior—whether it is a prelude to mating or a fight—seems to depend upon the context.

Flickers also have several other means of transmitting information, including an extensive vocabulary of scolding, alarm, and contact calls; and like all woodpeckers, they drum with their bills on resonant surfaces, particularly in the spring. Drumming by both sexes, together with loud, rapid-fire "wick-wick-wick" location calls, is especially important in the establishment of nesting territories. Early in the season, each pair lays claim to a relatively large area, perhaps three hundred meters in diameter, which they defend according to a strict sexual protocol: male against males, female against females. (Later on, their protectiveness becomes focused on the immediate vicinity of the nest hole, and the same-sex alignment no longer holds.) Both partners are deeply attached to their home range and return year after year, with the result that pair bonds, once formed, persist for life. Though sexual triangles

The "red-shafted," western form of the Northern Flicker (shown here) interbreeds with the "yellow-shafted," eastern form. Although hybrids are basically a western phenomenon, a few have been seen as far east as Ottawa.

often develop during courtship, as two females (or males) compete for the favors of a desirable mate, the long-established, resident bird generally—perhaps always—wins.

Flickers are surprisingly tolerant in their selection of nest sites and will settle for ground burrows, nest boxes, attics, fenceposts, or utility poles if nothing better presents itself. Their preference, however, is to drill a hole near the top of a dead or dying tree (often a poplar), usually on the south or southeast side where they'll get the morning sun. The location is decided by negotiation between the male and female, which each drum, call, and tap to attract the other to likely-looking spots. As a rule, the site they finally choose is one that was recommended by the male, who also bears primary responsibility for digging or renovating the hole, incubating the eggs (five to ten in a clutch), and feeding the nestlings. Incubation lasts only eleven or twelve days, and the youngsters fledge at about the age of one month. Although some overwinter in southern Canada, the majority are gone from October through mid-April, enjoying the sunshine of Mexico and Central America.

Adult flickers are comparatively safe from predation, but eggs and nestlings sometimes fall prey to black bears, house cats, weasels, chipmunks, squirrels, mice, crows, and jays. Another enemy is the European Starling, a species that was introduced to the eastern United States in 1890 and reached British Columbia about 1950. An aggressive bird, easily able to best a flicker in a fight, the starling often usurps flicker nest sites. Many other species breed in flicker holes as well—Tree Swallows, American Kestrels, small owls, and bluebirds, to name a few—but these are native species to which the flicker has become adapted through generations of coexistence. Will the starling upset the natural balance and crowd the flicker out? So far at least, this does not seem to have taken place. For one thing, a displaced flicker has the ability to make itself a new home; for another, the females can lay replacement eggs by the dozen if one or more clutches are lost. It seems reasonable to conclude that the flicker will continue to cope.

Facial markings are the means by which Northern Flickers distinguish males from females. If a mustache is experimentally added to a female (who, like the bird shown here, normally would not have one) her mate mistakes her for a male and attacks her viciously. If the mustache is then removed, he courts her again.

Order Passeriformes

Songbirds

When the songbirds leave us in the fall, following the sun, the empty woods suddenly lose a measure of their delight. There is no obvious reason why these birds and their singing should please us as they do. After all, bird songs are signals devised by other species to facilitate communications among themselves and have nothing to do with us. Yet, mysteriously, we are moved by their beauty. What, we may wonder, is the basis of the ancient kinship through which we and the songbirds share our interest in pitch, rhythm, dynamics, and other components of melody?

This question is, of course, unanswerable, and so we may as well turn our attention to more mundane concerns. The first question that needs to be dealt with is "what is a songbird?" The order Passeriformes, to which the songsters belong, is a riot of diversity—the largest, most complex, and most highly evolved order of birds. Nearly five thousand species (mostly small to medium-sized land birds) are included on its membership roles, or about three-fifths of all living birds. Their outstanding group characteristic is the structure of their feet, which are specialized for perching, with three toes pointing forward and one (the strongest) pointing back. Because of the way the muscles attach, a "perching bird" can do no more than open and close its toes; but by the same token, it is protected against falling, since its feet lock tightly when they grasp a branch. This means the bird cannot be swept off by a windstorm or tumble when asleep.

The perching birds are the most recent offshoot of the avian family tree; it is only over the last ten or eleven million years that they have diverged to their present luxuriant variety. Because their evolution has been rapid and is still ongoing, the relationships among subgroups within the order—families, sub-

families, tribes, genera—are not always clear. The order is like a forward-flowing river, yet the taxonomist must describe it as if it were a series of lakes and still pools. Current attempts at classification are, therefore, approximate and will no doubt be subject to continued improvement.

One point on which biologists are already sure is that there are two major types of perching birds. The first and more primitive group, the suborder Tyranni, includes kingbirds, peewees, and flycatchers. These species qualify as perching birds but not as songbirds. The "true songbirds" all belong to the second and much larger subdivision, the suborder Passeres. In Canada and the northern states alone, this category is represented by over two hundred species and seventeen native families: the larks; swallows; jays and crows; chickadees; bushtits; nuthatches; creepers; wrens; dippers; thrushes, kinglets, and gnatcatchers; mockingbirds; pipits; waxwings; shrikes; vireos; wood-warblers, tanagers, grosbeaks, buntings, blackbirds, and sparrows; finches, redpolls, and crossbills. From a taxonomic point of view, a songbird can simply be defined as a member of one of these families. Thus, a raw-voiced Common Raven qualifies, whereas the tender and melodious Mourning Dove (a member of the order Columbiformes) most emphatically does not.

While not all songbirds are musical, they all have an exceptionally well developed vocal apparatus. This is not the larynx, or voice box, with which we and other mammals produce sound, but an organ unique to birds, known as the syrinx. Situated at the base of the windpipe, the syrinx is fitted with membranes that tighten and relax to achieve changes in pitch, though most birds have little means of controlling these functions. Flycatchers, for example, have only two pairs of muscles attached to the syrinx. Songbirds, by contrast, all have more than four pairs, and some have as many as nine. This accounts for the suppleness and precision of their singing.

Before we go any further, we have to pause for another definition: just what is a "bird song"? Biologists have found it useful to distinguish between two sorts of avian vocalizations. On the one hand, there are "calls," short, accoustically simple utterances that typically require a prompt response from another bird. For example, calls may be used to signal danger or hunger or the whereabouts of a companion or mate. Such vocalizations are produced by all ages and both sexes at all times of the year.

Songs, on the other hand, are relatively long and complicated and may be repeated for hours at a time without any immediate stimulus. (The record for Most Bird Songs in a Single Day is held by a Red-eyed Vireo: 22,197.) Usually, singing is limited to the breeding season and, with few exceptions, is restricted to males. In most species, bird song can be thought of as a secondary sexual characteristic, a badge of masculinity like the human mustache and beard. If female birds are injected with testosterone, they begin to sing. Singing ability in the males is tied to their annual reproductive cycle: outside the breeding season, when hormone levels are low, the "song centers" in their brains shrink, so that they temporarily seem to forget how to sing.

Bird song has two primary functions: territorial and sexual. In some species, song is entirely territorial, in others entirely sexual, while in most it has a dual significance. In a territorial context, song may serve as a substitute for fighting: if you can scare an intruder away with a well-timed declaration of occupancy, you don't have to brawl with him. In sexual encounters, singing permits males to attract females and helps females choose mates of the right species. Not only that, but the male's song may have a profound effect on

his partner's physiology and behavior—stimulating her to ovulate and build nests. In this way, it helps to coordinate the reproductive activities of the mated pair.

Interestingly, experiments have shown that female birds respond much more strongly to normal, complex song than they do to artificially simplified renditions, and this fact may help explain the surprising variability of bird song. Most male songbirds have not one but several versions of their territorial/sexual song, which they sing with either "immediate variety," one song following another—ABC-DEF—or "eventual variety"—AAAA-BBBB-CCCC. In both cases, the objective seems to be to minimize tedious repetition. In addition to its effect on females, this variability may be important in retaining the attention of male neighbors and other territorial rivals, who would gradually lose interest in a monotonous sound. Another way in which a varied repertoire may possibly influence male listeners is by creating the illusion that an area is occupied by many birds rather than one, thereby discouraging newcomers from settling.

In every species of songbirds that has been studied to date, the males' song repertoires are acquired partially through learning. In most songbirds, there is a "sensitive period" some time during the early months of life, when the youngster absorbs a vocabulary of appropriate syllables and phrases. These he strings together in a warbling baby-talk, or subsong, as he perfects his vocal coordination and learns to guide his voice by ear. By the next spring, he will be ready to burst into mature song, following a pattern that is typical of his species, but with variations that may be uniquely his. There is mounting evidence, at least for some species, that new songs continue to be learned and composed in adulthood. All in all, recent discoveries about bird song suggest a capacity for learning, innovation, discrimination, and memory that discredit our old notions about the limitations of "bird brains."

Barn Swallow

Barn Swallow

Since the beginning of history and beyond, the Barn Swallow, *Hirundo rustica,* has been a favorite of humankind. The most widely distributed of all songbirds, this graceful and companionable species breeds in the North Temperate Zone across North America and Eurasia and winters from the tropics south to Patagonia and the Philippines. At our latitude, it is almost always found near farmsteads and country homes, where it can be seen swooping around buildings, speeding in and out of entranceways, or cavorting over fields and ponds, now high overhead, now low to the ground. Like other members of the swallow family, the Barn Swallow is quintessentially a "bird of the air," as light and tireless in flight as an albatross or swift. Thanks to its streamlined body and long, narrow-cut wings, it is fully sixty percent more fuel-efficient than most

other birds and thus can afford to drink and bathe on the wing, by skimming over water; feed on the wing, by darting after flies; even court on the wing, in zestful, erratic pursuits that liven the early spring skies.

Barn Swallows return to us by late April or early May and announce their presence in song: a liquid, trilling melody that is broken at intervals by short, tambourine-like rasps. Among the first orders of business for each breeding pair is the establishment of a territory, which in this species amounts to little more than the nest site and a flyway from the nest to a favorite perch; forty or more pairs will sometimes congregate in a loose colony, though solitary nestings are also common. In ages past, before Europeans arrived in North America, the birds nested in caves or on sheltered cliffs; but today they almost invari-

The familiar Barn Swallow can be identified by its deeply forked "swallow tail" and its coloration: metallic blue above and light cinnamon brown below. In Korea and Japan, it has long been a mark of good luck to have Barn Swallows nesting on your home.

ably choose barns and sheds or the undersides of bridges, even when natural sites are available. Settlement has therefore permitted the birds to expand their range both to the north and south, a process that is still continuing.

The nests themselves are made of clay: neat, semicircular cups of mud, hair, and straw that are mounted on vertical or, less commonly, horizontal surfaces. Sometimes, they're located on the outsides of buildings, protected by the eaves, and near the gourd-shaped constructions of Cliff Swallows; but usually they're indoors on rafters and walls. Selecting a spot where there's a crack, a bolt, or the remains of an old nest to provide purchase for the first gobs of mud, the swallows carry in clay one mouthful at a time, positioning and shaping each pellet with the bill and molding the walls from the inside with the whole body. Completing such a shelter occupies both partners for an average of six to eight days, during which time they may make four thousand trips for building supplies and travel, cumulatively, some two hundred kilometers. Not surprisingly, many pairs prefer instead to put a few hours work into renovating their nest from the previous year, by building up the rim and adding a new feather bed. Birds which take this labor-saving approach are reproductively more successful than those that build anew—that is, they are more likely to rear second broods.

Perhaps half or two-thirds of the Barn Swallow population is able to raise two families in a given year; a few pairs manage three. Laying begins in May and is followed by two weeks of incubation and three weeks of caring for nestlings, which are possessed by the universal and urgent hunger of the very young. When the chicks are ready to fly, the parents coax them out of the nest by withholding food, fluttering about, and uttering soft, persuasive calls; yet the adults will continue to feed and defend their offspring (which they can distinguish from other young Barn Swallows) for another week or two. It is during this interval, between fledging and independence, that the adults may begin constructing or refurbishing a nest for a second brood. In some cases, the still-dependent young seem to get in their parents' way at every turn, interrupting their work to the point that they may give it up for a while. But in other instances, the youngsters pitch in and help with the new nest. Later on, they and other unrelated juveniles may also assist in feeding the second family, which requires attention through August and sometimes into September.

Their reproductive efforts at an end for the year, Barn Swallows gather in huge flocks over marshes and sloughs, often in company with Tree and Cliff swallows and other allied species. Unsuccessful nesters, pairs rearing only one brood, and young of the year begin to congregate in August, and the last swallow is gone by late September. There's an old folk belief that the birds disappear into the marsh mud, where they hibernate, but the truth is that they move south, some of them journeying fifteen thousand kilometers to their wintering grounds. This puts them in the same league as the champions among long-distance migrators, the Arctic Terns, which annually cover sixteen thousand kilometers on their migratory trek between the Arctic and Antarctic.

Blue Jay

The Blue Jay, *Cyanocitta cristata,* is a member of the crow family or Corvidae, a group that includes the whole raucous congregation of crows, ravens, rooks, magpies, nutcrackers, and jays, more than a hundred species in all. Not only are they amongst the largest of the songbirds, they are also widely reputed to be the smartest birds in the world. The American Crow, for example, can be taught to count to three or four and also to imitate human speech, though without understanding. Blue Jays are capable mimics as well, credited with copying a wide variety of manmade and natural sounds, from the squeal of a chair being dragged across a floor to the chittering of chickadees and the screams of Red-tailed and Red-shouldered hawks. While this is no proof of intelligence per se, it does at

Within days of being ready to leave the nest, these young Blue Jays will spend the rest of the summer wandering with their parents. The family will disperse in the fall.

Blue Jay

least presuppose a certain measure of attentiveness and mental flexibility. More impressive are the results of laboratory experiments in which Blue Jays were tested on their ability to learn simple tasks and to discriminate objects; here the birds scored as well as some of the higher mammals, including cats, marmosets, and squirrel monkeys. But most surprising of all are the occasional reports of creativity and problem-solving in Blue Jays. Consider the case of a captive jay whose food pellets kept slipping through the wire grating of its cage and lodging out of reach. Everactive, ever-exploratory, this bird accidentally discovered that a shred of newspaper could be used as a rake, to reach and recover the food. Not only did he remember this invention, but he was also able to transfer the behavior to new objects, such as feathers and paper clips. What's more, other jays kept in the room soon started using tools in the same way, presumably through observation and learning.

Similar adaptability is sometimes seen in the wild, as well. Like a number of other species, Blue Jays commonly perform a behavior known as "anting," in which they catch ants and place or wipe them among their wing feathers. Believe it or not, this is probably comforting, for the strong formic-acid secretions of the ants are thought to sooth skin irritations caused by molting or mite infestations. What makes the Blue Jay's anting so interesting is its variability, for the birds have been known to use such exotic substances as vinegar, mustard, burning cigarettes, soap suds, and hair tonic. How could they know that these things work, except by trial-and-error learning?

The hallmark of intelligent behavior is versatility: it frees the individual from inflexibly instinctual control. The feeding patterns of most birds, to take one obvious and basic example, are fairly rigidly programmed, so that both the range of possible food stuffs and the ways of handling them are limited. To fly-catchers, for example, only flying insects of a certain size are recognizable as food, and nothing else is worth investigating. But to Blue Jays, almost anything is a potential meal: weed seeds, grain, corn, berries, caterpillars, grasshoppers, mice, leftover sandwiches, nuts and seeds on a feeding shelf, or the eggs and young of other birds taken from a nest. While their physical adaptations for exploiting these diverse resources are unexceptional—the most noteworthy being a stout bill for cracking acorns and nuts—Blue Jays have the advantage of such mental qualities as curiosity and an excellent memory, which, on the one hand, motivate them to taste and probe and, on the other, permit them to profit from their gustatory experiments.

But it would be a mistake to insist too much on the Blue Jays' intellectual powers, for their behavior is seldom genuinely rational and often appears disorganized. To prove this, you need only watch a flock feeding in an oak tree and caching acorns. One bird wedges its prize into a crevice in the bark, where the first wind storm must surely bring it down. Another flies off a few hundred meters (or a few kilometers), pokes an acorn into the ground, covers it carefully with leaf litter or carries in stones to protect it, and then flies away—only to return within minutes to dig the morsel up. Sometimes a second jay, close on the tail of the first, rushes down to harvest the hidden food, though the oak tree is still laden with a ready supply of fruit. Alternatively, and more often perhaps, it may be that no one will ever see the acorn again and that the jay has unintentionally planted an oak for the benefit of generations to come. Though jays can carry several acorns at once, with one or more in their expandable throat pouch and one in the bill, they always hide them separately, several meters apart, inadvertently leaving room for growth. But this is the result of a long, evolutionary adjustment between jays and oaks, not of reasoning.

Sometimes, one assumes, these food caches must function as an emergency food supply, and Blue Jays have, in fact, been known to recover and eat nuts after a lapse of several days. But can they find them months later, when the landscape has been transfigured with snow, as nutcrackers and European jays are known to do?

Even at the northern edge of their range, Blue Jays are only partially migratory, with most of the adult birds remaining on or near their breeding grounds through the hungry winter months. First-year birds may be more likely to travel south, but even they seldom go more than a few hundred kilometers. One indication that food supplies have a bearing on the Blue Jay's migratory habits is the fact that migration is becoming less common, presumably because of the growing numbers of well-provided birdfeeders. Winter feeding stations, together with the maturation of ornamental plants in towns and cities, are also thought to be responsible for the Blue Jay's recent city-hopping expansion into New Mexico, Wyoming, Montana, Oregon, Washington, and British Columbia, areas from which they were virtually absent until the mid-1970s. What effect this will have on the Steller's Jay, the resident western "blue jay" (recognizable by its dark hue and lack of white markings), is uncertain, though the two species are so similar that they can interbreed. For the moment, differences in habitat seem to be keeping them apart, with Steller's Jays concentrated in coniferous forests and Blue Jays in urban areas.

Especially for the portion of the population that is nonmigratory, the Blue Jay's breeding season starts early in the year, sometimes on warm days in late February. Shrieking "jay" and a variety of other creaking, squeaking, and grating syllables, the birds aggregate in flocks of three to six, usually a single female with her coterie of scrapping suitors. Through a combination of intimidation, fighting, and a peculiar bobbing display, one male eventually eliminates his rivals and is able to proceed to the next stages of courtship, in which he feeds his mate and offers her sticks with which to make a mock nest. The actual nest is usually built in dense conifers or thick shrubbery, within six or seven meters of the ground, and consists of a bulky mass of twigs, bark, moss, paper, and the like, sometimes cemented with mud, and lined with fine rootlets. Both birds build, but the female is far more adept. There are four or five eggs in an average clutch, which are incubated by the female alone for about two and a half

Blue Jays are "publicity seekers" who draw notice with their brilliant markings and varied calls. Through vocalization and body posture, they communicate amongst themselves with considerable subtlety.

weeks, usually in May or June. The male, meanwhile, feeds his mate on or near the nest and guards his territory in a somewhat lackadaisical fashion, taking action only against Blue Jays that feed on the ground, rest, preen, or show other signs of being at home. A bird that stays in the tree tops or that is feeding its troupe of wandering fledglings will probably be ignored. The arrival of a predator, however—a Great Horned Owl or a bird-eating hawk—elicits a far more energetic and determined response, not only from the resident pair but from neighboring jays, who mob around their enemy and harry it with knife-edged shouts of alarm. Not infrequently, jays may find themselves the object of similar assaults by other birds—American Robins, for example—which attack Blue Jays during their occasional nest-raids. But whatever the dangers and difficulties of their existence, Blue Jays are remarkably long-lived for songbirds. A life span of six years is about average, and ten, twelve, even fifteen years have been recorded for free-living birds.

Black-capped Chickadee

There are days in midwinter when the air is heavy with cold and life scarcely seems possible in this part of the world. Without parkas and longjohns, toques and boots, scarves and mitts, would we survive? Without central heating? Yet this is a routine achievement for many small and medium-sized songbirds, including the Golden-crowned Kinglet; Snow Bunting; Pine Grosbeak; all the various nuthatches, waxwings and redpolls; and our four species of chickadees (Mountain, Boreal, Chestnut-backed, and Black-capped, by name). Of these, the Black-capped Chickadee, *Parus atricapillus,* with its neat black-and-white markings and clear "chick-a-dee" call, is amongst the most familiar and easily recognized. (Birdwatchers in the Rockies should note that the very similar Mountain Chickadee has white "eyebrows," which are not found on the Black-cap; the Carolina Chickadee of the northeastern states can be distinguished by voice.) Sometimes, when food is short and the weather unusually fierce, the more northerly populations of Black-caps shift south for the winter; but as a rule, the species is resident throughout its range, prepared to face the rotating seasons with vivacity and apparent good cheer.

The central problem in the Black-caps' winter existence is to maximize energy intake while minimizing inefficiency and waste. So you won't be surprised to learn that their puffy little bodies are clothed in an abundance of downy feathers, to reduce heat loss. The need for insulation also explains why, on winter nights, the birds huddle in thickets of dense coniferous growth, seeking shelter from the cold. During the brief hours of daylight, by contrast, their lives are given over almost entirely to a single-minded search for food. Agile to the point of being acrobatic, they forage in woods and sometimes in clearings, hopping along branches, clinging to tree trunks, balancing on weed heads, now right side up or sideways, now hanging upside down. Although they occasionally collect seeds and small fruits, they concentrate their attentions on spiders and forest insects: weevils, aphids, sawflies, moths, et cetera, together with eggs and larvae. In winter, their food supplies are augmented by morsels that were originally caught several months earlier (in late summer and fall) and tucked away under loose bark or inside dry leaves. Chickadees are also frequent visitors at winter feeding stations and are so tame and adaptable that they can be taught to take nuts from your hand.

If you stop to reflect for a moment, there is one aspect of the Black-caps' winter behavior that may perplex you, and that is their habit of living in flocks. These groupings, which usually include half a dozen or a dozen birds, form in

Black-capped Chickadee

145

Black-capped Chickadees are exceptionally intelligent and trusting. They can often be attracted by an imitation of their "tseep" contact note or their "chick-a-dee" call.

late summer and persist till the following spring. But don't these aggregations increase the competition for food, just when supplies are most limited? What are the benefits for an individual bird? One probable advantage is improved protection from predators, since group members warn one another of danger. A sharp "tsee" call means "Red alert: predator approaching. Everyone freeze"; and everyone does so, until one of their number signals "All clear," by calling "chick-a-dee." Another plus may be a more wide-ranging and dependable food search. Obviously, birds foraging as a company and sharing in each other's discoveries will eat more frequently than if they were foraging alone. This is crucial for wintering chickadees, which must feed almost constantly. When members of another species join the flock for a time (nuthatches, kinglets, woodpeckers, or other chickadees), Black-caps may take advantage of their food-finds, as well, thereby exploiting resources they might never have encountered on their own.

If you have a chance to observe Black-caps

at a feeding station, you will notice that the number of birds on the shelf varies from day to day and from hour to hour. Yet banding studies reveal that the total membership of most chickadee flocks is remarkably constant: you are likely to be seeing the same birds, in different combinations, all winter long and, often, from year to year. In fact, by feeding them, you are helping to sustain a complex society, in which interactions amongst individuals are governed by a strict dominance hierarchy. A subordinate bird will sometimes recognize a social superior ten or fifteen meters away and instantly cede place at the feeder; little or no energy is wasted on hostilities. Status depends on sex and experience, with top rank going to whichever male last nested near the center of the flock's winter range. Other males are arranged below him, with juveniles on the bottom levels. With the top, or "alpha," bird in the lead, the males defend an area of ten or fifteen hectares—a collective territory—within which all flock members can feed without interference from neighboring groups of Black-caps. By restricting their activities to this private preserve, the birds become thoroughly acquainted with the local resources and don't lose time hunting for food.

Like the males, females have their own rank order, though theirs is more variable: newcomers may have ascendancy over long-time residents, and the mate of the alpha male is not always in the first rank. Perhaps because of their territorial aggressiveness, males, even those from the lowest orders, are usually dominant over females. In theory, this should put the females at a disadvantage, since the males could limit their chances to feed, but there is actually little interaction between the sexes in winter. In general, females choose to feed in shorter trees, on smaller branches, and farther out on the canopy than do males; thus, they have their own sphere, in which the males seldom challenge them. It is the low-status juveniles, which are dominated by high-ranking birds of their own sex, that bear the weight of the social system. In years of food shortage, they will face starvation first, thereby sparing adult birds that have proven their ability to breed.

Winter flocks break up by the end of March,

as the alpha bird becomes increasingly aggressive toward his male underlings. Soon, he and his mate (who is usually his partner from the previous year and a member of his winter flock) are left in possession of most of the winter range; subordinate birds settle on the periphery of the flock territory or farther afield. It is at this time of year, when the birds are becoming established on their breeding territories, that you are most likely to hear their whistled "fee-bee"—"spring soon"—and to see whirling chases and fights. By May, a typical pair will have excavated a nest hole in the soft, rotten wood of a dying branch or tree, and lined it with rabbit hair and soft plant down. Here the female lays her eggs, usually six to eight in a clutch, and incubates them for about two weeks; the male feeds her frequently during this period. Interestingly, the alpha pair usually produces more eggs and rears more fledglings than even its closest subordinates. When the young achieve independence at the age of five or six weeks, they disperse; by late August, most will have found places in winter flocks. Young birds have not been known to winter with their parents and seldom return to their natal areas.

House Wren

Of the eight species of wrens in our area, none is more familiar than that ardent little busybody, the House Wren, *Troglodytes aedon*. Boundlessly energetic—now flitting from perch to perch; now rustling through dry leaves; now foraging high in the trees; its upcocked tail constantly a-twitch—the House Wren is in many ways typical of its kind. But it can be distinguished from other wrens by its appearance (the lack of a distinct line over the eye) and by its habitat. Although House Wrens are still to be found in the shrubby coulees and woodland edges that they have always occupied, they are now more common around human homes, where they add interest and vigor to the scene with their scolding chatter and loud, bubbling song.

Among the Ojibwa Indians, the House Wren was aptly known as "Big-noise-for-its-size."

Unlike other songbirds, which tend to give voice most freely at twilight and in the early stages of the breeding cycle, male House Wrens are strenuous singers, who vocalize throughout the day and the nesting season. As you might expect, the songs are a means of claiming territory, and two contesting males will sometimes face each other on a branch and conduct a verbal "shoot-out," which ends when one of them concedes defeat and leaves. Frequently, though, disputes cannot be settled so peaceably: aggressive impulses rise, one of the combatants gives chase, and the birds end up scrapping on the ground. The territory holder usually wins these skirmishes—but not always, with the result that boundary lines are constantly in flux. Among the unsettling forces in boundary disputes are the late-arriving males, usually yearlings, who attempt to mus-

House Wren

147

The wren's scientific name, *Troglodytes,* means "cave-dwelling," a reference to their habit of nesting in holes. This House Wren will feed its young on small insects and spiders, the same diet on which it sustains itself.

cle in between established birds.

Aside from territory, the other great source of drama in a male wren's life is finding a mate. When an unattached female appears within his domain, the male becomes tense with excitement: his wings may start to quiver, his tail flicks up, and his singing voice rises to a shrill squeak. But the female seems far less interested in him and his passions than she is in his nesting sites. On average, a House Wren territory encompasses about half a hectare and includes three or four nest holes. Almost any small cavity will do: a freshly painted bird house or a rusty tin can, a woodpecker hole or a watering pot, a crevice in a rotten stump or the inside of an old shoe! Before the female arrives, the male will already have built a "dummy nest" of dry twigs (or, occasionally, bits of metal) in each suitable location on his territory, often cramming the space so full that there is barely room for the female to squeeze in. Later in the season, this tangle of sticks will help keep out predators and provide the wrens with a hiding place.

If the female approves of the male's efforts, she sets to work adding a soft cup of feathers and plant down to one of the dummy nests; and this is where she lays her eggs, usually six to eight in a clutch. Incubation lasts about two weeks and is done entirely by the female, but both parents guard the nest—and with good reason. Although cats, foxes, and owls are a danger to fledglings, the most serious threat to eggs and nestlings comes from other House Wrens. The males are often expansionists, who fly surreptitious reconnaissance missions into one another's territories. If they locate an untended nest, they may puncture the eggs or kill the nestlings and dump them out, presumably acting on their impulse to clean cavities before using them. The likelihood of this happening depends both on the availability of nest sites (the denser the population, the more raids occur) and on the "personalities" of the males in the vicinity. A particularly aggressive individual may destroy half a dozen nests in the course of the season, including eggs or young of other species such as bluebirds and

148

chickadees.

The male's interest in acquiring new nest sites and building dummy nests persists long after his first family of the year has been begun. Sometimes, his continued singing and activity will attract a second female to his territory, so that he has two mates at the same time. More often, however, he focuses his attentions on his first brood until they are out of the nest and nearing independence, then leaves them in the care of their mother, while he remates for a second brood. Occasionally, the reverse occurs: the female takes off, leaving the male in charge. Or both may stay to tend the young as long as they need care (about two weeks) and then renest together or with new partners. The casual couplings and uncouplings, both within seasons and from year to year, can make for some very complicated genealogies.

First broods are usually initiated in May, with second nestings in July. But by September, the intense feelings of the mating period begin to subside, as the wrens molt and undergo a change of appearance, habitat, and behavior. Darker than in summer, the birds disappear into the underbrush, where they do little to attract our attention. Audubon thought they were a different species, the "wood wren." Within a few weeks, all will have headed south for their wintering grounds in Mexico and the Gulf Coast states. The next spring, first-year birds will disperse to new areas for nesting, but experienced breeders return year after year to the same neighborhoods.

Bluebirds

In all the world, North America is the only place where bluebirds naturally occur. We have three species, all quite similar in life cycle and behavior but sufficiently different in appearance so that we (and the birds themselves) can distinguish amongst them. The Eastern Bluebird, *Sialia sialis,* has a rusty-red belly and throat, the color being less intense in females than in males. The Western Bluebird, *S. mexicana,* which breeds in south-central British Columbia and across the western third of the United States, also has a red breast, but it can be identified by its blue throat and, sometimes, by patches of red-brown on its back; females again are duller than the males. But in the so-called Mountain Bluebird, *S. currucoides* (which actually breeds across the foothills and parklands, too), the sexes are much more distinct, with mouse-brown females, touched with color on the tail, rump, and wings, and brilliant, turquoise males. Mountain Bluebirds never have chestnut markings.

With the exception of a few individuals that linger in southern British Columbia or the Niagara Peninsula, all three species of bluebirds normally leave Canada each October for wintering grounds in the United States and farther south. The first returnees are back by the end of March, bright and unexpected in the drab late-winter scene. The March winds howl, the temperature falls to –20°C, and late snows cover the fields, yet the bluebirds may survive, providing the bad weather doesn't last too long. Eastern Bluebirds, for example, sometimes huddle inside a nest box to keep warm—as many as fourteen at a time.

But if their early arrival poses difficulties, it also has compensations, for the bluebirds get first pick of suitable nesting sites. Bluebirds are cavity-nesters, with a preference for small woodpecker holes and nest boxes built to their specifications; but these sites are also used by Tree Swallows, House Wrens, Northern Flickers, Deer Mice, Flying Squirrels, and, sometimes, bumblebees and wasps. Competition, both between and within species, is intense and can be violent.

Unhappily, the bluebirds' age-old method of dealing with this problem—by being first in line—is no longer adequate to maintain their populations. Intensive farming and urban sprawl have destroyed habitat; two introduced birds—the House Sparrow and European Starling—have been added to the list of nest-site competitors; the use of insecticides

■ Eastern Bluebird
■ Mountain Bluebird
■ Range Overlap

149

has reduced their food supply. The result: a sharp decline in all three bluebird species. The key to a partial recovery, over the last twenty-five years, has been the provision of thousands of nest boxes along highways and country roads. If you want to add more, make them 13 x 13 x 28 centimeters (width x length x height), with an entrance hole 20 centimeters above the floor and 4 centimeters in diameter; it's a good idea to drill two small holes just under the roof for ventilation. Nail the boxes to fence posts, about 200 meters apart, in an area of short-cropped vegetation where there are overhead wires or branches for perches and nearby trees to shelter fledglings. And get them up early in the year—sometime in March.

Supposing that you succeed in attracting bluebirds, what behaviors can you expect to see around the box? Bluebirds sometimes arrive on their nesting grounds already paired, but let's say your box has been claimed by an unmated male Eastern Bluebird. His overriding concerns will be two-fold: to defend his territory (an area of from five to thirty hectares that will be used for courting, mating, nesting, and food-getting) and to attract a mate. Naturally conspicuous, he draws even more attention to himself by singing, sometimes in aggressive "song duels" with neighboring males, and by flying loops, zigzags, and slow-winged "butterfly" flights within his boundaries. He also draws attention to his nest hole (or holes) by approaching in full song, often using a showy wingbeat, and rocking back and forth in the entranceway. Then he hops inside and ducks his head in and out, so that he appears and disappears. If a female is present, this game of peekaboo may entice her to the hole and inside with the male; but she's cautious, no doubt aware that her suitor's message is both defensive and sexual. Significantly, her first action when they emerge from the box is to oust the male from his perch, by biting and shoving, if necessary. It's as if she wants to say, "This hole is now mine, too; I have some rights around here and won't be

Facing page: The Eastern Bluebird was known by the early settlers as the "blue robin," in appreciation of its richly colored breast.

Bluebirds have exceptional eyesight, an attribute that is invaluable in hunting insects. Usually, they hunt from a perch, but Mountain Bluebirds (like the bird shown here) can hover in midair while seeking prey.

chased away." Without this gesture of dominance, a pair bond cannot be established. For his part, the male pecks at his mate during both courtship and copulation but frequently alternates these attacks with offers of food.

Although male bluebirds seem to enjoy handling nesting material—carrying it, working it with their bills, eating it, letting it fall—it is the females who build the nests and incubate the eggs. Three to six is an average clutch, with an incubation period of about two weeks; the youngsters attain full independence at thirty-five or forty days of age. Long before this happens, their mother may have left them in their father's care and started a second nest, often on the same territory and with the same mate. (Separation or relocation is common if the pair's original nesting attempt has failed.) Occasionally, young from the first brood are still in the area ·when the second one hatches; and, though scarcely more than infants themselves, still wearing the spotty-breasted plumage of their youth, they may help their parents bring in caterpillars, grasshoppers, spiders, and the like for their younger brothers and sisters. Although this behavior may look like altruism, it is actually an example of "selfish genes" at work. Siblings are genetically very similar, so caring for a brother or sister is a way of caring for some of your own DNA. The next spring, as yearlings, these "helpful" youngsters will look after their own broods.

American Robin

American Robin

From the moment you see the first robin redbreast hopping across the lawn, you know it must be spring. Never mind that the grackles, bluebirds, and Red-winged Blackbirds have been back for several days; never mind that there are still patches of snow on the ground. When the robins return, the new year has officially begun. Traveling in ragged flocks, these "wandering thrushes," *Turdus migratorius,* move north gradually, advancing and retreating along the leading edge of the warm temperatures, and finally settle with us in March or April, the exact date depending on weather and latitude. The males (with their bright red breasts) generally arrive first. Over the next two weeks, as the females (recognizable by their duller plumage) and yearlings move in, the males mount to the tree tops and telephone wires and begin to sing. "Cheer up, cheeriup, cheerily": the song pours forth with almost unlimited variation of accent, duration, and pitch; sometimes, individual birds can be identified by peculiarities in the pattern of their caroling. Although we associate robin song with spring, it actually continues throughout the breeding period and presumably functions in the attraction of mates and the maintenance of territories. Early in the season, when both mates and territories are in doubt, some males sing virtually nonstop; but as a rule, they take their cue from the sun and confine their serenades to dawn and dusk. And so it happens, as a poetic ornithologist once put it, that "a wave of Robin song arises on the Atlantic coast to hail the coming day, and so, preceding the rising sun, rolls across the land until at last it breaks and dies away upon the distant shores of the Pacific Ocean."

One reason that robins rank so high in the affections of North Americans is that they share our habitat. In pre-settlement times, robins were a forest species, and they can still be found nesting along rivers and lakes and other openings in the woods. Here they forage for the fruits and small, soft-bodied animals that make up their diet. But their needs are even more readily met amongst the ornamental plantings and short-cropped lawns of suburbia. As this type of landscape has expanded, so have the robin's population and range. Simply by mowing and watering your grass, you are providing the local robins with a first-class opportunity to feed, since earthworms are brought to the surface by the rumble of the machinery and by the water flooding into their lairs. If you get down on your hands and knees, you will be able to see them, the tips of their plump, pink bodies filling the entrances of their burrows, a few millimeters below ground. That is what a robin looks for, too, when it zigzags across the lawn, cocking its head first one way, then the other, so that each eye is focused in turn on a patch of turf. If it finds a worm, the bird immediately jabs at the hole with its bill; the slightest inaccuracy and the prey will vanish underground. If the strike is successful, the bird still faces the task of tugging its slippery, resisting quarry out of the ground.

Please note that robins have proven to be extremely susceptible to pesticide residues in their prey. The best advice about using such poisons is: don't.

Feeding is not the only aspect of robin behavior that you can study in your backyard. In the spring, you may watch as rival males face-off on the lawn and then leap straight up into the air, biting, clawing, and battering each other with their wings. The issue is territory— the right to occupy this piece of land that you like to think of as yours. The same concern sometimes leads an individual into a prolonged contest with an imaginary challenger, such as his own reflection in a windowpane or hubcap. But the passions subside as the weeks pass, boundaries are drawn, and thereafter you are most likely to observe the resident pair, with neighboring robins visiting your yard only occasionally. In May and June, you may notice that you're seeing much more of the resident male than of his mate, until one day, in June or July, he shows up with a retinue of three or

Although the American Robin is the essential bird of spring for many of us, it is also becoming an increasingly common winter bird, even where the climate is quite extreme. Decorative plantings, such as Mountain Ash, make it possible for a few individuals to survive over the winter.

Three or four eggs is a typical clutch for the American Robin; a pair may nest two or three times in a year.

Facing page: Young robins are plump, unsuspecting creatures, whose frequent food calls often attract the attention of house cats and other predators. Their first week out of the nest is especially perilous.

four bob-tailed, spotty-breasted young, which bounce around behind him and beg whenever he finds something to·eat.

The female, meanwhile, has been building and tending the nest. Indeed, no sooner has the first brood fledged than she's at it again: two nestings a year are typical throughout the robin's range, and three are not uncommon in the south. (Although robins usually change mates from year to year, they seldom do so between clutches in the same year.) Sometimes the female will refurbish her original nest for the second brood, but more often she starts afresh, first selecting a sturdy branch, crotch, or ledge, then constructing an outer wall or foundation of coarse grass and twigs. This she lines with wet clay, which she brings in one mouthful at a time and works into place with her body; during dry spells she may pick up beakfuls of dust and dip them in puddles or birdbaths to make her own mud. The finishing touch is a bed of fine grass. If you want to help her with her task, you can provide a nesting shelf: a board, fifteen or twenty centimeters on a side, which is furnished with drain holes. Put it two to six meters above ground, in a place where it will be sheltered from sun and rain. The bird may also accept bits of string (no more than thirty centimeters long so she won't get snarled in them) and a tray of mud.

Generally speaking, the male takes little or no interest in nest-building, incubation, or brooding. In fact, throughout the breeding season, he leads a distinctly double life. Attentive by day to the urgencies of defending his territory or feeding young, he retires at night to the peaceful and companionable atmosphere of a "roost." There, under the cover of dense foliage, robins may congregate by the dozens or hundreds to spend the night. At first, while the females are on the nest and the young unfledged, only the adult males assemble, but the flock grows as the young birds start to arrive. Eventually, toward the end of summer, the females are also free to join. Just what function these daily reunions serve in robin society is far from clear, though they may provide some sort of preparation for migration and the non-breeding season, when the birds will travel and forage in flocks. Most robins winter in the Gulf states, though not always (perhaps rarely) in the company of the birds with which they spend the summer. The next spring, however, each population will again converge on its familiar breeding grounds, with many individuals seeking out the same few hundred square meters of shrubs and lawn that they occupied the year before. Roosting areas tend to be reused as well, sometimes for a decade or more.

Waxwings

From the sounds they make, you might imagine that waxwings were hung all over with tiny silver bells that jingle whenever they move. In the winter, their tinkling calls, uttered continuously and by many voices at once, often provide the first hint that waxwings have arrived in the neighborhood. Follow the music to its source, and you will see a tight, ever-shifting flock of starling-sized birds swooping from yard to yard, from berry-tree to berry-tree. Mountain ash, or rowan, fruit is favored particularly. Surprisingly tame (or totally absorbed in their task), they may let you stand under and amongst them long enough to notice their black masks, mobile crests, and yellow-tipped tails and to appreciate the velvety sleekness of their plumage. These characteristics mark them as waxwings; but which species do they belong to? We have two, which occasionally associate in mixed flocks: the Bohemian, or northern, Waxwing, *Bombycilla garrulus,* has white bars on its wings and a rusty patch on the underside of the tail, while the slightly smaller Cedar, or southern, Waxwing, *Bombycilla cedrorum,* lacks wingbars and has white under the tail. The Bohemians are common winter birds in western Canada and the western and midwestern states and make only occasional wintertime sweeps across the continent. Cedars, by contrast, breed from coast to coast, though seldom much above the international boundary; they winter south to Panama.

Have you ever wondered about the name "waxwing"? Most adults of both species have waxy-looking red tips on some or all of their secondary flight feathers, which form a dotted line of color at midwing. One theory is that these droplets protect the feather tips from abrasion, but it is also possible that they have a social significance. Perhaps, like variations in hair and eye color in humans, variations in the number and arrangement of these markings help the birds to tell one another apart. This is pure speculation, for very little is known about interactions among waxwings. Exceptionally gregarious, they associate in flocks of three or four dozen birds (sometimes fewer, sometimes many more) from late summer until spring, and, as we will see, often maintain a social life even while nesting.

One obvious means of communication among waxwings is their calls, and even human ears have been able to distinguish seven variations on the basic waxwing "zeee," each with its own significance: hunger, aggression, distress, location, and so on. The birds also have social displays, notably a minuet-like "dance" which may be performed by two birds in privacy or by several pairs in a flock. The ceremony begins with the couple side by side on a branch, facing the same direction and looking straight ahead. Then one of them (the male) hops toward his partner and rubs her bill or offers her a petal or berry from his mouth. She responds by hopping away, hopping back, and returning his gift or attention. Then it's his turn again—hop to the side, hop back, exchange—and so it goes through a dozen or more repetitions. Although not restricted to the breeding season, this pretty ritual is probably an aspect of courtship and pair maintenance. But why do a group of waxwings sometimes stand in a row and pass a berry back and forth? No one knows, and many other, more significant questions about leadership, dominance, and permanence in waxwing flocks remain unanswered as well.

One reason waxwings are hard to study is that they are so unpredictable. These are the gypsies of the bird world, capable of appearing almost anywhere within their range at almost any time and in any number. The key to understanding this and other aspects of their behavior is their food supply. Although they eat petals, sap, and insects (which they catch in flight), the basic item on their menu is small fruit: saskatoons or June berries, wild cherries, cedar berries, strawberries, rosehips. Compared to the insects and seeds on which most songbirds subsist, such food is watery and low in nutrients. Hence, waxwings eat often and enthusiastically. But berries are also patchy, perishable, and relatively unreliable from year to year, so that the birds have to search constantly to keep up their food supply. This

■ Cedar Waxwing
■ Bohemian Waxwing
■ Range Overlap

Both species of waxwings share the same wonderfully fine, soft plumage. This is a Cedar Waxwing.

helps to account for their wanderings and to explain their sociable natures. By living in a flock, an individual benefits from the food-finds of its fellows, yet loses little by sharing its own discoveries, since, when food is found, there is generally plenty for all.

Not surprisingly, the timing of nesting is also influenced by the birds' diet. Cedar Waxwings, for example, return to their breeding grounds when spring is almost past—usually around the first of June—and seldom lay eggs until late June or July. This presumably insures that the young will hatch when the berry crop is at its best. As unpredictable in their choice of nest sites as in their movements, the birds seem somehow to size up the fruit-

producing potential of an area before deciding to stay. Sometimes a pair of "Cedar-birds" will nest alone, but often up to a dozen pairs form a loose "colony," all in the same grove though not in one tree. Neighbors often get together to go foraging. Yet there are limits to their conviviality during the breeding season, for each pair claims a small area around the nest within which other waxwings may not trespass. If you should see a waxwing perched consistently on the same wire or branch, it is probably a male guarding his territory.

Somewhere below him, his mate is tending the nest. Waxwings build bulky cups, about fifteen centimeters in diameter, out of twigs, mosses, lichens, grasses, and whatever else is

With its feathers fluffed against the cold, this Bohemian Waxwing is prepared to endure winter's worst. The purpose of the waxy red wingtips is not known.

Raising a brood (or two)
of demanding young can tax
Cedar Waxwings to the limit
of their strength.

available; they have been known to take string from an outstretched hand and to pull hair from a person's head! The birds are surreptitious in approaching the nest, but the female sometimes gives its location away with a noisy outburst of begging—the male feeds her many times a day throughout the two-week incubation. It's like a magic act: the male arrives with nothing in his mouth, gives his head a little jerk, and, presto, a whole berry appears in his bill; he can carry eight or ten at once in his throat. Later, with some assistance from his mate, he will feed their four or five nestlings, at first bringing in insects and then fruit. If, as sometimes happens, the pair opt to have a second brood, they will somehow manage to feed and protect their first family, renew their courtship, and build a new nest, all at the same time; the male will also be called upon to feed his mate, who is under the strain of producing a clutch of eggs. Pushing themselves to the limit, working fourteen- to eighteen-hour days, the birds (like many other songbirds) often lose weight while raising their young.

Among waxwings, reproductive success obviously depends on close cooperation between mates, and there are signs that this all-important relationship may be strengthened by an emotional bond. If a person captures one member of a pair, its partner will often fly close by and twitter anxiously; if one bird dies, its mate may call in distress for as long as two days. We cannot know if waxwings feel affection, but the evidence is suggestive. In the words of a wise old saying, "One touch of Nature makes the whole world kin."

Shrikes

The first thing to notice about a shrike is its bill, particularly the hooked tip and the "tooth" on the upper mandible. Do they remind you of anything you've seen before? (If not take a look at the American Kestrel on page 71.) Judging from its form, the shrike's bill clearly belongs to a predator. But then examine the bird's feet: four slender toes, three pointed forward and one back, all attached at the same height. (On a falcon, the toes would be stout and armed with talons, and the hind toe would be slightly raised.) While it's true

These Loggerhead Shrikes belong to a remarkable group of songbirds that prey on small birds and mammals.

that the shrike's claws are relatively strong and sharp, its feet clearly belong to a perching bird. Though seemingly contradictory, these two descriptions—predator and perching bird—are both accurate, for shrikes are songbirds that prey on other animals, including vertebrates.

Of the seventy-four species of shrikes in the world, most are native to tropical Africa. Two regularly occur in our area, the Northern Shrike, *Lanius excubitor,* and the Loggerhead Shrike, *L. ludovincianus.* The former, as its name suggests, generally breeds in the taiga

north of 60°; but from October to April, it can be found throughout settled areas of southern Canada and in the northernmost tier of states. The Loggerhead, on the other hand, nests in the mid-latitudes and winters farther south. Thus, as a rule, winter sightings will be Northerns, summer sightings Loggerheads. But what of spring and fall, when the two may temporarily overlap? Loggerheads and Northerns look very much alike: both are about the size of robins and dressed in gray, black, and white, with a black mask; both have a rapid, undulating flight and a patch of white on the underwing that flashes with each stroke. But it is still possible to tell them apart, since Northerns are slightly larger, with delicately barred breasts, a light-colored base on the lower bill, and no black on the forehead, while Loggerheads are smaller, unbarred, dark-billed, and marked with black between the eyes.

As a rule, Loggerheads are with us from around the first of April until the end of August. The best place to look for them is in parkland country or thin woods, where there are fields for hunting and bare branches or wires for perching. Perhaps you'll see your bird on one of its conspicuous lookouts or notice it swooping down, skimming along just above the ground, and rising abruptly to another vantage point. Perhaps it will dash out and catch an insect in midair. Another even more characteristic maneuver is a ground attack, a direct and silent descent toward the prey, followed by last-minute dodging and hovering in midair as the hunter perfects its aim.

Phenomenally perceptive and alert, a Loggerhead can detect a moving grasshopper (one of its staple foods) up to seventy meters away and orient toward it unerringly. When the quarry is a mouse or small songbird, the shrike is even more precise, controlling not only the direction of its attack but the placement of the killing bite. Large insects may be grabbed anywhere on the head or thorax, but vertebrates, which are potentially dangerous and likely to get away, are dispatched with a sudden, disabling snip to the back of the neck. In this way, a fifty-gram Loggerhead can take a twenty-five gram rodent or an adult Northern Mockingbird.

What happens next may surprise you. Be-

cause the shrike's feet are weak, it cannot hold large prey while tearing it apart. Instead it carries the carcass to a nearby thicket or fence and impales it on a thorn, sharp twig, or wire barb or wedges it in a crevice. With its meal thus secured, the shrike can rip off bite-sized shreds. The movement pattern involved in impaling is innate (a tendency to drag prey along branches and other surfaces until it gets stuck), but a knowledge of possible impaling sites is learned through trial and error. As birds go, shrikes are surprisingly smart and are even capable of reasoning. One individual, confined in a cage with limited impaling facilities, tore off a chunk of meat that was still too large to swallow. Seeing that all its spikes were filled, the bird dropped the oversized piece, removed one of the hanging carcasses in order to empty a place, and put up the bit it was working on. Loggerheads also have keen memories, and if a carcass is not consumed in one meal, or if a bird goes on hunting when it's too full to eat, it will remember the location of its cache and return to it. Food is usually recovered within twenty-four hours, but it can be left for a week or more and then reclaimed. Sometimes, when good impaling sites are scarce, a shrike hangs a dozen or more carcasses in one area—sometimes in a single bush—and almost all of them will be used in time. To the ancients, these outdoor larders were reminiscent of their own open-air meatmarkets; hence the Latin generic *Lanius,* or "butcher."

During incubation and brooding, female Loggerheads have been known to raid their mate's impaled caches to feed themselves or their young. In general, the division of labor at the nest follows a typical songbird pattern: the female builds the nest (a bulky mass of twigs and grass hidden in dense brush), lays the eggs (around five or six to a clutch), incubates, and broods. The male, meanwhile, feeds the female, helps feed the nestlings, and stands guard. Both parents are aggressive and loyal in defending the nest. The rate of reproduction is often high, with most pairs rearing at least one fledgling, and some producing second broods. Yet Loggerhead populations are significantly depressed throughout the eastern half of North America and nobody knows why. As is usual in such cases, the finger of suspicion points at habitat loss or pesticides or both.

Loggerhead Shrike

Yellow Warbler

Yellow Warbler

The American warblers, or "wood-warbler" group, are sometimes thought of as the butterflies of the avian world. There are over a hundred species in all, most of them brightly colored—blue, orange, red, chestnut, yellow—and all of them ceaselessly active, as they flit and hop among the branches in their search for insect food. More than forty species breed at our latitude, including a bewildering variety of Golden-wings, Orange-crowns, Black-throats, Yellow-throats, Chestnut-sides, Bay-breasts, Prairies, Pines, and Palms, a diversity that becomes most apparent during the spring and fall migrations. Traveling by night, mixed flocks of warblers move north and south in waves; by day, they feed and rest, bringing sudden life to wooded areas of both city and countryside. Since each species has its own set of distinguishing characteristics, which may differ by season, sex, and age, trying to identify these restless migrants provides unending sport and satisfaction for bird-watchers.

The most widely distributed and best known of the wood-warblers is the Yellow Warbler, *Dendroica petechia*. During the nesting season, you can expect to find it in gardens and roadside thickets, where it goes calmly about its business even in the presence of people; but its natural habitat is moist woods, particularly the willow-thatched shores of marshes and streams. In all plumages, this is the yellowest of all our warblers—hence the nickname "wild canary." It is also the only one with yellow (not white) on the inner webs of the tail, a marking that is diagnostic at all times of the year.

If your ear is well tuned to subtle differences in pitch, range, tempo, rhythm, and duration, you can also hope to tell the species by the males' song, a rapid, musical "tsee-tsee-tsee-tsee-tseesi-weesee" (or words to that effect). Actually, Yellow Warblers have two types of song, so-called "accented-ending songs," which finish with a crescendo and an ascending phrase; and "unaccented ending songs," which have a less prominent cadence. The latter are most often heard in midseason and seem to be associated with territorial defense, since they

The overgrown youngster in the nest of this Yellow Warbler is a Brown-headed Cowbird, a species that is always reared by foster parents—often by warblers or Song Sparrows.

are usually uttered along a boundary or in the presence of another male Yellow Warbler. Interestingly, these songs are extremely variable, perhaps permitting neighbors to recognize each other individually, but they are not particularly distinctive of the species, since they closely resemble the territorial songs of the American Redstart and certain other warblers. Songs with accented endings, by contrast, are more rigidly prescribed—they are performed in much the same way by all the males in the population—and are more distinctive of Yellow Warblers. Not surprisingly, they are heard most often in May and June, during the mating season, when finding a mate of the right species takes precedence over individual expression.

Yellow Warblers generally nest sometime in June. The female is the house-builder in the family, though the male may follow her closely as she gathers grass, plant down, and the like and carries it to the chosen site, usually an upright crotch in a bush or small tree, one or two meters above ground. Working with impressive dexterity, the female fashions an elegant, firmly woven cup; lines it; and shapes it with her body, readying it to receive her four or five eggs. Incubation (by the female alone) lasts about eleven days, and the young are tended in the nest for an equal length of time, a period that sees them transformed from half-naked little grubs with bulging eyes and abdomens into drab but fully feathered Yellow Warblers, capable of flight. To accomplish this miracle, the parents work fifteen-hour days, bringing in caterpillars, inchworms, aphids, and other insects for their ever-hungry brood. Even after the young have fledged, they trail after their parents for a time, squawking and fluttering their wings as they beg to be fed.

In addition to (or instead of) attending to their own offspring, Yellow Warblers often find themselves cast in the role of foster-parents to another species, the Brown-headed Cowbird. Like the cuckoos of the Old World, cowbirds are "obligatory nest parasites," which means that they always lay their eggs in the nests of other birds and never take any part in rearing

Also known as the "summer yellowbird" and "golden warbler," the Yellow Warbler is our only wild bird that appears all yellow from a distance. The brownish-red stripes on the breast of the male can only be seen at close range.

their young. When you think about it, this is amazing—a radical reworking of the basic patterns of avian reproduction and a tribute to the inexhaustible creativity of natural selection. This same inventive process has also been at work on the cowbirds' host species, including the Yellow Warbler. A nestling cowbird is large, fast-growing, and ravenous, with the result that it deprives the hosts' own young of space, food, and, often, of their lives. Obviously, the best strategy, from the hosts' point of view, is to keep the cowbird from hatching. But how? Some species simply toss the egg out, but the female Yellow Warbler isn't big enough to grasp the egg in her bill. Instead, she may choose to abandon her nest and either rebuild or give up for the year. More frequently, she just builds a new floor, thereby burying the cowbird egg (perhaps with one of her own), and starts a new clutch on top. In this way, the cowbird is deprived of warmth and cannot develop. If the nest is parasitized again, the warbler may add another floor, and another, until she has as many as six "basements" under her nest cup, each containing one or two cowbird eggs. But if the cowbird egg is added late in the laying period, when the warbler's clutch is almost complete, she will likely accept it. Some pairs have succeeded in raising a cowbird and up to four of their own offspring.

Not so long ago, the now ubiquitous cowbird was a "bison bird," restricted to the western plains. With the expansion of agriculture, it has expanded too, both to the east and west, thereby making contact with species that are not adapted to cope with it. One example is Kirtland's Warbler, a bird of the southern and eastern Great Lakes region, which now nests exclusively in central Michigan. Through a combination of habitat loss, nest parasitism, and high winter mortality, this species has been reduced to about two hundred breeding pairs. Habitat protection and a local program of cowbird trapping has helped to stabilize the population; but winter mortality is uncontrollable, and Kirtland's Warbler is listed as endangered in both Canada and the United States.

Song Sparrow

If you've always assumed that sparrows were drab and dreary little birds with nothing to say for themselves except "chirp," get ready for a surprise. The Song Sparrow, *Melospiza melodia,* is one of the most versatile and original songsters on the continent. A typical Song Sparrow melody is a vivid flourish of sound, two or three seconds long, higher in pitch than the top keys on the piano, and made up of three or four slow, clear, staccato notes; a buzzy vibrato tone; and a combination of trills, whistles, slurs, and other phrases. Within this general pattern, there is room for almost limitless variety, which is detectable electronically, though not always apparent to the human ear. On average, every male has eight to ten distinctly different songs (some have twenty or more), most or all of which are uniquely his. Neither his father, nor his brothers, nor his closest neighbors are likely to share even one of his themes. And if it should happen, as it occasionally does, that two birds do sing exactly the same tune, each will have his own set of variations. By adding, subtracting, and substituting elements—a phrase here, a trill there—a Song Sparrow can create up to two hundred versions of a single song. Typically, he'll sing six or eight of these in one burst, switch to a second tune and vary it, continue with a third, and so on, running through six or ten songs before repeating one. It may take him several hours to work through his whole repertoire.

Why this emphasis on virtuosity? For one thing, female Song Sparrows appreciate it: they show a preference for males with many songs. The males, for their part, use song as a means of identifying one another or, at least, of distinguishing neighbors from outsiders. A familiar song coming from the other side of a well-established territorial border causes less concern than an unfamiliar song, which reveals the presence of an intruder. As a rule, each male has four to seven next-door neighbors, which means he must come to recognize roughly forty to seventy songs, plus variations, a task that calls for considerable powers of discrimination and memory. Yet there is every reason to believe that Song Sparrows are able to do it.

If the differences between individuals are important to Song Sparrows, so are the similarities. While neighbors generally don't share entire songs, they often have several song-elements, or "syllables," in common. A syllable that is used frequently in one area may be unknown in a population only an hour's drive away. To the human ear, the air-time accorded to any particular whistle or tweet is of no great significance; but such subtleties obviously matter to Song Sparrows, for they respond much more strongly to songs from their own region than to foreign "dialects."

The fact that dialects develop and persist among Song Sparrows has at least three implications. In the first place, it means that there must be some mechanism by which local peculiarities can be passed from generation to generation. This mechanism is learning. Young males start acquiring their songs at five to twelve weeks of age, just after they've become independent of their parents but before they leave their home area on migration. Thus, during this critical period, a youngster ordinarily gets a chance to hear and imitate many of the adult males in his neighborhood. If he is experimentally deprived of this experience, he will still come up with a medley of tunes, but they will be too long, too slow, too simple, and too monotone to pass for normal. The existence of dialects also implies that there is an innovative or creative force at work, so that local idiosyncrasies can develop in the first place; and this is improvisation. Not only are young Song Sparrows able to rearrange song-elements that they learn from adult birds, they can also invent new syllables. (By the time they reach maturity during their second spring, their repertoires have become fixed.) Finally, if dialects are to remain distinct, local populations must be separate, with little genetic or social exchange. In fact, yearlings of both sexes almost always breed within three hundred meters of their birthplaces, and adults return to the same or neighboring territories year after year.

Song Sparrow

Though unassuming in appearance, the Song Sparrow is remarkable for its ability to perform, remember, and create songs.

A Song Sparrow territory usually encompasses about half a hectare of scrubland—weeds, grass, and brush—where the birds can forage for insects and seeds and find cover for their nests. Two clutches per year are typical and three not uncommon, with the first being laid in April or May, before the leaves are out. Accordingly, an early nest is almost always built on the ground, under a concealing thatch of dry plants, while later ones are often in shrubs. The three to six heavily splotched eggs are incubated by the female for almost two weeks, during which time the male stands a tuneful watch over the territory but seldom approaches the nest. How is it, then, that he knows so promptly when the infants hatch? Does the mother catch his attention by showing signs of excitement? However it happens, the male plays a full role in feeding the nestlings. Interestingly, when the young birds

166

leave home at ten days of age, the brood is organized into two single-parent families, so that each fledgling is consistently fed by the same adult. In broods with an odd number of young, the mother usually takes the extra one but gradually cedes some of her duties to the male, thereby freeing herself to start another nest. Fledgling Brown-headed Cowbirds are shared in the same way as the sparrows' own offspring.

Thanks to their extravagant fertility, Song Sparrows cope successfully with a very high rate of cowbird parasitism. They are also subject to heavy predation by bird-eating hawks such as Cooper's and Sharp-shins and by egg- and nestling-nabbers like crows and Blue Jays. For every ten eggs that a Song Sparrow lays, only four are likely to yield fledglings, with predators getting most of the rest. Over-winter mortality is also high, and the average life expectancy for the species is only two or two and a half years. Yet populations are buoyant and are normally held in check not by any of these external forces but by the sparrows' own territoriality, which limits the number of birds that breed.

Red-winged Blackbird

According to the dictionary, a marsh is "a tract of wetlands, often with cattails and grasses." But for birdlovers, this definition leaves out at least one essential factor—blackbirds. From late March until autumn, almost every marshy stand on the continent is abloom with one or two species of these vivacious and colorful birds. The Yellow-headed Blackbird is basically a westerner, found throughout the Canadian prairies and across the western half to two-thirds of the United States. As a rule, you'll find the males perched atop cattails in the more open, central parts of the marsh, uttering their "song," a metallic bray that wards off intruders. Their cousins, the Red-winged Blackbirds, *Agelaius phoeniceus,* are smaller and more melodious than the Yellow-heads. Where the two coexist, Redwings are apparently subordinant and are often excluded from the richest habitat (riches being defined amongst blackbirds by the availability of aquatic insects and insect larvae on the breeding grounds). But despite this disadvantage, Redwings ultimately get the upper hand, for they are far more adaptable than their overbearing relatives and are even able to breed in moist meadows and hayfields a long way from water. Partly because of this versatility, the Redwing is now thought to be one of the most numerous species of bird in North America, with a fall population of around 400 million.

How does one identify a Red-winged Blackbird? Although it would be convenient if they all had red wings, this is not the case. In fact, more than half the population isn't even black. The females, for example, are reed-brown, with black and white streaks on the underside, and only occasionally have orange-red on their shoulders. Young of the year are like their mothers, but second-year males are darker and sport bright epaulets that are mottled with black. Significantly, these young males, with their imperfect markings, are seldom able to breed, because they cannot maintain territories against older males. Crimson epaulets, which characteristically occur on males past their second year, are a badge of maturity and masculinity and are prominently displayed in the well-named "song spread" display with which the birds defend their boundaries. You might watch for this behavior the next time you visit a marsh. Without his showy markings (or without his song), a male Redwing is much less able to intimidate intruders and will almost certainly lose at least part of his holdings. This, in turn, will likely reduce his opportunities to mate. Not surprisingly, male Redwings place a high value on their epaulets

Red-winged Blackbird

The red epaulets of the male Redwing are of great practical and psychological importance to the bird. This individual is performing the "song spread" display.

and will work for hours or days at restoring them if they're dyed black for an experiment.

Even among males with normal, adult markings, there are always a substantial number of evolutionary "losers"—birds that are unable to obtain breeding territories. Early in the season, competition for habitat is intense, and a territory holder will wear himself gaunt guarding his domain. (Nine hundred square meters is an average holding.) The payoff comes when the females arrive, a week or two after the males. Let one of them land even briefly on a territory, and she is immediately claimed by the resident male. Should she move into a neighboring territory, he darts across the line and chases her back. She seems scarcely to care which male breeds with her, as long as she can find a suitable nest site within his realm. If, as occasionally happens, her mate is absent when she's ready to copulate, she'll accept the attentions of the next-door neighbor or a chance visitor. And the next year, if her old mate is still in the area, she is likely to pass him by and form a new and equally evanescent pair bond.

If the females are nonchalant about their relationships with males, they are more passionate in encounters with members of their own sex. Every female maintains a subterritory within her male's domain, from which she excludes all other females, using the song-spread and other aggressive actions. The male, by contrast, is eager to let the newcomers move in—more females means more offspring for him—and accordingly, he interferes in the battle on their behalf, even if it means striking a female that has already accepted him. In the end, each male's territory is usually occupied by from one to four spatting females and sometimes as many as ten or fifteen. The females are quite right to resent one another's presence, because crowded territories are often subject to higher-than-average rates of nest predation.

Highly sociable by nature, Red-winged Blackbirds may mass together by the thousands—or more. At a single winter roost in the southern states, there may be twenty or thirty million birds.

A female Red-winged Blackbird feeds her young. Not all Redwings have red wings.

A Redwing nest is a softly lined pouch, often attached to dead cattail stalks, and built by the female alone. Listen carefully in the spring and you may hear her ripping strips off cattail leaves to use in nest-making. Egg laying begins in May, typically four to a clutch; incubation lasts eleven or twelve days and is another female responsibility. The male may or may not help feed the nestlings, but he does assist when the youngsters fledge and have to run a gauntlet of hostile neighbors to get off the marsh. The mother stays with them in the uplands for about two weeks (though she may ultimately go back to rear a second brood), while the father returns to his other mates and to any "runts" that may have been left behind.

Once away from the wetlands, Redwings undergo a rapid change. Where once they were insect-eaters, they now switch to seeds; where once they were antagonistic to one another, they are now highly sociable and mass in huge flocks that work the croplands by day and settle on the marshes after dark. By late October, one roost in Quebec usually houses a cacophonous aggregation of 500,000 birds. Ever since the Iroquoians started growing maize, Redwings have taken a portion of the corn crop. Today, with their population at a record high, they are Public Enemy Number One in some localities. Damage extends to oats, barley, flax, and sunflowers, as well as corn. Control measures have ranged from bizarre (the use of cannonlike noisemakers and flashing shield-shaped kites) to brutal (drenching the birds with detergent and leaving them to die of exposure); but none can be counted a success. There are always birds to take the place of those that have been removed. The best prospects include the development of bird-resistant plant varieties, the use of lure crops, and other changes in farming practices.

Meadowlarks

Before the last Ice Age, there was probably just one species of meadowlark in North America. But as the glaciers advanced southward, they are thought to have driven the birds to the east and west, dividing them into separate populations and holding them apart for many thousands of years. The result: we now have two distinct species, the Eastern Meadowlark, *Sturnella magna,* and the Western Meadowlark, *Sturnella neglecta.*

In many ways, these two are still very much alike. In appearance, for example, they're almost identical—chunky, robin-sized birds with outer tail feathers that flash white in flight; plump yellow breasts; and black V's on their bibs. Western Meadowlarks tend to be slightly smaller and paler than their eastern counterparts, but the differences are too subtle to be useful in the field. Both species share a preference for wide-open spaces, and during the breeding season (from April to October), they can generally be found around farmyards, pastures, and uncultivated fields. Here, each breeding male claims a vaguely defined territory of about three hectares (often in the same area he occupied the preceding year) and defends it in tortuous, chaselike aerial duets, showy "jump-flights," and other displays that are common to both species. Similar behaviors are also seen during courtship, as the males each try to win the loyalty of two or three mates. The females in such a grouping coexist amicably with each other but nest apart, each choosing a ground-hollow or hoofprint for her neat cup of grass, complete with an over-arching canopy. A typical clutch for either species consists of four or five eggs, which are incubated by the mother alone for about two weeks. Though almost invisible to human eyes—look sharp, or your first clue to their whereabouts will be the crunch of shells under your feet—meadowlark eggs are readily nosed out by a horde of hungry predators, including dogs, cats, skunks, weasels, and foxes, ground squirrels, garter snakes, and voles; many broods are also destroyed by mowing and other farm work. As a consequence, fully two-thirds of the nests may fail, and even by attempting two broods (which is the rule), an average female only rears two or three offspring per year.

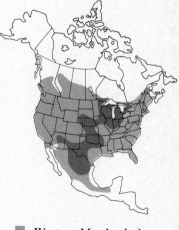

■ Western Meadowlark
■ Eastern Meadowlark
■ Range Overlap

Nestlings are fed on insects and insect larvae —up to three thousand grasshopper nymphs or the equivalent for each young during its eleven or twelve days in the nest—with weed seeds being added to the menu as the birds mature. All in all, both Eastern and Western species deserve a four-star rating as destroyers of agricultural pests.

Thus, in many aspects of their biology and behavior, Eastern and Western meadowlarks are essentially alike. So what is it that prevents them from merging through interbreeding? They've been in touch with each other now for several centuries (perhaps longer), yet hybrids are exceedingly rare. How do the birds distinguish their own kind, and why has it been important for them to do so?

The answer to the first question— How?—will be obvious to anyone who has heard Eastern and Western meadowlarks in

song. It is amazing that two species can look and act so much alike, yet sound so totally dissimilar! Eastern birds sing in falsetto, a slurred "see you, see yeer" that is capable of numerous simple variations. A normal Eastern male has fifty to one hundred rather similar songs, which he sings in bouts, several repetitions of one being followed by several repetitions of another, until he has worked his way through his whole repertoire. Westerners, by contrast, have a mellow alto voice and produce a song in two phrases, the first slow and monotone, the second a throaty, gurgling descent: "Oh I can see your white petticoat," or "top of the morning, top of the morn." A Western male has only five to twelve songs, which he cycles through in much the same manner as an Eastern bird would do, but his variations are generally more complex and distinct. The alarm calls of the two species are

Meadowlarks are not really larks but highly colored members of the blackbird group. This is a female Western Meadowlark.

also entirely different: a buzzy "dzert" in the East and a low "chupp" in the West. Occasionally, where their ranges overlap, males are found with songs and, more rarely, calls of both types, a virtuosity that develops through youthful learning; but even in these cases, the "pure" Eastern and Western characteristics of individual melodies are not lost. "Intermediate" songs, which combine the timbre of one species with the phrasing of the other, are virtually never heard.

Now for a surprise. As obvious as these distinctions are, male meadowlarks seem scarcely to notice them, for they engage in their full range of territorial behavior against members of the other species, despite the fact that their opponents sing the "wrong" songs. Nor are the males more discriminating when it comes to potential mates. Any female mead-

owlark will elicit courtship; even a starling will sometimes do. But the females are not so easily wooed. By and large, they insist on males that know the appropriate calls and tunes. The only exception occurs on an advancing frontier, where members of one species are vastly outnumbered by the other. Under these circumstances, a sexually ready female may reluctantly accept a mate of the wrong species, because she has little choice. But this decision is self-defeating, since the offspring of mixed unions are sterile. Whatever their apparent similarities, Eastern and Western meadowlarks are genetically incompatible, a fact that goes far toward explaining why their vocalizations have not converged. Females need a cue by which to identify males of their own species, in order to increase the likelihood of producing fertile young.

This Eastern Meadowlark is tending young in a well-protected ground nest. The nesting behavior of both Eastern and Western Meadowlarks is very similar.

Northern Oriole

Northern Oriole

The Northern Oriole, *Icterus galbula,* is sometimes known as the "firebird," in tribute to the fiery beauty of the male's breeding colors. See him in the spring, standing straight and tall in front of his intended partner, dazzling her with the blazing orange of his breast. Down he jerks, until he's almost prone, his head on a level with his feet. For a moment, all the female can see is the black of his pate, blotting out the glow. But as the male rocks forward, his brilliant rump flares into view; and so it goes, an alternating show of light and dark, with which he woos his mate.

For birdwatchers, the male's plumage is the key to distinguishing between the two subspecies of Northern Oriole. The western form, Bullock's Oriole, occurs from the Great Plains to the Pacific slope in the United States, with extensions into British Columbia, southeastern Alberta, and southwestern Saskatchewan. It can be recognized by the male's black crown and orange cheeks, by the large white patch on the wings, and by the black tips on the outer tail feathers. The Baltimore Oriole, in contrast, breeds from Alberta to Texas and east to the Atlantic coast. A male in this population has an all-black head, a small white bar on each wing, and orange tips on the sides of its tail. The females of both types are similar—variably dressed in olive and brown—though Baltimores tend to be more yellowish on their underparts.

Male Baltimore and Bullock's orioles are so easily distinguished that, until quite recently, they were thought to represent separate species. But a species, according to the classical definition, is reproductively isolated. That is to say, members of one species will not normally breed with those of another. Yet Baltimore and Bullock's orioles interbreed freely all along the line where they come in contact. In fact, there is a "hybrid zone" some two- to three-hundred kilometers wide, stretching from Saskatchewan to central Texas, within which birds of the pure Bullock's or Baltimore type are almost never found. In all likelihood, the birds were divided into two populations during the last Ice Age but were subsequently reunited along the wooded banks of certain rivers that reach across the plains. With the coming of settlement and the planting of shade trees and shelterbelts, oriole habitat was markedly increased on the prairies, birds moved in from east and west, and the mixed-blood community began to flourish and grow.

Yet oddly enough, the hybrid zone does not seem to be enlarging: Baltimore Oriole characteristics are not spreading farther west, nor Bullock's farther east. What is it that limits the intermingling? Could it be that birds with intermediate characteristics are not accepted as mates by orioles in the "pure" populations on either side of the hybrid zone? Or maybe the barrier has to do with differences in physiology. Of the two forms, Bullock's Orioles are adapted to more arid conditions—areas with high temperatures, low rainfall, constant winds—while Baltimores are better suited to temperate climes. Bullock's Orioles, for example, often build well-supported nests that are attached to several branches and to the main tree trunk, thereby securing them against high winds, a behavior that does not seem to be included in the repertoire of Baltimore Orioles that breed on the Great Plains.

Wherever they occur and whichever subspecies they belong to, Northern Orioles are justly acclaimed for their ability as nest-builders. A typical oriole nest is a hanging, woven pouch of plant fibers, hair, and string, about ten or fifteen centimeters deep, with an opening at the top. It is usually suspended from the outer branches of a tall shade tree and is often over a roadway, stream, or some other clearing, so the birds can easily get in and out. Since orioles are latecomers in the spring (they usually return sometime in May), the female doesn't begin building until the trees are in leaf, making nests hard to find and the process of construction difficult to observe. But, with luck, maybe you'll someday watch as the female oriole brings in the first long threads, one at a time, wraps each around her chosen branch, and, as the mass grows, begins intertwining them with rapid thrusting movements

Baltimore Oriole? Bullock's Oriole? Northern Oriole? To determine which subspecies this is, please see the text.

Northern Orioles are also
sometimes known as "hang
nests" or "hammock birds."

of her bill. As the first wall nears completion, she starts on another, anchoring it to a nearby twig. Working with the same feverish energy as before, now from above, now from the side, now from below, her weight half-supported on the swinging ball of threads, she draws the sides together and weaves in the loose ends. From time to time, she climbs inside the pocket, turns about, and shakes her whole body to mold the nest to size, until the leaves and sometimes the tree itself are trembling. Such a nest will often last for several years, yet is never reused; the female builds a new one every spring. Construction takes about a week; the male, meanwhile, guards the territory and sings.

The orioles' eggs and young (usually four or five to a nest) are relatively safe in their little hammocks far above the ground, yet they are still sometimes vulnerable to attack by crows, Screech Owls, tree squirrels, and the like. Losses are kept to a minimum by the adult birds, which are second to none in the vigilance and fury with which they defend their progeny. Consider the plight of the unsuspecting young magpie that flew up to an oriole nest, thinking to find itself a breakfast of warm eggs, and ended up instead lying stunned beneath the tree, the victim of a well-placed blow from the father oriole. Fledgling orioles are much harder to protect since they spend their first week out of the nest calling almost constantly for food (caterpillars and other insects, sometimes fruit); many are no doubt lost to predators attracted by their "cry-baby" complaints.

In midsummer, the orioles suddenly and prematurely disappear, as the adults seek seclusion to molt. The females show up again about late July, when they form flocks of several dozen birds, including young of the year. Adult males never join these groupings, preferring instead the privacy of their nesting territories. Here they give few hints of their whereabouts, until August, when they reveal themselves with a minor revival of the robust, flutelike themes that were heard in spring. (Incidentally, the Northern Oriole is one of the very few species in which females also have well developed and individually distinctive songs, but they are only reported to sing in spring.) By the end of August, most of the orioles have left for the tropics, but a hardy few now winter in the Atlantic states and southeastern Canada, where they take advantage of parklike plantings and backyard feeding-shelves.

Distribution Maps

The distribution maps in this book show the approximate breeding (not wintering) ranges of the birds being discussed. Although based on a number of sources, they derive primarily from the new edition of W. Earl Godfrey's *Birds of Canada* (1986) and from Eirik Blom's work in National Geographic's *Field Guide to the Birds of North America* (1983). These are both excellent publications with fine maps. But please bear in mind that the boundaries shown are, of necessity, sometimes arbitrary. Birds do not feel obliged to confine their activities within the hard-and-fast lines that we draw on maps.

Bird Names

In the "binomial system" of scientific nomenclature, all species have two-part names. The first name refers to a group of closely related species, the genus. In the case of loons, for example, the generic name is *Gavia*. All loons share this name. The second name applies only to a particular species. Thus, the Common Loon is *Gavia immer,* while the Arctic Loon is *Gavia arctica.* In this book, scientific names are provided for all species that are discussed in detail. Officially accepted English names are capitalized when they appear in full.

A complete listing of scientific and English names for North American birds is available in the *American Ornithologists' Union checklist of North American birds,* 6th ed., 1983.

References

The literature on birds is vast, and many additional items might have been mentioned here. For reasons of space, however, this list includes only sources that support the specific statements made in this book. Major sources are marked with asterisks.

General References

Items under this heading were consulted repeatedly in preparing the text.

American Ornithologists' Union. 1983. *American Ornithologists' Union check-list of North American birds,* 6th ed. Lawrence, Kansas: Allen Press.

Austin, O. L., Jr. 1961. *Birds of the world: a survey of the twenty-seven orders and one hundred and fifty-five families.* New York: Golden Press.

Beebe, F. L., 1974. *Field studies of the Falconiformes of British Columbia: vultures, hawks, falcons, eagles.* B.C. Provincial Museum Occ. Paper Ser. No. 17.

Bellrose, F. C., 1976. *Ducks, geese and swans of North America.* Harrisburg, Pa.: Stackpole.

Brown, L., and Amadon, D. 1968. *Eagles, hawks and falcons of the world.* 2 vol. New York: McGraw-Hill.

Burton, J. A., ed. 1973. *Owls of the world: their evolution, structure and ecology.* n.p.: Peter Lowe.

Feduccia, A. 1980. *The age of birds.* Cambridge, Mass.: Harvard University Press.

Fyfe, R. W. 1977. Status of Canadian raptor populations. *Proc. World Conf. Birds of Prey, Vienna* 1: 34–38.

Godfrey, W. E. 1967. *The birds of Canada.* Ottawa: National Museum of Canada.

Guiguet, C. J. 1954–1978. *The birds of British Columbia.* B.C. Provincial Museum Handbooks 1–10.

Laboratory of Ornithology, Cornell University. 1975. *A field guide to western bird songs: western North America and the Hawaiian islands.* 3 long-play recordings. Boston: Houghton Mifflin.

Johnsgard, P. A. 1973. *Grouse and quails of North America.* Lincoln, Neb.: University of Nebraska Press.

———. 1978. *Ducks, geese, and swans of the world.* Lincoln, Neb.: University of Nebraska Press.

Mansell, W. M. 1980. *North American birds of prey.* Toronto: Gage.

Palmer, R. S., ed. 1962, 1976. *Handbook of North American birds.* 3 vol. New Haven, Conn.: Yale University Press.

Peters, H. S., and Burleigh, T. D. 1951. *The birds of Newfoundland.* Newfoundland Dept. Nat. Res.

Peterson, R. T. 1961. *A field guide to western birds.* Boston: Houghton Mifflin.

———. 1963. *The birds.* New York: Time Inc.

———. 1980. *A field guide to the birds east of the Rockies,* 4th ed. Boston: Houghton Mifflin.

Reilly, E. M., Jr. 1968. *The Audubon illustrated handbook of American birds.* New York: McGraw-Hill.

Rising, T., and Rising, J. 1982. *Canadian songbirds and their ways.* Montreal: Tundra.

Salt, W. R., and Salt, J. R. 1976. *The birds of Alberta.* Edmonton: Hurtig.

Scott, S. L., ed. 1983. *Field guide to the birds of North America.* Washington, D.C.: National Geographic.

Snyder, L. L. 1951. *Ontario birds.* Toronto: Clarke Irwin.

Squires, W. A. 1952. *The birds of New Brunswick.* New Brunswick Museum Monogr. Ser. No. 4.

Terres, J. K. 1980. *The Audubon Society encyclopedia of North American birds.* New York: Knopf.

Thomson, A. L., ed. 1964. *A new dictionary of birds.* New York: McGraw-Hill.

Tufts, R. W. 1961. *The birds of Nova Scotia.* Halifax: Nova Scotia Museum.

Udvardy, M. D. F. 1977. *The Audubon Society field guide to North American Birds: western region.* New York: Knopf.

Van Tyne, J., and Berger, A. J. 1976. *Fundamentals of ornithology.* New York: John Wiley and Sons.

Introduction

Brodkorb, P. 1971. Origin and evolution of birds. In *Avian biology,* ed. D. S. Farner; J. R. King; and K. C. Parkes, vol. 1, pp. 20–55. New York: Academic Press.

Committee on the Status of Endangered Wildlife in Canada. 1983. *List of species with designated status as of April 1983.* Distributed by the Canadian Nature Federation.

Desmond, A. J. 1975. *The hot-blooded dinosaurs: a revolution in palaeontology.* London: Blond and Briggs.

Hardin, G. 1960. The competitive exclusion principle. *Science* 131: 1282–98.

McGowan, C. 1984. Evolutionary relationships of ratites and carinates: evidence from ontogeny of the tarsus. *Nature* 307: 733–35.

Mead, C. 1983. *Bird migration*. Feltham, Middlesex: Country Life Books.

Mosquin, T., and Suchal, C., eds. 1977. *Canada's threatened species and habitats*. Canadian Nature Federation Sp. Pub. No. 6.

Ostrom, J. H. 1973. The ancestry of birds. *Nature* 242: 136.

———. 1980. The evidence for endothermy in dinosaurs. In *A cold look at warm-blooded dinosaurs,* eds. R. D. K. Thomas and E. C. Olson, pp. 15-54. American Association for the Advancement of Science Symposium No. 28.

Papi, F., and Wallraff, H. G., eds. 1982. *Avian navigation: International Symposium on Avian Navigation (ISAN), Tirrenia (Pisa), September 11-14, 1981*. Berlin: Springer-Verlag.

Storer, R. S. 1975. Bird. *Encyclopaedia Britannica Macropaedia* 2: 1053–62.

Vincent, J., ed. 1966 (updated 1971). *The red data book*. Morges, Switzerland: IUCN.

Welty, J. C. 1975. *The life of birds*. Philadelphia: W. B. Saunders.

Loons

Barklow, W. E. 1979. Graded frequency variations of the tremolo call of the Common Loon (*Gavia immer*). *Condor* 81: 53–64.

Canadian Wildlife Service. 1973. *Loon*. Hinterland Who's Who Series.

Fox, G. A.; Yonge, K. S.; and Sealy, S. G. 1980. Breeding performance, pollutant burden and eggshell thinning in Common Loons *Gavia immer* nesting on a boreal forest lake. *Ornis Scand*. 11: 243–48.

Heimberger, M.; Euler, D.; and Barr, J. 1983. The impact of cottage development on Common Loon reproductive success in central Ontario. *Wilson Bull*. 95: 431–39.

Henderson, A. D. 1924. The Common Loon in Alberta. *Condor* 26: 143–45.

McIntyre, J. W. 1974. Territorial affinity of a Common Loon. *Bird-Banding* 45: 178.

———. 1978. Wintering behavior of Common Loons. *Auk* 95: 396–403.

Munro, J. A. 1945. Observations of the loon in the Cariboo parklands, British Columbia. *Auk* 62: 38–49.

Nelson, D. H. 1983. A Common Loon nest from New Hampshire containing four eggs. *Wilson Bull*. 95: 672–73.

*Olson, S. T., and Marshall, W. H. 1952. *The Common Loon in Minnesota*. Minnesota Museum of Natural History Occ. Paper No. 5.

Ream, C. H. 1976. Loon productivity, human disturbance, and pesticide residues in northern Minnesota. *Wilson Bull*. 88: 427–32.

Rummel, L., and Goetzinger, C. 1975. The communication of intraspecific aggression in the Common Loon. *Auk* 92: 333–46.

———. 1978. Aggressive display in the Common Loon. *Auk* 95: 183–86.

Schorger, A. W. 1947. The deep diving of the loon and old-squaw and its mechanism. *Wilson Bull*. 59: 151–59.

Sjölander, S., and Ägren, G. 1972. Reproductive behavior of the Common Loon. *Wilson Bull*. 84: 296–308.

Sutcliffe, S. A., ed. 1979. *The Common Loon: proceedings of the second North American conference of Common Loon research and management*. National Audubon Society Cons. Paper.

Titus, J. R., and Van Druff, L. W. 1981. Response of the Common Loon to recreational pressure in the Boundary Waters Canoe Area. *Wildl. Monogr*. No. 79.

Vermeer, K. 1973a. Some aspects of the breeding and mortality of Common Loons in east-central Alberta. *Can. Field-Nat*. 87: 403–8.

———. 1973b. Some aspects of the nesting requirements of Common Loons in Alberta. *Wilson Bull*. 85: 429–35.

Zicus, M. C. 1975. Loon predation on a Canada Goose gosling. *Auk* 92: 611–12.

Grebes

Dubois, A. D. 1919. An experience with Horned Grebes (*Colymbus auritus*). *Auk* 36: 170–80.

Faaborg. J. 1976. Habitat selection and territorial behavior of the small grebes of North Dakota. *Wilson Bull*. 88: 390–99.

Finley, W. L. 1907. The grebes of southern Oregon. *Condor* 9: 97–101.

Glover, F. A. 1953. Nesting ecology of the Pied-billed Grebe in northwestern Iowa. *Wilson Bull*. 65: 32–39.

Kilham, L. 1954. Courtship behavior of the Pied-billed Grebe. *Wilson Bull*. 66: 65.

Kirby, R. E. 1976. Breeding chronology and interspecific relations of Pied-billed Grebes in northern Minnesota. *Wilson Bull*. 88: 493–95.

McAllister, N. M. 1958. Courtship, hostile behavior, nest-establishment and egg laying in the Eared Grebe (*Podiceps caspicus*). *Auk* 75: 290–311.

McAllister, N. M., and Storer, R. W. 1963. Copulation in the Pied-billed Grebe. *Wilson Bull*. 75: 166–73.

*Munro, J. A. 1901. *The grebes: studies of waterfowl in British Columbia*. Occ. Papers B.C. Prov. Mus. No. 3.

Nero, R. W.; Lahrman, F. W.; and Bard, F. G. 1958. Dryland nest-site of a Western Grebe colony. *Auk* 75: 347–49.

Storer, R. W. 1969. The behavior of the Horned Grebe in spring. *Condor* 71: 180–205.

————. 1974. Podicipediformes. *Encyclopaedia Britannica Macropaedia* 14: 596–97.

Sugden, L. G. 1977. Horned Grebe breeding habitat in Saskatchewan parklands. *Can. Field-Nat.* 91: 372–76.

Wetmore, A. 1920. Observations of the habits of birds at Lake Burford, New Mexico. *Auk* 37: 221–47, 393–412.

Storm-Petrels

Ainslie, J. A., and Atkinson, R. 1937. On the breeding habits of Leach's Fork-tailed Petrel. *Brit. Birds* 30: 234–48.

Cramp, S., chief ed. 1977. *Handbook of the birds of Europe, the Middle East, and North Africa.* Oxford: Oxford University Press.

Fisher, J., and Lockley, R. M. 1954. *Sea-birds: an introduction to the natural history of the sea-birds of the North Atlantic.* London: Collins.

Gross, W. O. 1935. The life history cycle of Leach's Petrel (*Oceanodroma leucorhoa leucorhoa*) on the outer sea islands of the Bay of Fundy. *Auk* 52: 382–99.

Grubb, T. C., Jr. 1970. Burrow digging techniques of Leach's Petrel. *Auk* 87: 587–88.

————. 1973. Colony location by Leach's Petrel. *Auk* 90: 78–82.

————. 1974. Olfactory navigation to the nesting burrow in Leach's Petrel (*Oceanodroma leucorhoa*). *Anim. Behav.* 22: 192–202.

————. 1979. Olfactory guidance of Leach's Storm-Petrel to the breeding island. *Wilson Bull.* 91: 141–43.

Harris, S. W. 1974. Status, chronology, and ecology of nesting storm petrels in northwestern California. *Condor* 76: 249–61.

Huntingdon, C. E. 1963. Population dynamics of Leach's Petrel, *Oceanodroma leucorhoa*. *Proc. XIII Intern. Ornithol. Congr.*: 701–5.

Lockley, R. M. 1973. *Ocean wanderers: the migratory sea birds of the world.* Harrisburg, Pa.: Stackpole.

Morse, D. H., and Buchheister, C. W. 1977. Age and survival of breeding Leach's Storm-Petrels in Maine. *Bird-Banding* 48: 341–49.

Morse, D. H., and Kress, S. W. 1984. The effect of burrow loss on mate choice in the Leach's Storm-Petrel. *Auk* 101: 158–60.

Ricklef, R. E.; White, S.; and Cullen, J. 1980. Postnatal development of Leach's Storm-Petrel. *Auk* 97: 768–80.

Wallraff, H. G., and Hund, K. 1982. Homing experiments with starlings subjected to olfactory nerve section. In *Avian navigation: International Symposium on Avian Navigation (ISAN), Tirrenia (Pisa), September 11-14, 1981,* eds. F. Papi and H. G. Wallraff. Berlin: Springer-Verlag.

Wilbur, H. M. 1969. The breeding biology of Leach's Petrel, *Oceanodroma leucorhoa*. *Auk* 86: 433–42.

Gannets, Pelicans, and Cormorants

Nettleship, D. N. 1976. Gannets in North America: present numbers and recent population changes. *Wilson Bull.* 88: 300–313.

Northern Gannet

Cramp, S., chief ed. 1977. *Handbook of the birds of Europe, the Middle East and North Africa.* Oxford: Oxford University Press.

Fisher, J., and Lockley, R. M. 1954. *Sea-birds: an introduction to the natural history of the sea-birds of the North Atlantic.* London: Collins.

Kirkham, I. R. 1981. Nesting Northern Gannets (*Morus bassanus*) killed by rock falls at Great Bird Rock, Quebec. *Can. Field-Nat.* 95: 202–3.

Nelson, B. 1964. Bass Rock Gannets. *Nat. Hist.* 73: 32–41.

Nelson, J. B. 1965. The behaviour of the Gannet. *Brit. Birds* 58: 233–88; 313–36.

————. 1978a. *The Gannet.* Berkhamsted: T & A D Poyser.

————. 1978b. *The Sulidae: gannets and boobies.* Oxford: Oxford University Press.

Nettleship, D. N. 1975. A recent decline of gannets, *Morus bassanus,* on Bonaventure Island, Quebec. *Can. Field-Nat.* 89: 125–33.

————. 1976. Gannets in North America: present numbers and recent population changes. *Wilson Bull.* 88: 300–313.

American White Pelican

Bartholomew, G. A., Jr.; Dawson, W. R.; and O'Neill, E. J. 1953. A field study of the temperature regulation in young White Pelicans, *Pelecanus erythrorhynchos*. *Ecology* 34: 554–60.

*Behle, W. H. 1958. *The bird life of Great Salt Lake.* Salt Lake City: University of Utah Press.

Cottam, C.; Williams, C. S.; and Sooter, C. A. 1942. Cooperative feeding of White Pelicans. *Auk* 59: 444–45.

Evans, R. M. 1980. Development of behavior in seabirds: an ecological perspective. In *Behavior of marine animals: marine birds,* ed. J. Berger, B. L. Olla, and H. E. Winn, pp. 271–322. New York: Plenum Press.

*Hall, E. R. 1925. Pelicans versus fishes in Pyramid Lake. *Condor* 27: 147–60.

Houston, C. S. 1962. Hazards faced by colonial birds. *Blue Jay* 20: 74–77.

Johnson, R. F., Jr. and Sloan, N. F. 1978. White Pelican production and survival of young at Chase Lake National Wildlife Refuge, North Dakota. *Wilson Bull.* 90: 346–52.

Knopf, F. L. 1979. Spatial and temporal aspects of colonial nesting of White Pelicans. *Condor* 81: 353–63.

———. 1980. On the hatching interval of White Pelican eggs. *Proc. Okla. Acad. Sci.* 60: 26–28.

Lies, M. F., and Behle, W. H. 1966. Status of the White Pelican in the United States and Canada through 1964. *Condor* 68: 279–92.

Low, J. B.; Kay, L.; Ramussen, D. I. 1950. Recent observations of the White Pelican on Gunnison Island, Great Salt Lake, Utah. *Auk* 67: 345–56.

Markham, B. 1979. Status report on White Pelican *Pelecanus erythrorhynchos* in Canada 1978. Committee on the Status of Endangered Wildlife in Canada.

O'Malley, J. B. E., and Evans, R. M. 1980. Variations in measurements among white pelican eggs and their use as a hatch date predictor. *Can. J. Zool.* 58: 603–8.

———. 1982a. Flock formation in white pelicans. *Can. J. Zool.* 60: 1024–31.

———. 1982b. Structure and behavior of white pelican formation flocks. *Can. J. Zool.* 60: 1388–96.

Roney, K. 1978. Pelicans, cormorants and Great Blue Herons in Saskatchewan in 1976. *Blue Jay* 36: 28–35.

———. 1982. 1980 nest census of Saskatchewan's pelican and cormorant colonies. *Blue Jay* 40: 158–60.

Schaller, G. B. 1964. Breeding behavior of the White Pelican at Yellowstone Lake, Wyoming. *Condor* 66: 3–23.

Sloan, N. F. 1982. Status of breeding colonies of White Pelicans in the United States through 1979. *Amer. Birds* 36: 250–54.

Strait, L. E., and Sloan, N. F. 1975. Movements and mortality of juvenile White Pelicans from North Dakota. *Wilson Bull.* 87: 54–59.

*Vermeer, K. 1970. Distribution and size of colonies of white pelicans, *Pelecanus erythrorhynchos,* in Canada. *Can. J. Zool.* 48: 1029–32.

———. 1971. The pelican—protection or extinction. *Can. Aud.* 33: 103–4.

Double-crested Cormorant

Ellison, L. N., and Cleary, L. 1978. Effects of human disturbance on breeding of Double-crested Cormorants. *Auk* 95: 510–17.

Kury, C. R. 1975. Human interference and gull predation in cormorant colonies. *Biol. Conserv.* 8: 23–34.

*Lewis, H. F. 1929. *The natural history of the Double-crested Cormorant* (Phalacrocorax auritus auritus (Lesson)). Ottawa: Ru-Mi-Lou Books.

———. 1931. Additional information concerning the Double-crested Cormorant. *(Phalacrocorax auritus auritus* (Lesson)). *Auk* 48: 207–14.

Lock, A. R., and Ross, R. K. 1973. The nesting of the Great Cormorant (*Phalacrocorax carbo*) and the Double-crested Cormorant (*Phalacrocorax auritus*) in Nova Scotia in 1971. *Can. Field-Nat.* 87: 43–49.

McLeod, J. A., and Bondar, G. F. 1953. A brief study of the Double-crested Cormorant on Lake Winnipegosis. *Can. Field-Nat.* 67: 1–11.

Markham, B. J. 1978. Status report on Double-crested Cormorant *Phalacrocorax auritus* in Canada 1978. Committee on the Status of Endangered Wildlife in Canada.

Meyerriecks, A. J. 1972. Tool-using by a Double-crested Cormorant. *Wilson Bull.* 84: 482–83.

Siegal-Causey, D., and Hunt, G. L., Jr. 1981. Colonial defense behavior in Double-crested and Pelagic Cormorants. *Auk* 98: 522–31.

Tate, J., Jr., and Tate, D. J. 1982. The Blue List for 1982. *Amer. Birds* 36: 126–35.

Vermeer, K. 1970a. Colonies of Double-crested Cormorants and White Pelicans in Saskatchewan. *Can. Field-Nat.* 84: 39–42.

———. 1970b. Some aspects of the nesting of Double-crested Cormorants at Cypress Lake, Saskatchewan in 1969; a plea for protection. *Blue Jay* 28: 11–13.

———. 1973. Great Blue Heron and Double-crested Cormorant colonies in the prairie provinces. *Can. Field-Nat.* 87: 427–32.

Weseloh, D. V.; Brechtel, S.; and Burns, R. D. 1977. Recent population changes in Double-crested Cormorants and California and Ring-billed Gulls in Alberta, Canada, with a note on White Pelicans. *Proc. Conf. Colonial Waterbird Group:* 10–18.

Bitterns and Herons

Godfrey, W. E. 1983. Personal communication.

American Bittern

Byers, E. 1951. Feeding behavior of young American Bitterns. *Wilson Bull.* 63: 334–36.

Chapin, J. P. 1922. The function of the oesophagus in the bittern's booming. *Auk* 39: 196–202.

Gabrielson, I. N. 1914. Ten days' bird study in a Nebraska swamp. *Wilson Bull.* 87: 51–68.

Hancock, J., and Elliott, H. 1978. *The herons of the world.* New York: Harper and Row.

Kushlan, J. A. 1976. Feeding behavior of North American herons. *Auk* 93: 86–94.

Middleton, D. S. 1949. Close proximity of two nests of American Bitterns. *Wilson Bull.* 61: 113.

Mousley, H. 1939. Home life of the American Bittern. *Wilson Bull.* 51: 83–85.

Torrey, B. 1889. The 'booming' of the bittern. *Auk* 6: 1–8.

Vesall, D. B. 1940. Notes on nesting habits of the American Bittern. *Wilson Bull.* 52: 207–8.

Great Blue Heron

Bayer, R. D. 1982. Great Blue Heron eggshell thickness at Oregon estuaries. *Wilson Bull.* 94: 198–201.

DesGranges, J.-L. 1979. *Great blue heron.* Canadian Wildlife Service Hinterland Who's Who series.

Hancock, J., and Elliott, H. 1978. *The herons of the world.* New York: Harper and Row.

Henny, C. J., and Bethers, M. R. 1971. Population ecology of the Great Blue Heron with special reference to western Oregon. *Can. Field-Nat.* 85: 205–9.

Henny, C. J., and Kurtz, J. E. 1978. Great Blue Herons respond to nesting habitat loss. *Wildl. Soc. Bull.* 6: 35–37.

Hjertaas, D. G. 1982. Great Blue Herons and raccoons at Nicolle Flats. *Blue Jay* 40: 36–41.

Krebs, J. R. 1974. Colonial nesting and social feeding as strategies for exploiting food resources in the Great Blue Heron (*Ardea herodias*). *Behavior* 51: 99–131.

Kushlan, J. A. 1976. Feeding behavior of North American herons. *Auk* 93: 86–94.

McAloney, K. 1973. The breeding biology of the Great Blue Heron on Tobacco Island, Nova Scotia. *Can. Field-Nat.* 87: 137–40.

Mark, D. M. 1976. An inventory of Great Blue Heron (*Ardea herodias*) nesting colonies in British Columbia. *Northwest Sci.* 50: 32–41.

Mock, D. W. 1976. Pair-formation displays of the Great Blue Heron. *Wilson Bull.* 88: 185–230.

———. 1979. Display repertoire shifts and "extramarital" courtship in herons. *Behaviour* 69: 57–71.

Pratt, H. M. 1970. Breeding biology of Great Blue Herons and Common Egrets in central California. *Condor* 72: 407–16.

———. 1972. Nesting success of Great Blue Herons and Common Egrets at Canyon Ranch in 1971. *Amer. Birds* 26: 699–702.

———. 1973. Breeding attempts by juvenile Great Blue Herons. *Auk* 90: 897–99.

———. 1980. Directions and timing of Great Blue Heron foraging flights from a California colony: implications for social facilitation of food finding. *Wilson Bull.* 92: 489–96.

Quinney, T. E. 1983. Comparison of Great Blue Heron, *Ardea herodias,* reproduction at Boot Island and other Nova Scotia colonies. *Can. Field-Nat.* 97: 275–78.

Quinney, T. E., and Smith, P. C. 1980. Comparative foraging behaviour and efficiency of adult and juvenile Great Blue Herons. *Can. J. Zool.* 58: 1168–73.

Vermeer, K. 1969. Great Blue Heron colonies in Alberta. *Can. Field-Nat.* 83: 237–42.

———. 1970. Insular Great Blue Heron colonies on large Manitoba lakes. *Blue Jay* 28: 84–86.

Vermeer, K., and Anweiler, G. G. 1970. Great Blue Heron colonies in Saskatchewan in 1970. *Blue Jay* 28: 158–61.

Vermeer, K., and Hatch, D. R. M. 1972. Additional information on Great Blue Heron colonies in Manitoba. *Blue Jay* 30: 89–92.

Vermeer, K., and Risebrough, R. W. 1972. Additional information on egg shell thickness in relation to DDE concentrations in Great Blue Heron eggs. *Can. Field-Nat.* 86: 384–85.

Swans, Geese, and Ducks

Johnsgard, P. A. 1965. *Handbook of waterfowl behavior.* Ithaca, N.Y.: Comstock.

Smith, A. G.; Stoudt, J. H., and Gollop, J. B. 1964. Prairie potholes and marshes. In *Waterfowl tomorrow,* ed. J. P. Linduska, pp. 39–50. U.S. Dept. Int. Fish Wildl. Serv.

Todd, F. S. 1979. *Waterfowl: ducks, geese and swans of the world.* New York: Harcourt Brace Jovanovich.

Swans

Bailey, R. O., and Batt, B. D. J. 1974. Hierarchy of waterfowl feeding with Whistling Swans. *Auk* 91: 488–93.

Banko, W. E., and Mackay, R. H. 1954. Our native swans. In *Waterfowl tomorrow,* ed. J. P. Linduska, pp. 155–64. U.S. Dept. Int. Fish Wildl. Serv.

Gunn, W. W. H. 1973. Environmental stress on the Whistling Swan. *Wildfowl* 24: 5–7.

*———. 1979. *Whistling Swan.* Canadian Wildlife Service Hinterland Who's Who series.

Irwin, J. C. 1975. Mortality factors in Whistling Swans at Lake St. Clair, Ontario. *J. Wildl. Dis.* 11: 8–12.

King, J. G., and Conant, B. 1981. The 1980 census of Trumpeter Swans on Alaskan nesting habitats. *Amer. Birds* 35: 789–93.

Lensink, C. J. 1973. Population structure and productivity of Whistling Swans on the Yukon Delta, Alaska. *Wildfowl* 24: 21–25.

Lumsden, H. G. 1979. The Whistling Swan in James Bay and the southern region of Hudson Bay. *Arctic* 28: 194–200.

Mackay, R. H. 1975. *Trumpeter Swan.* Canadian Wildlife Service Hinterland Who's Who series.

———. 1979. Status report on the Trumpeter Swan *Olor bucinnator* in 1978. Committee on the Status of Endangered Wildlife in Canada.

McKelvey, R. W. 1979. Swans wintering on Vancouver Island, 1977–1978. *Can. Field-Nat.* 93: 433–36.

Nieman, D. J.; Godwin, J. K.; and Smith, J. R. 1983.

Whistling Swans breeding in Saskatchewan parkland. *Blue Jay* 41: 92–98.

Scott, P., and the Wildfowl Trust. 1972. *The Swans.* London: Michael Joseph.

Smith, I. D., and Blood, D. A. 1972. Native swans wintering on Vancouver Island over the period 1969–71. *Can. Field-Nat.* 86: 213–16.

Todd, F. S. 1979. *Waterfowl, ducks, geese and swans of the world.* New York: Harcourt Brace Jovanovich.

Canada Goose

Collias, N. E., and Jahn, L. R. 1959. Social behavior and breeding success in Canada Geese (*Branta canadensis*) confined under semi-natural conditions. *Auk* 76: 479–507.

Cooper, J. A. 1979. The history and breeding biology of the Canada Geese of Marshy Point Manitoba Canada. *Wildl. Monogr.* 61: 1–87.

*Hanson, H. C. 1973. *Canada Goose.* Canadian Wildlife Service Hinterland Who's Who series.

Johnsgard, P. A. 1965. *Handbook of waterfowl behavior.* Ithaca, N.Y.: Comstock.

———. 1968. *Waterfowl: their biology and natural history.* Lincoln, Neb.: University of Nebraska Press.

Lorenz, K. 1966. *On Aggression.* London: Methuen.

Radesater, T. 1974a. Form and sequential associations between the triumph ceremony and other behavior patterns in the Canada Goose *Branta canadensis* L. *Ornis Scand.* 5: 87–101.

———. 1974b. On the ontogeny of orienting movements in the Triumph Ceremony in two species of geese (*Anser anser* L. and *Branta canadensis* L.) *Behaviour* 50: 1–15.

———. 1975. Interactions between male and female during the Triumph Ceremony in the Canada Goose (*Branta canadensis* L.) *Z. Tierpsychol.* 39: 189–205.

Raveling, D. G. 1969. Social classes of Canada Geese in winter. *J. Wildl. Manage.* 33: 304–18.

*———. 1970. Dominance relationships and agonistic behavior of Canada Geese in winter. *Behaviour* 37: 291–317.

———. 1979a. The annual cycle of body composition of Canada Geese with special reference to control of reproduction. *Auk* 96: 234–52.

———. 1979b. Traditional use of migration and winter roost sites by Canada Geese. *J. Wildl. Manage.* 43: 229–35.

———. 1981. Survival, experience, and age in relation to breeding success of Canada Geese. *J. Wildl. Manage.* 45: 817–29.

Sherwood, G. A. 1967. Behavior of family groups of Canada Geese. *Trans. N. Am. Wild. Conf.* 32: 340–55.

Williams, T. C.; Klonowski, T. J.; and Berkeley, P.

1976. Angle of Canada Geese V flight formation measured by radar. *Auk* 93: 554–59.

Zicus, M. C. 1981. Canada Goose brood behavior and survival estimates at Crex Meadows, Wisconsin. *Wilson Bull.* 93: 207–17.

Mallard

Abraham, R. L. 1974. Vocalizations of the Mallard (*Anas platyrhynchos*). *Condor* 76: 401–20.

Dzubin, A. 1955. Some evidences of home range in waterfowl. *Trans. N. Am. Wildl. Conf.* 20: 278–98.

———. 1957. Pairing display and spring and summer flights of the Mallard. *Blue Jay* 15: 10–13.

———. 1969. Comments on carrying capacity of small ponds for ducks and possible effects of density on mallard production. In *Saskatoon Wetlands Seminar,* pp. 138–60. Canadian Wildlife Service Rep. Ser. No. 6.

Dzubin, A., and Gollop, J. B. 1972. Aspects of mallard breeding ecology in Canadian parkland and grassland. In *Population ecology of migratory birds,* pp. 113–51. U.S. Fish Wildl. Res. Rep. No. 2.

Hess, E. H. 1972. Imprinting in a natural laboratory. *Sci. Amer.* 227: 24–31.

———. 1973. *Imprinting.* New York: Van Nostrand Reinhold.

Johnsgard, P. A. 1960. A quantitative study of sexual behavior of Mallards and Black Ducks. *Wilson Bull.* 72: 133–55.

———. 1968. *Waterfowl: their biology and natural history.* Lincoln, Neb.: University of Nebraska Press.

Krapu, G. L.; Klett, A. T.; and Jorde, D. G. 1983. The effect of variable spring water conditions on Mallard reproduction. *Auk* 100: 689–98.

Lebret, T. 1961. The pair formation in the annual cycle of the mallard, *Anas platyrhynchos* L. *Ardea* 49: 97–158.

Lister, R. 1973. *Mallard.* Canadian Wildlife Service Hinterland Who's Who series.

Rahmani, A. F. 1979. Pre-natal vocalization and imprinting in birds. *J. Bombay Nat. Hist. Soc.* 76: 510–13.

Smith, A. G.; Stoudt, J. H.; and Gollop, J. B. 1964. Prairie potholes and marshes. In *Waterfowl tomorrow,* ed. J. P. Linduska, pp. 39–50. U.S. Dept. Int. Fish Wildl. Serv.

Titman, R. D., and Lowther, J. K. 1975. The breeding behavior of a crowded population of mallards. *Can. J. Zool.* 53: 1270–83.

Weidmann, U., and Darley, J. 1971. The role of the female in the social display of Mallards. *Anim. Behav.* 19: 287–98.

Wright, B. S. 1973. *Black Duck.* Canadian Wildlife Service Hinterland Who's Who series.

Goldeneyes

Bent, A. C. 1925 (Reprint 1962). *Life histories of North American waterfowl, part II*. New York: Dover.

Brewster, W. 1900. Notes on the breeding habits of the American golden-eyed duck or whistler (*Clangula clangula americana*). *Auk* 17: 207–16.

Carter, B. C. 1958. *The American Goldeneye in central New Brunswick*. Canadian Wildlife Service Wildl. Mgmt. Bull. Ser. 2 No. 9.

Erskine, A. J. 1959. A joint clutch of Barrow's Goldeneye and Bufflehead eggs. *Can. Field-Nat.* 73:131.

———. 1960. Further notes on interspecific competition among hole-nesting ducks. *Can. Field-Nat.* 74: 161–62.

Grenquist, P. 1963. Hatching losses of Common Goldeneyes in the Finnish Archipelago. *Prkc. XIII Intern. Ornithol. Congr.*: 685–89.

Johnson, L. L. 1967. The Common Goldeneye duck and the role of nesting boxes in its management in north-central Minnesota. *J. Minn. Acad. Sci.* 34: 110–13.

Lumsden, H. G.; Page, R. E.; and Gauthier, M. 1980. Choice of nest boxes by Common Goldeneyes in Ontario. *Wilson Bull.* 92: 497–505.

McLaren, W. D. 1969. Further data on interspecific competition at a joint Bufflehead-Goldeneye nest site. *Can. Field-Nat.* 83: 59–61.

Prince, H. H. 1968. Nest sites used by Wood Ducks and Common Goldeneyes in New Brunswick. *J. Wildl. Manage.* 32: 489–500.

Rever, M., and Miller, R. S. 1973. Common Goldeneyes and the Emma Lake nest boxes. *Blue Jay* 31: 27–30.

Vultures, Eagles, Hawks, and Falcons

Brown, L. 1970. *Eagles*. New York: Arco.

Fyfe, R. W. 1976. Bringing back the Peregrine Falcon. *Nature Canada* 5: 10–11, 14–15, 17.

Heintzelman, D. S. 1975. *Autumn hawk flights: the migrations in eastern North America*. New Brunswick, N. J.: Rutgers University Press.

Pennycuick, C. J. 1973. The soaring flight of vultures. *Sci. Amer.* 229 (6): 102–9.

Savile, D. B. O. 1957. Adaptive evolution in the avian wing. *Evolution* 11: 212–24.

Snyder, N. F. R., and Wiley, J. W. 1976. Sexual size dimorphism in hawks and owls of North America. *Ornithol. Monogr.* No. 20.

Turkey Vulture

Bagg, A. M., and Parker, H. M. 1951. The Turkey Vulture in New England and eastern Canada up to 1950. *Auk* 68: 315–33.

Hatch, D. E. 1970. Energy conserving and heat dissipating mechanisms of the Turkey Vulture. *Auk* 87: 111–24.

Heintzelman, D. S. 1975. *Autumn hawk flights: the migrations in eastern North America*. New Brunswick, N. J.: Rutgers University Press.

Jackson, J. A.; Prather, I. D.; and Conner, R. N. 1978. Fishing behavior of Black and Turkey vultures. *Wilson Bull.* 90: 141–43.

Jackson, T. H. 1903. The Turkey Vulture and its young. *Bird-Lore* 5: 184–87.

Pennycuick, C. J. 1973. The soaring flight of vultures. *Sci. Amer.* 229 (6): 102–9.

Stewart, P. A. 1977. Migratory movements and mortality rate of Turkey Vultures. *Bird-Banding* 48: 122–24.

Temple, S. A. 1969. A case of Turkey Vulture piracy on Great Blue Herons. *Wilson Bull.* 81: 94.

Terres, J. K. 1968. *Flashing wings: the drama of bird flight*. Garden City, N.Y.: Doubleday.

Titus, K., and Mosher, J. A. 1980. Turkey Vulture predation of Ruffed Grouse chick. *Can. Field-Nat.* 94: 327–28.

Wenzel, B. M. 1982. Functional status and credibility of avian olfaction. In *Avian navigation: International Symposium on Avian Navigation (ISAN), Tirrenia, Pisa, September 11–14, 1981*. eds. F. Papi and H. G. Wallraff, pp. 352–61. Berlin: Springer-Verlag.

Bald Eagle

Andrew, J. A., and Mosher, J. A. 1982. Bald Eagle nest site selection and nesting habitat in Maryland. *J. Wildl. Manage.* 46: 383–90.

Broley, C. L. 1958. The plight of the American Bald Eagle. *Audubon* 60: 162–63.

Bromley, R. G., and Trauger, D. L. 1974. Ground nesting of Bald Eagles near Yellowknife, Northwest Territories. *Can. Field-Nat.* 88: 73–75.

Brown, L. 1970. *Eagles*. New York: Arco.

———. 1977. *Eagles of the world*. New York: Universe Books.

Davis, D. W. 1966. A plea for conservation of the Bald Eagle in Saskatchewan. *Blue Jay* 24: 160–67.

Gerrard, J. M. 1973. The Bald Eagles in Canada's northern forests. *Nature Canada* 2: 10–14.

Gerrard, J. M., and Gerrard, P. N. 1982. Spring migration of Bald Eagles near Saskatoon. *Blue Jay* 40: 97, 99, 101, 103–4.

Gerrard, J. M.; Whitfield, D. W. A.; Gerrard, P.; Gerrard, P. N.; and Maher, W. J. 1978. Migratory movements and plumage of subadult Saskatchewan Bald Eagles. *Can. Field-Nat.* 92: 375–82.

Gerrard, J. M.; Whitfield, D. W. A.; and Maher, W. J. 1976. Osprey-Bald Eagle relationships in Saskatchewan. *Blue Jay* 34: 240–46.

Grier, J. W. 1974. Reproduction, organochlorines, and mercury in northwestern Ontario Bald Eagles. *Can. Field-Nat.* 88: 469–75.

Grubb, T. C., Jr. 1971. Bald Eagles stealing fish from Common Mergansers. *Auk* 88: 928–29.

Hancock, D. 1964. Bald eagles wintering in the southern Gulf Islands, British Columbia. *Wilson Bull.* 76: 111–20.

———. 1970. *Adventures with eagles.* Saanichton, B. C.: Wildlife Conservation Center.

Hensel, R. J., and Troyer, W. A. 1964. Nesting studies of the Bald Eagle in Alaska. *Condor* 66: 282–86.

Herrick, F. H. 1932, 1933. Daily life of the American eagle: early phase. *Auk* 49: 307–23, 428–35; 50: 35–53.

Leighton, F. A.; Gerrard, J. M.; Gerrard, P.; Whitfield, D. W. A.; and Maher, W. J. 1979. An aerial census of Bald Eagles in Saskatchewan. *J. Wildl. Manage.* 43: 61–69.

Merrell, T. R., Jr. 1970. A swimming Bald Eagle. *Wilson Bull.* 82: 220.

Ofelt, D. H. 1974. Food habits of nesting bald eagles in southeast Alaska. *Condor* 77: 337–38.

Platt, J. B. 1976. Bald Eagles wintering in a Utah desert. *Amer. Birds* 30: 783–88.

Southern, W. E. 1963. Winter populations, behavior, and seasonal dispersal of Bald Eagles in northwestern Illinois. *Wilson Bull.* 75: 42–55.

Sprunt, A., IV. 1965. Population trends of the Bald Eagle in North America. In *Peregrine falcon populations: their biology and decline,* ed. J. J. Hickey, pp. 347-51. Madison, Wisc.: University of Wisconsin Press.

Sprunt, A., IV; Robertson, W. B., Jr.; Postupalsky, S.; Hensel, R. J.; Knoder, C. E.; and Ligas, F. J. 1973. Comparative productivity of six Bald Eagle populations. *Trans. N. Am. Wildl. Conf.* 38: 96–106.

Truslow, F. K. 1961. Eye to eye with eagles in the Everglades. *Nat. Geog.* 119: 123–47.

Whitfield, D. W. A.; Gerrard, J. M.; Maher, W. J.; and Davis, D. W. 1974. Bald eagle nesting habitat, density, and reproduction in central Saskatchewan and Manitoba. *Can. Field-Nat.* 88: 399–407.

Northern Harrier

Breckenridge, W. J. 1935. An ecological study of some Minnesota Marsh Hawks. *Condor* 37: 268–76.

Clark, R. J., and Ward, J. G. 1974. Interspecific competition in two species of open country raptors *Circus cyaneus* and *Asio flammeus*. *Proc. Pa. Acad. Sci.* 48: 79–87.

Craighead, J. J., and Craighead, F. C., Jr. 1956. *Hawks, owls and wildlife.* Harrisburg, Pa.: Stackpole.

Errington, P. L., and Breckenridge, W. J. 1936. Food habits of Marsh Hawks in the glaciated prairie region of north-central United States. *Am. Midl. Nat.* 7: 831–48.

Hamerstrom, F. 1969. A harrier population study. In *Peregrine falcon populations: their biology and decline,* ed. J. J. Hickey, pp. 367–83. Madison, Wisc.: University of Wisconsin Press.

Rice, W. R. 1982. Acoustical location of prey by the Marsh Hawk: adaptation to concealed prey. *Auk* 99: 403–13.

Schipper, W. J. A.; Buurma, L. S.; and Bossenbroek, P. 1975. Comparative study of hunting behaviour of wintering Hen Harriers *Circus cyaneus* and Marsh Harriers *Circus aeruginosus*. *Ardea* 63: 1–29.

Sealy, S. G. 1967. Notes on the breeding biology of the Marsh Hawk in Alberta and Saskatchewan. *Blue Jay* 25: 63–69.

Shelley, L. O. 1935. Notes on the growth, behavior and taming of young Marsh Hawks. *Auk* 52: 287–99.

Sharp-shinned Hawk

Canadian Wildlife Service. 1973. *Hawks (accipiters).* Canadian Wildlife Service Hinterland Who's Who series.

Mueller, H. C.; Mueller, N. S.; and Parker, P. G. 1981. Observation of a brood of Sharp-shinned Hawks in Ontario, with comments on the functions of sexual dimorphism. *Wilson Bull.* 93: 85–92.

Platt, J. B. 1976. Sharp-shinned Hawk nesting and nest site selection in Utah. *Condor* 78: 102–3.

Reynolds, R. T. 1972. Sexual dimorphism in accipiter hawks: a new hypothesis. *Condor* 74: 191–97.

Snyder, N. F. R.; Snyder, H. A.; Lincer, J. L.; and Reynolds, R. T. 1973. Organochlorines, heavy metals, and the biology of North American accipiters. *BioSci.* 23: 300–305.

Snyder, N. F. R., and Wiley, J. W. 1976. Sexual size dimorphism in hawks and owls of North America. *Ornithol. Monogr.* No. 20.

Tate, J., Jr., and Tate, D. J. 1982. The Blue List for 1982. *Amer. Birds* 36: 126–35.

Red-tailed Hawk

Adamcik, R. S.; Todd, A. W.; and Keith, L. B. 1979. Demographic and dietary responses of Red-tailed Hawks during a Snowshoe Hare fluctuation. *Can. Field-Nat.* 93: 16–27.

Austing, G. R. 1964. *The world of the Red-tailed Hawk.* New York: Lippincott.

Fitch, H. S., and Bare, R. O. 1978. A field study of the Red-tailed hawk in eastern Kansas. *Trans. Kansas Acad. Sci.* 81: 1–13.

Fitch, H. S.; Swenson, F.; and Tillotson, D. F. 1946. Behavior and food habits of the Red-tailed Hawk. *Condor* 48: 205–37.

Henny, C. J., and Wight, H. M. 1972. Population ecology and environmental pollution: Red-tailed and Cooper's Hawks. In *Population ecology of migratory birds,* pp. 229–49. U.S. Fish Wildl. Res. Rep. No. 2.

Houston, C. S. 1975. Close proximity of Red-tailed Hawk and Great Horned Owl nests. *Auk* 92: 612–14.

Luttich, S. T.; Keith, L. B.; and Stephenson, J. D. 1971. Population dynamics of the Red-tailed Hawk (*Buteo jamaicensis*) at Rochester, Alberta. *Auk* 88: 75–87.

Luttich, S.; Rusch, D. H.; Meslow, E. C.; and Keith, L. B. 1970. Ecology of Red-tailed Hawk predation in Alberta. *Ecology* 51: 190–203.

McInvaille, W. B., Jr., and Keith, L. B. 1974. Predator-prey relations and breeding biology of the Great Horned Owl and Red-tailed Hawk in central Alberta. *Can. Field-Nat.* 88: 1–20.

Meslow, E. C., and Keith, L. B. 1966. Summer food habits of Red-tailed Hawks near Rochester, Alberta. *Can. Field-Nat.* 80: 98–100.

Orians, G., and Kuhlman, F. 1956. Red-tailed Hawk and Great Horned Owl populations in Wisconsin. *Condor* 58: 371–85.

Savage, A., and Savage, C. 1981. *Wild mammals of western Canada.* Saskatoon: Western Producer Prairie Books.

Seidensticker, J. C. IV, and Reynolds, H. V. III. 1971. The nesting, reproductive performance, and chlorinated hydrocarbon residues in the Red-tailed Hawk and Great Horned Owl in south-central Montana. *Wilson Bull.* 83: 408–18.

Stinson, C. H. 1980. Weather-dependent foraging success and sibling aggression in Red-tailed Hawks in central Washington. *Condor* 82: 76–80.

Wiley, J. W. 1975. Three adult Red-tailed Hawks tending a nest. *Condor* 77: 480–82.

American Kestrel

Balgooyen, T. G. 1975. Another possible function of the American Kestrel's deflection face. *Jack-Pine Warbler* 53: 115–16.

———. 1976. Behavior and ecology of the American Kestrel (*Falco sparverius* L.) in the Sierra Nevada of California. *U. Calif. Pub. in Zool.* No. 103.

Cade, T. J. 1955. Experiments on winter territoriality of the American Kestrel, *Falco sparverius. Wilson Bull.* 67: 5–17.

Clay, W. M. 1953. Protective coloration in the American Sparrow Hawk. *Wilson Bull.* 65: 129–34.

Collopy, M. W. 1977 Food caching by female American Kestrels in winter. *Condor* 79: 63–68.

Hamerstrom, F.; Hamerstrom, F. N.; and Hart, J. 1973. Nest boxes: an effective management tool for kestrels. *J. Wildl. Manage.* 37: 400–403.

Mills, G. S. 1976. American Kestrel sex ratios and habitat separation. *Auk* 93: 740–48.

Mueller, H. C. 1974. Food caching behaviour in the American Kestrel (*Falco sparverius*). *Z. Tierpsychol.* 34: 105–14.

Nunn, G. L.; Klem, D., Jr.; Kimmel, T.; and Merriman, T. 1976. Surplus killing and caching by American Kestrels (*Falco sparverius*). *Anim. Behav.* 24: 759–63.

Roest, A. I. 1957. Notes on the American Sparrow Hawk. *Auk* 74: 1–19.

Savile, D. B. O. 1957. Adaptive evolution in the avian wing. *Evolution* 11: 212–24.

Willoughby, E. J., and Cade, T. J. 1964. Breeding behavior of the American Kestrel (Sparrow Hawk). *Living Bird* 3: 75–96.

Grouse

Bendell, J. F. 1973. *Ruffed Grouse.* Canadian Wildlife Service Hinterland Who's Who series.

Fish and Wildlife Branch, Sask. Dept. of Tourism and Natural Resources. 1979. Greater Prairie Chicken *Tympanuchus cupido pinnatus.* Committee on the Status of Endangered Wildlife in Canada, Endangered Canadian Wildlife series.

Hamerstrom, F., and Hamerstrom, F. 1961. Status and problems of North American grouse. *Wilson Bull.* 73: 284–94.

Ruffed Grouse

Allen, A. A. 1934. Sex rhythm in the Ruffed Grouse (*Bonasa umbellus* Linn.) and other birds. *Auk* 51: 180–99.

Archibald, H. L. 1975. Temporal patterns of spring space use by Ruffed Grouse. *J. Wildl. Manage.* 39: 472–81.

———. 1976a. Spatial relationships of neighboring male Ruffed Grouse in spring. *J. Wildl. Manage.* 40: 750–60.

———. 1976b. Spring drumming patterns of Ruffed Grouse. *Auk* 93: 808–29.

Aubin, A. E. 1972. Aural communication in Ruffed Grouse. *Can. J. Zool.* 50: 1225–29.

Bendell, J. F. 1973. *Ruffed Grouse.* Canadian Wildlife Service Hinterland Who's Who series.

Boag, D. A. 1976. Influence of changing grouse density and forest attributes on the occupancy of a series of potential territories by male ruffed grouse. *Can. J. Zool.* 54: 1727–36.

Boag, D. A., and Sumanik, K. M. 1969. Characteristics of drumming sites selected by Ruffed Grouse in Alberta. *J. Wildl. Manage.* 33: 621–28.

Brander, R. B. 1967. Movements of female Ruffed

Grouse during the mating season. *Wilson Bull.* 79: 28–36.

Bump, G.; Darrow, R. W.; Edminster, F. C.; and Crissey, W. F. 1947. *The Ruffed Grouse: life history, propagation, management.* N. Y. State Conservation Dept.

Chambers, R. E., and Sharp, W. M. 1958. Movement and dispersal within a population of Ruffed Grouse. *J. Wildl. Manage.* 22: 231–39.

Cringan, A. T. 1970. Reproductive biology of Ruffed Grouse in southern Ontario, 1964–69. *J. Wildl. Manage.* 34: 756–61.

Doerr, P. D.; Keith, L. B.; Rusch, D. H.; and Fischer, C. A. 1974. Characteristics of winter feeding aggregations of Ruffed Grouse in Alberta. *J. Wildl. Manage.* 38: 601–15.

Eng, R. L., and Gullion, G. W. 1962. The predation of Goshawks upon Ruffed Grouse on the Cloquet Forest Research Center, Minnesota. *Wilson Bull.* 74: 227–42.

Friesen, V. C. 1971. The crazy flight phenomenon of the Ruffed Grouse. *Blue Jay* 29: 121–24.

———. 1978. Further observations of the Ruffed Grouse's "crazy flight." *Blue Jay* 36: 193–99.

Godfrey, G. A., and Marshall, W. H. 1969. Brood break-up and dispersal of Ruffed Grouse. *J. Wildl. Manage.* 33: 609–20.

Gullion, G. W. 1967. Selection and use of drumming sites by male Ruffed Grouse. *Auk* 84: 87–112.

———. 1970. Factors influencing Ruffed Grouse populations. *Trans. N. Am. Wildl. Conf.* 35: 93–105.

———. 1976. Reevaluation of "activity clustering" by male grouse. *Auk* 93: 192–93.

———. 1977. Forest manipulation for Ruffed Grouse. *Trans. N. Am. Wildl. Conf.* 42: 449–58.

Gullion, G. W., and Marshall, W. H. 1968. Survival of Ruffed Grouse in a boreal forest. *Living Bird* 7: 117–67.

Hjorth, I. 1970. Reproductive behaviour in Tetraonidae, with special reference to males. *Viltrevy* 7: 183–596.

Hoffman, R. S. 1958. The role of predators in "cyclic" declines of grouse populations. *J. Wildl. Manage.* 22: 317–19.

McGowan, J. D. 1973. Fall and winter foods of Ruffed Grouse in interior Alaska. *Auk* 90: 636–40.

Maxson, S. J. 1978. Spring home range and habitat use by female Ruffed Grouse. *J. Wildl. Manage.* 42: 61–71.

Palmer, W. L. 1963. Ruffed Grouse drumming sites in northern Michigan. *J. Wildl. Manage.* 27: 657-62.

———. 1969. Time frequency between successive drumming performances of Ruffed Grouse. *Wilson Bull.* 81: 97–99.

Rusch, D. H.; Gillespie, M. M.; and McKay, D. I.

1978. Decline of a Ruffed Grouse population in Manitoba. *Can. Field-Nat.* 92: 123–27.

Rusch, D. H., and Keith, L. B. 1971a. Ruffed Grouse-vegetation relationships in central Alberta. *J. Wildl. Manage.* 35: 417–29.

———. 1971b. Seasonal and annual trends in numbers of Alberta Ruffed Grouse. *J. Wildl. Manage.* 35: 803–22.

Salo, L. J. 1978. Characteristics of ruffed grouse drumming sites in western Washington and their relevance to management. *Ann. Zool. Fennici* 15: 261–78.

Samuel, D. E.; Beightol, D. R.; and Brain, C. W. 1974. Analysis of the drums of Ruffed Grouse. *Auk* 91: 507–16.

Svoboda, F. J., and Gullion, G. W. 1972. Preferential use of aspen by Ruffed Grouse in northern Minnesota. *J. Wildl. Manage.* 36: 1166–80.

Theberge, J. B., and Gauthier, D. A. 1982. Factors influencing densities of territorial male Ruffed Grouse, Algonquin Park, Ontario. *J. Wildl. Manage.* 46: 263–68.

Wiley, R. H. 1974. Evolution of social organization and life-history patterns among grouse. *Quart. Rev. Biol.* 49: 201–26.

Sharp-tailed Grouse

Ammann, G. A. 1957. *The prairie grouse of Michigan.* Lansing, Mich.: Game Division, Dept. of Conservation.

Boag, D. A., and Alway, J. H. 1980. Effect of social environment within the brood on dominance rank in gallinaceous birds (Tetraonidae and Phasianidae). *Can. J. Zool.* 58: 44–49.

Evans, R. M. 1969. Territorial stability in Sharp-tailed Grouse. *Wilson Bull.* 81: 75–78.

Fish and Wildlife Branch, Sask. Dept. of Tourism and Nat. Res. 1979. Greater Prairie Chicken, *Tympanuchus cupido pinnatus.* Endangered Canadian Wildlife fact sheet. Committee on the Status of Endangered Wildlife in Canada.

Hamerstrom, F. N., Jr., and Hamerstrom, F. 1951. Mobility of the Sharp-tailed Grouse in relation to its ecology and distribution. *Am. Midl. Nat.* 46: 174–226.

Hjorth, I. 1970. Reproductive behaviour in Tetraonidae, with special reference to males. *Viltrevy* 7: 183–596.

Johnsgard, P. A., and Wood, R. E. 1968. Distributional changes and interaction between Prairie Chickens and Sharp-tailed Grouse in the Midwest. *Wilson Bull.* 80: 173–88.

Kermott, L. H., and Oring, L. W. 1975. Acoustical communication of male Sharp-tailed Grouse (*Pedioecetes phasianellus*) on a North Dakota dancing ground. *Anim. Behav.* 23: 375–86.

Moyles, D. L. J., and Boag, D. A. 1981. Where, when, and how male sharp-tailed grouse establish territories on arenas. *Can. J. Zool.* 59: 1576–81.

Sparling, D. W. 1981. Communication in prairie grouse. 1. Information content and intraspecific functions of principal vocalizations. *Behav. and Neur. Biol.* 32: 463–86.

Rails and Cranes

Aldrich, J. W. 1979. Status of the Canadian Sandhill Crane. *Proc. Int. Crane Workshop* 1: 139–48.

Bieniasz, K. A. 1979. The Greater Sandhill Crane in Routt County, Colorado. *Proc. Int. Crane Workshop* 1: 197–203.

Bowman, M. G., and Whitman, S. L. 1972. Simultaneous migration of Sandhill Cranes in Florida. *Auk* 89: 668.

Buller, R. J. 1979. Lesser and Canadian Sandhill Crane populations, age structure, and harvest. *U. S. Fish Wildl. Serv. Sp. Sci. Rep.* 221: 1–10.

Drewien, R. C.; Littlefield, C. D.; Walkinshaw, L. H.; and Braun, C. E. 1975. Conservation committee report on status of Sandhill Cranes. *Wilson Bull.* 87: 297–302.

Drewien, R. C., and Kuyt, E. 1979. Teamwork helps the Whooping Crane. *Nat. Geog.* 155: 680–93.

Gollop, M. A. 1979. Status report on Whooping Crane *Grus canadensis* in Canada 1978. Committee on the Status of Endangered Wildlife in Canada.

Harvey, J. M.; Lieff, B. C.; MacInnes, C. D.; and Prevett, J. P. 1968. Observations on behavior of Sandhill Cranes. *Wilson Bull.* 80: 421–25.

Hyde, D. O. 1957. My Greater Sandhill Cranes. *Audubon* 59: 264–68.

Johnson, D. H., and Stewart, R. E. 1972. The Sandhill Crane with emphasis on aspects related to North Dakota. *Prairie Nat.* 4: 65–76.

Kuyt, E. 1982. *Whooping Crane.* Canadian Wildlife Service Hinterland Who's Who series.

*Lewis, J. C. 1977. Sandhill Crane. In *Management of migratory shore and upland game birds in North America,* ed. Glen C. Sanderson, pp. 5–44. Washington, D.C.: International Association of Fish and Wildlife Agencies.

Lewis, J. C., and Masatomi, H., ed. 1981. *Crane research around the world: Proc. of the International Crane Symposium at Sapporo, Japan in 1980 and papers from the World Working Group on Cranes, International Council for Bird Preservation.* Baraboo, Wisc.: Int. Crane Foundation.

Littlefield, C. D. 1976. Sandhill Cranes feed on ducklings. *Wilson Bull.* 88: 503-4.

Lovvorn, J. R., and Kirkpatrick, C. M. 1982. Recruitment and socially-specific flocking tendencies of eastern Sandhill Cranes. *Wilson Bull.* 94: 313–21.

Miller, R. S. 1973. The brood size of cranes. *Wilson Bull.* 85: 436–41.

Stephen, W. J. D. 1979. Status report on the Greater Sandhill Crane *Grus canadensis* in Canada 1978. Committee on the Status of Endangered Wildlife in Canada.

Tebbel, P. D., and Ankney, C. D. 1979. Biology of Sandhill Cranes in the southern Algoma District, Ontario. *Proc. Int. Crane Workshop* 1: 129–34.

Walkinshaw, L. H. 1949. *The Sandhill Cranes.* Cranbrook Institute of Science, Bull. No. 29.

———. 1973. *Cranes of the world.* New York: Winchester Press.

Shorebirds, Gulls, and Auks

Gollop, B. 1979. Eskimo Curlew, *Numenius borealis.* Endangered Canadian Wildlife fact sheet. Committee on the Status of Endangered Wildlife in Canada.

Nettleship, D. N., and Birkhead, T. R., ed. 1984. *The Atlantic alcidae: the evolution, distribution and biology of the auks inhabiting the Atlantic Ocean and adjacent water areas.* New York: Academic Press.

Ouellet, H. 1979. Piping Plover, *Charadrius melodius.* Threatened Canadian Wildlife fact sheet. Committee on the Status of Endangered Wildlife in Canada.

Killdeer

Davis, E. 1943. A study of wild and hand reared Killdeers. *Wilson Bull.* 55: 223–33.

Deane, C. D. 1944. The broken-wing behavior of the Killdeer. *Auk* 61: 243–47.

Furniss, O. C. 1933. Observations on the nesting of the Killdeer plover in the Prince Albert district in central Saskatchewan. *Can. Field-Nat.* 47: 135–38.

Hall, H. M. 1960. *A gathering of shore birds.* New York: Devin-Adair.

Lenington, S., and Mace, T. 1975. Mate fidelity and nesting site tenacity in the Killdeer. *Auk* 92: 149–51.

Mundahl, J. T. 1982. Role specialization in the parental and territorial behavior of the Killdeer. *Wilson Bull.* 94: 515–30.

Phillips, R. E. 1972. Sexual and agonistic behaviour in the Killdeer *(Charadrius vociferus). Anim. Behav.* 20: 1–9.

Pickwell, G. 1925. The nesting of the Killdeer. *Auk* 42: 485–96.

———. 1930. The sex of the incubating Killdeer. *Auk* 47: 499–507.

Quilliam, H. R. 1975. *Killdeer.* Canadian Wildlife Service Hinterland Who's Who series.

Stout, G. D., ed. 1967. *The shorebirds of North America.* New York: Viking.

Wass, M. L. 1974. Killdeer nesting on graveled roofs. *Amer. Birds* 28: 983–84.

Spotted Sandpiper

Hall, H. M. 1960. *A gathering of shore birds.* New York: Devin-Adair.

Hays, H. 1972. Polyandry in the Spotted Sandpiper. *Living Bird* 11: 43–57.

Knowles, E. H. M. 1942. Nesting habits of the Spotted Sandpiper. *Auk* 59: 583–84.

Nelson, T. 1930. Growth rate of the Spotted Sandpiper chick with notes on nesting habits. *Bird-Banding* 1: 1–13.

Oring, L. W.; Lank, D. B.; and Maxson, S. J. 1983. Population studies of the polyandrous Spotted Sandpiper. *Auk* 100: 272–85.

Oring, L. W., and Knudson, M. L. 1972. Monogamy and polyandry in the Spotted Sandpiper. *Living Bird* 11: 59–73.

Oring, L. W., and Maxson, S. J. 1978. Instances of simultaneous polyandry by a Spotted Sandpiper, *Actitis macularia. Ibis* 120: 349–53.

Stout, G. D., ed. 1967. *The shorebirds of North America.* New York: Viking.

American Woodcock

Baird, J. C. 1977. *American Woodcock.* Canadian Wildlife Service Hinterland Who's Who series.

Dunford, R. D., and Owen, R. B., Jr. 1973. Summer behavior of immature radio-equipped woodcock in central Maine. *J. Wildl. Manage.* 37: 462–69.

Hale, J. B., and Gregg, L. E. 1976. Woodcock use of clearcut aspen areas in Wisconsin. *Wildl. Soc. Bull.* 4: 111–15.

Hall, H. M. 1946. *Woodcock ways.* New York: Oxford University Press.

Owen, R. B., Jr., and Morgan, J. W. 1975. Summer behavior of adult radio-equipped woodcock in central Maine. *J. Wildl. Manage.* 39: 179–82.

Peterson, R. T. 1963. *The birds.* New York: Time Incorporated.

Sheldon, W. G. 1961. Summer crepuscular flights of American Woodcocks in central Massachusetts. *Wilson Bull.* 73: 126–39.

*———. 1967. *The book of the American Woodcock.* Amherst, Mass.: University of Massachusetts Press.

Wishart, R. A., and Bider, J. R. 1976. Habitat preferences of Woodcock in southwestern Quebec. *J. Wildl. Manage.* 40: 523–31.

Herring Gull

Brown, R. G. B. 1967. Breeding success and population growth in a colony of Herring and Lesser Blackbacked Gulls *Larus argentatus* and *L. fuscus. Ibis* 109: 502–15.

Burger, J. 1977. Nesting behavior of Herring Gulls: invasion into *Spartina* salt marsh areas of New Jersey. *Condor* 79: 162–69.

———. 1981. On becoming independent in Herring Gulls: parent-young conflict. *Amer. Nat.* 117: 444–56.

Burger, J., and Shisler, J. 1978. Nest site selection and competitive interactions of Herring and Laughing Gulls in New Jersey. *Auk* 95: 252–66.

Drury, W. H. 1973. *Herring Gull.* Canadian Wildlife Service Hinterland Who's Who series.

Drury, W. H., Jr., and Smith, W. J. 1968. Defense of feeding areas by adult Herring Gulls and intrusion by young. *Evolution* 22: 193–201.

Graham, F., Jr. 1975. *Gulls: a social history.* New York: Random House.

Haycock, K. A., and Threlfall, W. 1975. The breeding biology of the Herring Gull in Newfoundland. *Auk* 92: 678–97.

Hunt, G. L., Jr. 1972. Influence of food distribution and human disturbance on the reproductive success of Herring Gulls. *Ecology* 53: 1051–61.

Ingolfsson, A., and Estrella, B. T. 1978. The development of shell-cracking behavior in Herring Gulls. *Auk* 95: 577–79.

Kadlec, J. A. 1971. Effects of introducing foxes and raccoons on Herring Gull colonies. *J. Wildl. Manage.* 35: 625–36.

Kadlec, J. A., and Drury, W. H. 1968. Structure of the New England Herring Gull population. *Ecology* 49: 644–76.

Moore, F. R. 1976. The dynamics of seasonal distribution of Great Lakes Herring Gulls. *Bird-Banding* 47: 141–59.

Nettleship, D. N. 1977. Seabird resources of eastern Canada: status, problems and prospects. In *Canada's threatened species and habitats,* ed. T. Mosquin and C. Suchal, pp. 96–108. Ottawa: Canadian Nature Federation.

Parsons, J. 1971. Cannibalism in Herring Gulls. *Brit. Birds* 64: 528–37.

Paynter, R. A., Jr. 1949. Clutch-size and the egg and chick mortality of Kent Island Herring Gulls. *Ecology* 30: 146–66.

*Tinbergen, N. 1953. *The Herring Gull's world: a study of the social behaviour of birds.* London: Collins.

———. 1956. On the functions of territory in gulls. *Ibis* 98: 401–11.

Verbeek, N. A. M. 1977. Comparative feeding behavior of immature and adult Herring Gulls. *Wilson Bull.* 89: 415–20.

Vermeer, K.; Robertson, I.; Campbell, R. W.; Kaiser, G.; and Lemon, M. 1983. *Distribution and densities of marine birds on the Canadian West coast.* Canadian Wildlife Service.

Weseloh, D. U., and Blokpoel, H. 1979. *Ring-billed Gull.* Canadian Wildlife Service Hinterland Who's Who series.

Puffins

Chapdelaine, G. 1980. *Onzième inventaire et analyse des fluctuations de populations d'oiseaux marins dans les refuges de la côte nord du Golfe Saint-Laurent. Can. Field-Nat.* 94: 34–42.

Corkhill, P. 1973. Food and feeding ecology of puffins. *Bird Study* 20: 207–20.

Fisher, J., and Lockley, R. M. 1954. *Sea-birds: an introduction to the natural history of the sea-birds of the North Atlantic.* London: Collins.

Grant, P. R. 1971. Interactive behaviour of puffins (*Fratercula arctica* L.) and skuas (*Stercorarius parasiticus* L.). *Behaviour* 40: 263–81.

Harris, M. P. 1976a. Lack of a 'desertion period' in the nestling life of the puffin *Fratercula arctica. Ibis* 118: 115–18.

———. 1976b. The present status of the puffin in Britain and Ireland. *Brit. Birds* 69: 239–64.

———. 1983. Parent-young communication in the puffin *Fratercula arctica. Ibis* 125: 109–14.

Homer, S. 1982. The quiet famine. *Equinox* 1: 43–56.

*Lockley, R. M. 1953. *Puffins.* New York: Devin-Adair.

*Nettleship, D. N. 1972. Breeding success of the Common Puffin (*Fratercula arctica* L.) on different habitats at Great Island, Newfoundland. *Ecol. Monogr.* 42: 239–68.

———. 1977. Seabird resources of eastern Canada: status, problems and prospects. In *Canada's threatened species and habitats,* eds. T. Mosquin and C. Suchal, pp. 96–108. Canadian Nature Federation Sp. Pub. No. 6.

Nettleship, D. N., and Birkhead, T. R., ed. 1984. *The Atlantic alcidae: the evolution, distribution and biology of the auks inhabiting the Atlantic Ocean and adjacent water areas.* New York: Academic Press.

Penicaud, P. 1978. *L'activité de deux colonies de macareux* Fratercula arctica *aux Sept-Iles. Alauda* 46: 43–52.

Pigeons and Doves

Alison, R. M. 1976. Mourning Doves wintering in Ontario. *Can. Field-Nat.* 90: 174–76.

Armstrong, E. R., and Noakes, D. L. G. 1981. Food habits of Mourning Doves in southern Ontario. *J. Wildl. Manage.* 45: 222–30.

Beams, H. W., and Meyer, R. K. 1931. The formation of pigeon "milk." *Physiol. Zool.* 4: 486–500.

Caldwell, L. D. 1964. Dove production and nest site selection in southern Michigan. *J. Wildl. Manage.* 28: 732–38.

Coon, R. A.; Nichols, J. D.; and Percival, H. F. 1981. Importance of structural stability to success of Mourning Dove nests. *Auk* 98: 389–92.

Craig, W. 1911. The expressions of emotion in the pigeons. II. The Mourning Dove *(Zenaidura macroura* Linn.) *Auk* 27: 398–407.

Dolton, D. D. 1977. *Mourning Dove status report, 1976.* U.S. Fish and Wildl. Serv. Sp. Sci. Rep. No. 208.

Dunks, J. H.; Tomlinson, R. E.; Reeves, H. M.; Dolton, D. D.; Braun, C. E.; and Zapatka, T. P. 1982. *Migration, harvest, and population dynamics of Mourning Doves banded in the central management unit, 1976-77.* U.S. Fish Wildl. Ser. Sp. Sci. Rep. No. 249.

Frankel, A. I., and Baskett, T. S. 1961. The effect of pairing on cooing of penned Mourning Doves. *J. Wildl. Manage.* 25: 372–84.

Goodwin, D. 1967. *Pigeons and doves of the world.* London: Trustees of the British Museum (Natural History).

Jackson, G. L., and Baskett, T. S. 1964. Perch-cooing and other aspects of breeding behavior of Mourning Doves. *J. Wildl. Manage.* 28: 293–307.

LaPerriere, A. J., and Haugen, A. O. 1972. Some factors influencing calling ability of wild Mourning Doves. *J. Wildl. Manage.* 36: 1194–98.

McClure, H. E. 1943. *Ecology and management of the Mourning Dove,* Zenaidura macroura *(Linn.), in Cass County, Iowa.* Iowa State College of Agriculture Res. Bull. No. 310.

Mirachi, R. E., and Scanlon, P. F. 1981. Effects of orphaning on captive fledgling Mourning Doves. *J. Wildl. Manage.* 45: 218–22.

Morse, D. H. 1975. Mourning Doves breeding in an unusual habitat: the coastal spruce forest. *Wilson Bull.* 87: 422-24.

*Nice, M. M. 1922, 1923. A study of the nesting of Mourning Doves. *Auk* 39: 457-74; 40: 37-58.

Peters, H. S. 1961. The past status and management of the Mourning Dove. *Trans. N. Am. Wildl. Conf.* 26: 371–74.

Ranford, R. B. 1974. Early nesting of a Mourning Dove. *Ont. Field Biol.* 28: 46.

Thomforde, L. T. 1972. Migration and mortality of banded mourning doves. *J. Minn. Acad. Sci.* 38: 72–76.

Tomlinson, R. E.; Wight, H. M.; and Baskett, T. S. 1960. Migrational homing, local movement, and mortality of Mourning Doves in Missouri. *Trans. N. Am. Wildl. Conf.* 25: 253–67.

Cuckoos

Bent, A. C. 1940. *Life histories of North American cuckoos, goatsuckers, hummingbirds, and their allies.* U.S. National Museum Bull. 176.

Hamilton, W. J., III, and Hamilton, M. E. 1965. Breeding characteristics of Yellow-billed Cuckoos in Arizona. *Proc. Calif. Acad. Sci.* 32: 405–32.

Hamilton, W. J., III, and Orians, G. H. 1965. Evolution of brood parasitism in altricial birds. *Condor* 67: 361–82.

*Spencer, O. R. 1943. Nesting habits of the Black-billed Cuckoo. *Wilson Bull,* 55: 11–22.

Owls

Earhart, C. E., and Johnson, N. K. 1970. Size dimorphism and food habits of North American owls. *Condor* 72: 251–64.

Marshall, J. T., Jr. 1974. Strigiformes. *Encyclopaedia Britannica Macropaedia* 17: 734–37.

Sillman, A. J. 1973. Avian vision. In *Avian biology,* eds. D. S. Farner; J. R. King; and K. C. Parkes, vol. 3, pp. 349–87. New York: Academic Press.

Sparks, J., and Soper, T. 1970. *Owls: their natural and unnatural history.* New York: Taplinger.

*Walker, L. W. 1974. *The book of owls.* New York: Knopf.

Walls, G. L. 1967. *The vertebrate eye and its adaptive radiation.* New York: Hafner.

Great Horned Owl

Adamcik, R. S., and Keith, L. B. 1978. Regional movements and mortality of Great Horned Owls in relation to Snowshoe Hare fluctuations. *Can. Field-Nat.* 92: 228–34.

Adamcik, R. S.; Todd, A. W.; and Keith, L. B. 1978. Demographic and dietary responses of Great Horned Owls during a Snowshoe hare cycle. *Can. Field-Nat.* 92: 156–66.

Austing, G. R., and Holt, J. B., Jr. 1966. *The world of the Great Horned Owl.* New York: Lippincott.

Baumgartner, F. M. 1938. Courtship and nesting of the Great Horned Owls. *Wilson Bull.* 50: 274–85.

———. 1939. Territory and population in the Great Horned Owl. *Auk* 56: 274–82.

Bent, A. C. 1937. *Life histories of North American birds of prey, part 2.* U.S. National Museum Bull. 167.

Emlen, J. T. 1972. Vocal stimulation in the Great Horned Owl. *Condor* 75: 126–27.

Errington, P. L. 1932. Studies on the behavior of the Great Horned Owl. *Wilson Bull.* 44: 212–20.

———. 1938. The Great Horned Owl as an indicator of vulnerability in prey populations. *J. Wildl. Manage.* 2: 190–205.

Fitch, H. S. 1947. Predation by owls in the Sierran foothills of California. *Condor* 49: 137–51.

Houston, C. S. 1971. Brood size of the Great Horned Owl in Saskatchewan. *Bird-Banding* 42: 103–5.

———. 1975. Reproductive performance of Great Horned Owls in Saskatchewan. *Bird-Banding* 46: 302–4.

———. 1978. Recoveries of Saskatchewan-banded Great Horned Owls. *Can. Field-Nat.* 92: 61–66.

*Keith, L. B. 1977. *Great Horned Owl.* Canadian Wildlife Service Hinterland Who's Who series.

Orians, G., and Kuhlman, F. 1956. Red-tailed Hawk and Horned Owl populations in Wisconsin. *Condor* 58: 371–85.

Red Eagle, Chief. 1929. A glimpse of owl life. *Bird-Lore* 31: 261–62.

Rusch, D. H.; Meslow, E. C.; Doerr, P. D.; and Keith, L. B. 1972. Response of Great Horned Owl populations to changing prey densities. *J. Wildl. Manage.* 36: 282–96.

Smith, D. G. 1969. Nesting ecology of the Great Horned Owl *Bubo virginianus. Brigham Young University Sci. Bull.* 10: 16-25.

Smith, D. G., and Smith, B. A. 1972. Hunting methods and success of newly-fledged Great Horned Owls. *Bird-Banding* 43: 142.

Stewart, P. A. 1969. Movements, population fluctuations, and mortality among Great Horned Owls. *Wilson Bull.* 81: 155–62.

Wolhuter, B. R. 1968. Second report of Great Horned Owl preying on Short-eared Owl. *Bird-Banding* 39: 319.

Snowy Owl

Banfield, A. W. F. 1974. *The mammals of Canada.* Toronto: University of Toronto Press.

Bent, A. C. 1937. *Life histories of North American birds of prey, part 2.* U.S. National Museum Bull. 167.

Boxall, P. C., and Lein, M. R. 1982. Territoriality and habitat selection of female snowy owls *(Nyctea scandiaca)* in winter. *Can. J. Zool.* 60: 2344–50.

Catling, P. M. 1973. Food of Snowy Owls wintering in southern Ontario, with particular reference to the Snowy Owl hazard to aircraft. *Ont. Field Biol.* 27: 41–45.

Chamberlin, M. L. 1980. Winter hunting behavior of a Snowy Owl in Michigan. *Wilson Bull.* 92: 116–20.

Custer, T. W. 1973. Snowy Owl predation on Lapland Longspur nestlings recorded on film. *Auk* 90: 433–35.

Gross, A. O. 1947. Cyclic invasions of the Snowy Owl and the migration of 1945–1946. *Auk* 64: 584–601.

Höhn, E. O. 1973. Winter hunting of Snowy Owls in farmland. *Can. Field-Nat.* 87: 468–69.

Karalus, K. E., and Eckbert, A. W. 1974. *The owls of North America (north of Mexico).* Garden City, N.Y.: Doubleday.

Lein, M. R., and Webber, G. A. 1979. Habitat selection by wintering Snowy Owls *(Nyctea scandiaca). Can. Field-Nat.* 93: 176–78.

*Parmelee, D. F. 1972. Canada's incredible arctic owls. *Beaver* 303 (summer): 30–41.

Parker, G. R. 1974. A population peak and crash of lemmings and Snowy Owls on Southampton

Island, Northwest Territories. *Can. Field-Nat.* 88: 151–56.

*Sutton, G. M., and Parmelee, D. F. 1956. Breeding of the Snowy Owl in southeastern Baffin Island. *Condor* 58: 273–82.

Taylor, P. S. 1973. Breeding behavior of the Snowy Owl. *Living Bird* 12: 137–54.

*Watson, A. 1957. The behaviour, breeding, and food-ecology of the Snowy Owl *Nyctea scandiaca. Ibis* 99: 419–62.

Weir, R. D. 1973. Snowy Owl invasion on Wolfe Island, winter 1971-72. *Ont. Field Biol.* 27: 3–17.

———. 1974. *Snowy Owl.* Canadian Wildlife Service Hinterland Who's Who series.

Wiggins, I. L. 1953. Foraging activities of the Snowy Owl *(Nyctea scandiaca)* during a period of low lemming population. *Auk* 70: 366–67.

Williams, P. L., and Frank, L. G. 1979. Diet of the Snowy Owl in the absence of small mammals. *Condor* 81: 213–14.

Burrowing Owl

Arbib, R. 1979. The Blue List for 1980. *Amer. Birds* 33: 830–35.

Bent, A. C. 1937. *Life histories of North American birds of prey, part 2.* U.S. National Museum Bull. 167.

Brenckle, J. F. 1936. The migration of the Western Burrowing Owl *(Speotyto cunicularia hypogoea). Bird-Banding* 7: 166–68.

Butts, K. O. 1976. Burrowing Owls wintering in the Oklahoma panhandle. *Auk* 93: 510–16.

Coulombe, H. N. 1971. Behavior and population ecology of the Burrowing Owl, *Speotyto cunicularia,* in the Imperial Valley of California. *Condor* 73: 162–76.

Courser, W. D. 1979. Continued breeding range expansion of the Burrowing Owl in Florida. *Amer. Birds* 33: 143–44.

Karalus, K. E., and Eckbert, A. W. 1974. *The owls of North America (north of Mexico).* Garden City, N. Y.: Doubleday.

Marti, C. D. 1974. Feeding ecology of four sympatric owls. *Condor* 76: 45–61.

Martin, D. J. 1973a. Selected aspects of Burrowing Owl ecology and behavior. *Condor* 75: 446–56.

———. 1973b. A spectrographic analysis of Burrowing Owl vocalizations. *Auk* 90: 564–78.

Robertson J. McB. 1929. Some observations on the feeding habits of the Burrowing Owl. *Condor* 31: 38–39.

Tate, J., Jr., and Tate, D. J. 1982. The Blue List for 1982. *Amer. Birds* 36: 126–35.

Thomsen, L. 1971. Behavior and ecology of Burrowing Owls on the Oakland Municipal Airport. *Condor* 73: 177–92.

Walker, L. W. 1952. Underground owls. *Nat. Hist.* 61: 78–81.

*Wedgwood, J. A. 1976. Burrowing Owls in south-central Saskatchewan. *Blue Jay* 34: 26–44.

———. 1979. Status report on the Burrowing Owl *Athene cunicularia* in Canada 1978. Committee on the Status of Endangered Wildlife in Canada.

Great Gray Owl

Bell, G. P.; Phelan, F. J. S.; and Wypkema, R. C. P. 1979. The owl invasion of Amherst Island, Ontario, January–April 1979. *Amer. Birds* 33: 245–46.

Brunton, D. F., and Pittaway, R., Jr. 1971. Observations of the Great Gray Owl on winter range. *Can. Field-Nat.* 85: 315–22.

Godfrey, W. E. 1967. Some winter aspects of the Great Gray Owl. *Can. Field-Nat.* 81: 99–101.

Houston, S. 1957. The Great Gray Owl in Saskatchewan. *Blue Jay* 15: 150–53.

Kondla, N. G. 1973. The Great Gray Owls raise two young southeast of Edmonton, Alberta. *Blue Jay* 31: 98–100.

Law, C. 1960. The Great Gray Owl of the woodlands. *Blue Jay* 18: 14–16.

Muir, D. 1972. At a nest of the Great Gray Owl. *Nature Canada* 1 (2): 20–22.

Nero, R. W. 1969. The status of the Great Gray Owl in Manitoba, with special reference to the 1968–69 influx. *Blue Jay* 27: 191–209.

———. 1971. Spirit of the boreal forest: the Great Gray Owl. *Beaver* 302: 26–29.

———. 1978. Beware: mother on nest. *Internat. Wildl.* 8 (2): 13–15.

———. 1979. Status report on Great Gray Owl *Strix nebulosa* in Canada. Committee on the Status of Endangered Wildlife in Canada.

*———. 1980. *The Great Gray Owl: phantom of the northern forest.* Washington, D.C.: Smithsonian Institution Press.

Oeming, A. F. 1955. In quest of the rare Great Gray Owl. *Can. Geog.* 51: 236–43.

———. 1974. Great Gray Owls. In *The book of owls,* ed. L. W. Walker, pp. 153–72. New York: Knopf.

Vickery, P. D., and Yunick, R. P. 1979. The 1978–79 Great Gray Owl incursion across northeastern North America. *Amer. Birds* 33: 242–44.

Northern Saw-whet Owl

Austing, G. R. 1958. The unsuspicious Saw-whet Owl. *Audubon* 60: 272–75.

Bent, A. C. 1937. *Life histories of North American birds of prey, part 2.* U.S. National Museum Bull. 167.

Catling, P. M. 1971. Spring migration of Saw-whet Owls at Toronto, Ontario. *Bird-Banding* 42: 110–14.

———. 1972. Food and pellet analysis studies of the

Saw-whet Owl (*Aegolius acadicus*). *Ont. Field Biol.* 26: 1–15.

Forbes, J. E., and Warner, D. W. 1974. Behavior of a radio-tagged Saw-whet Owl. *Auk* 91: 783–95.

Holroyd, G. L., and Woods, J. G. 1975. Migration of the Saw-whet Owl in eastern North America. *Bird-Banding* 46: 101–5.

Johns, S. 1977. Saw whet Owl attacks Robin. *Blue Jay* 35: 172.

Johns, S., and Johns, A. 1978. Observations on the nesting behaviour of the Saw-whet Owl in Alberta. *Blue Jay* 36: 36–38.

Mueller, H. C., and Berger, D. D. 1967. Observations on migrating Saw-whet Owls. *Bird-Banding* 38: 120–25.

Randle, W., and Austing, R. 1952. Ecological notes on Long-eared and Saw-whet Owls in southwestern Ohio. *Ecology* 33: 422–26.

Santee, R., and Granfield, W. 1939. Behavior of the Saw-whet Owl on its nesting grounds. *Condor* 41: 3–9.

Schaeffer, F. S. 1973. Tactile bristles of Saw-whet Owls are sensitive to touch. *Bird-Banding* 44: 125.

Taylor, R. B. 1962. Fall Saw-Whet concentrations in Ontario. *Blue Jay* 20: 118–19.

Terrill, L. Mc I. 1931. Nesting of the Saw-whet Owl (*Cryptoglaux acadica acadica*) in the Montreal district. *Auk* 48: 169–74.

Walker, L. W. 1974. *The book of owls.* New York: Knopf.

Weir, R. D.; Cooke, F.; Edwards, M. H.; and Stewart, R. B. 1980. Fall migration of Saw-whet Owls at Prince Edward Point, Ontario. *Wilson Bull.* 92: 475–88.

Nightjars

Armstrong, J. T. 1965. Breeding home range in the nighthawk and other birds; its evolutionary and ecological significance. *Ecology* 46: 619–29.

*Bent, A. C. 1940. *Life histories of North American cuckoos, goatsuckers, hummingbirds and allies.* U.S. National Museum Bull. 176.

Bowles, J. H. 1921. Nesting habits of the nighthawks at Tacoma, Wash. *Auk* 38: 203–17.

Dexter, R. W. 1952. Banding and nesting studies of the Eastern Nighthawk. *Bird-Banding* 23: 109–14.

Griffin, D. R. 1958. *Listening in the dark: the acoustical orientation of bats and man.* New Haven, Conn.: Yale University Press.

Miller, A. H. 1925. The boom-flight of the Pacific Nighthawk. *Condor* 27: 141–43.

Sparks, J., and Soper, T. 1970. *Owls: their natural and unnatural history.* New York: Taplinger.

Sutherland, C. A. 1963. Notes on the behavior of Common Nighthawks in Florida. *Living Bird* 2: 31–39.

Sutton, G. M., and Spencer, H. H. 1949. Observations at a nighthawk's nest. *Bird-Banding* 20: 141–49.

Tomkins, I. R. 1942. The "injury-feigning" behavior of the Florida Nighthawk. *Wilson Bull.* 54: 43–49.

Weller, M. W. 1958. Observations on the incubation behavior of the Common Nighthawk. *Auk* 75: 48–59.

Hummingbirds

Bent, A. C. 1940. *Life histories of North American cuckoos, goatsuckers, hummingbirds and their allies.* U.S. National Museum Bull. 176.

Bertin, R. I. 1982. The Ruby-throated Hummingbird and its major food plants: ranges, flowering phenology and migration. *Can. J. Zool.* 60: 210–19.

Ewald, P. W., and Williams, W. A. 1982. Function of the bill and tongue in nectar uptake by hummingbirds. *Auk* 99: 573–76.

Foster, W. L., and Tate, J., Jr. 1966. The activities and coactions of animals at sapsucker trees. *Living Bird* 5: 87–113.

Gass, C. L., and Lertzman, K. P. 1980. Capricious mountain weather: a driving variable in hummingbird territorial dynamics. *Can. J. Zool.* 58: 1964–68.

Grant, K. A., and Grant, V. 1968. *Hummingbirds and their flowers.* New York: Columbia University Press.

Hainsworth, F. R. 1973. On the tongue of a hummingbird: its role in the rate and energetics of feeding. *Comp. Biochem. Physiol.* 46A: 65–78.

Hainsworth, F. R.; Collin, B. G.; and Wolf, L. L. 1977. The function of torpor in hummingbirds. *Physiol. Zool.* 50: 215–22.

Hainsworth, F. R., and Wolf, L. L. 1972. Power for hovering flight in relation to body size in hummingbirds. *Amer. Nat.* 106: 589–96.

Johnsgard, P. A. 1983. *The hummingbirds of North America.* Washington, D.C.: Smithsonian Institution Press.

Lawrence, L. De K. 1974. *Ruby-throated Hummingbird.* Canadian Wildlife Service Hinterland Who's Who series.

Miller, R. S., and Miller, R. E. 1971a. Feeding activity and color preference of Ruby-throated Hummingbirds. *Condor* 73: 309–13.

———. 1971b. The memory of hummingbirds. *Blue Jay* 29: 29–30.

Miller, R. S., and Nero, R. W. 1983. Hummingbird-sapsucker associations in northern climates. *Can. J. Zool.* 61: 1540–46.

Pearson, O. P. 1953. The metabolism of hummingbirds. *Sci. Amer.* 188 (January): 69–72.

Pitelka, F. A. 1942. Territoriality and related problems in North American hummingbirds. *Condor* 44: 189–204.

Pojar, J. 1975. Hummingbird flowers of British Columbia. *Syesis* 8: 25–28.

Raven, P. H. 1973. Why are bird-visited flowers predominantly red? *Evolution* 26: 674.

*Skutch, A. F. 1973. *The life of the hummingbird.* New York: Crown Publishers.

Southwick, E. E., and Southwick, A. K. 1980. Energetics of feeding on tree sap by Ruby-throated Hummingbirds in Michigan. *Amer. Midl. Nat.* 104: 328–34.

Stiles, F. G. 1976. Taste preferences, color preferences, and flower choice in hummingbirds. *Condor* 78: 10–26.

Kingfishers

Bent, A. C. 1940. *Life histories of North American cuckoos, goatsuckers, hummingbirds, and their allies.* U.S. National Museum Bull. 176.

Cornwell, G. W. 1963. Observations on the breeding biology and behavior of a nesting population of Belted Kingfishers. *Condor* 65: 426–31.

Davis, W. J. 1982. Territory size in *Megaceryle alcyon* along a stream habitat. *Auk* 99: 353–62.

Kilham, L. 1974. Biology of young Belted Kingfishers. *Amer. Midl. Nat.* 92: 245–47.

Kirby, R. E., and Fuller, M. R. 1978. Observations and reinterpretation of kingfisher-raptor interactions. *Auk* 95: 598–99.

Salyer, J. C., II, and Lagler, K. F. 1949. The eastern Belted Kingfisher, *Megaceryle alcyon alcyon* (Linnaeus), in relation to fish management. *Amer. Fish. Soc. Trans.* 76: 97–117.

White, H. C. 1953. The eastern Belted Kingfisher in the Maritime provinces. *Fish. Res. Bd. Canada Bull.* 97: 1–44.

Downy Woodpecker

Helleiner, C. W. 1973. Possible imitative feeding behavior in two species of woodpeckers. *Can. Field-Nat.* 87: 315.

Jackson, J. A. 1970a. Some aspects of the population ecology of Downy Woodpeckers in relation to a feeding station. *Iowa Bird Life* 40: 27–34.

———. 1970b. A quantitative study of the foraging ecology of Downy Woodpeckers. *Ecology* 51: 318–23.

Kilham, L. 1962. Reproductive behavior of Downy Woodpeckers. *Condor* 64: 126–33.

———. 1970. Feeding behavior of Downy Woodpeckers. I. Preference for paper birches and sexual differences. *Auk* 87: 544–56.

———. 1974. Early breeding season behavior of Downy Woodpeckers. *Wilson Bull.* 86: 407–18.

Kisiel, D. S. 1972. Foraging behavior of *Dendrocopos villosus* and *D. pubescens* in eastern New York State. *Condor* 74: 393–98.

Lawrence, L. de K. 1966. A comparative life history

of four species of woodpeckers. *Ornithol. Monogr.* No. 5.

———. 1973. *Downy Woodpecker.* Canadian Wildlife Service Hinterland Who's Who series.

Stirling, D. 1968. Notes on food and feeding habits of some wintering birds. *Can. Field-Nat.* 82: 14–17.

Williams, J. B. 1975. Habitat utilization by four species of woodpeckers in a central Illinois woodland. *Amer. Midl. Nat.* 93: 354–67.

———. 1980. Intersexual niche partitioning in Downy Woodpeckers. *Wilson Bull.* 92: 439–51.

Northern Flicker

Bent, A. C. 1939. *Life histories of North American woodpeckers.* U.S. National Museum Bull. 174.

Bock, C. E. 1971. Pairing in hybrid flicker populations in eastern Colorado. *Auk* 88: 921–24.

Burns, F. L. 1900. A monograph of the flicker. *Wilson Bull.* 7: 1–82.

Conner, R. N. 1975. Orientation of entrances to woodpecker nest cavities. *Auk* 92: 371–74.

———. 1977. The effect of tree hardness on woodpecker nest entrance orientation. *Auk* 94: 369–70.

Dennis, J. V. 1969. The Yellow-shafted Flicker *(Colaptes auratus)* on Nantucket Island, Massachusetts. *Bird-Banding* 40: 290–308.

DeWeese, L. R., and Pillmore, R. E. 1972. Bird nests in an aspen tree robbed by Black Bear. *Condor* 74: 488.

Erskine, A. J., and McLaren, W. D. 1976. Comparative nesting biology of some hole-nesting birds in the Cariboo Parklands, British Columbia. *Wilson Bull.* 88: 611–20.

Inouye, D. W. 1976. Nonrandom orientation of entrance holes to woodpecker nests in aspen trees. *Condor* 78: 101–2.

Johnson, C. E. 1934. The chronicle of a flicker's courtship. *Auk* 51: 477–81.

Kilham, L. 1959. Early reproductive behavior of flickers. *Wilson Bull.* 71: 323–36.

———. 1973. Colonial type nesting in Yellow-shafted Flickers as related to staggering of nesting times. *Bird-Banding* 44: 317–18.

Kirby, V. C. 1980. An adaptive modification in the ribs of woodpeckers and piculets (*Picidae*). *Auk* 97: 521–32.

Knight, J., ed. 1974. *The nature of birds.* Toronto: Natural Science of Canada.

*Lawrence, L. de K. 1966. A comparative life-history of four species of woodpeckers. *Ornithol. Monogr.* No. 5.

Noble, G. K. 1936. Courtship and sexual selection of the flicker (*Colaptes auratus luteus*). *Auk* 53: 269–82.

Sherman, A. R. 1910. At the sign of the Northern Flicker. *Wilson Bull.* 22: 135–71.

Short, L. 1971. Woodpeckers without woods. *Nat. Hist.* 80: 66–74.

Udvardy, M. D. F. 1977. *The Audubon Society field guide to North American birds: western region.* New York: Knopf.

Songbirds

Armstrong, E. A. 1963. *A study of bird song.* London: Oxford University Press.

Falls, J. B., and Krebs, J. R. 1975. Sequence of songs in repertoires of western meadowlarks (*Sturnella neglecta*). *Can. J. Zool.* 53: 1165–78.

Hartshorne, C. 1973. *Born to sing: an interpretation and world survey of bird song.* Bloomington, Ind.: Indiana University Press.

Kroodsma, D. E.; Miller, E. H.; and Ouellet, H., eds., 1982. *Acoustic communication in birds.* 2 vols. New York: Academic Press.

Nottebohm, F. 1981. A brain for all seasons: cyclical anatomical changes in song control nuclei of the canary brain. *Science* 214: 1368–70.

Strauss, S. 20 April 1984. Bird brains: they're capable of more than humans believed. *Globe and Mail,* p. 14.

Welty, J. C. 1975. *The life of birds.* Philadelphia: W. B. Saunders.

Yasukawa, K. 1981. Song repertoires in the Red-winged Blackbird (*Agelaius phoeniceus*): a test of the Beau Geste hypothesis. *Anim. Behav.* 29: 114–25.

Barn Swallow

Bent, A. C. 1942. *Life histories of North American flycatchers, larks, swallows, and their allies.* U.S. National Museum Bull. 179.

Burtt, E. H., Jr. 1977. Some factors in the timing of parent-chick recognition in swallows. *Anim. Behav.* 25: 231–39.

Davis, E. M. 1937. Observations on nesting Barn Swallows. *Bird-Banding* 8: 66–72.

Erskine, A. J. 1979. Man's influence on potential nesting sites and populations of swallows in Canada. *Can. Field-Nat.* 93: 371–77.

Hails, C. J. 1979. A comparison of flight energetics in hirundines and other birds. *Comp. Biochem. Physiol.* 63A: 581–85.

Herroleon, P. 1957-59. *Over de broedbiologie van de Boerenzwaluw,* Hirundo rustica L. Le Gerfaut 47: 115–26, 265–78; 49: 11–30.

Jackson, J. A., and Burchfield, P. G. 1975. Nest-site selection of Barn Swallows in east-central Mississippi. *Amer. Midl. Nat.* 94: 503–9.

Meservey, W. R., and Kraus, G. F. 1976. Absence of "individual distance" in three swallow species. *Auk* 93: 177–79.

Myers, G. R., and Waller, D. W. 1977. Helpers at the nest in Barn Swallows. *Auk* 94: 596.

Samuel, D. E. 1971a. The breeding biology of Barn and Cliff Swallows in West Virginia. *Wilson Bull.* 83: 284–301.

———. 1971b. Vocal repertoires of sympatric Barn and Cliff Swallows. *Auk* 88: 839–55.

Skutch, A. F. 1961. Birds as helpers. *Condor* 63: 198–226.

Smith, W. P. 1933. Some observations of the nesting habits of the Barn Swallow. *Auk* 50: 414–49.

———. 1937. Further notes on the nesting of the Barn Swallow. *Auk* 54: 65–69.

Snapp, B. D. 1976. Colonial breeding in the Barn Swallow (*Hirundo rustica*) and its adaptive significance. *Condor* 78: 471–80.

Turner, A. K. 1982. Optimal foraging by the swallow (*Hirundo rustica*, L): prey size selection. *Anim. Behav.* 30: 862–72.

Weeks, H. P., Jr. 1977. Nest reciprocity in Eastern Phoebes and Barn Swallows. *Wilson Bull.* 89: 632–35.

Wood, H. B. 1937. Observations at a Barn Swallow's nest. *Wilson Bull.* 49: 96–100.

Blue Jay

Angell, T. 1978. *Ravens, crows, magpies, and jays.* Seattle: University of Washington Press.

Bock, C. E., and Lepthien, L. W. 1976. Changing winter distribution and abundance of the Blue Jay, 1962-1971. *Amer. Midl. Nat.* 96: 232–36.

Bossema, I. 1979. Jays and oaks: an eco-ethological study of a symbiosis. *Behaviour* 20: 1–117.

Darley-Hill, S., and Johnson, W. C. 1981. Acorn dispersal by the Blue Jay. *Oecologia* 50: 231–32.

Goodwin, D. 1976. *Crows of the world.* Ithaca, N.Y.: Comstock.

*Hardy, J. W. 1961. Studies in behavior and phylogeny of certain New World jays (*Garrulinae*). *University of Kansas Sci. Bull.* 42: 13–149.

Hunter, M. W., III, and Kamil, A. C. 1971. Object-discrimination learning set and hypothesis behavior in the northern bluejay (*Cyanocitta cristata*). *Psychon. Sci.* 22: 271–73.

Jones, T. B., and Kamil, A. C. 1973. Tool-making and tool-using in the northern Blue Jay. *Science* 180: 1076–78.

Kamil, A. C.; Lougee, M.; and Shulman, R. I. 1973. Learning set behavior in the learning-set experienced Blue Jay (*Cyanocitta cristata*). *J. Comp. Physiol. Psychol.* 82: 394–405.

Kamil, A. C., and Maudlin, J. E. 1975. Intraproblem retention during learning-set acquisition in blue-jays (*Cyanocitta cristata*). *Anim. Learning Behav.* 3: 125–30.

Middleton, R. J. 1974. Fifty-two years of banding Blue Jays at Norristown, Pennsylvania. *Bird-Banding* 45: 206–9.

Miller, F. W. 1952. Blue Jay, *Cyanocitta cristata,* "anting" with burning cigarettes. *Auk* 69: 87–88.

Nero, R. W. 1973. *Blue Jay*. Canadian Wildlife Service Hinterland Who's Who series.

Nice, M. M. 1955. Blue Jay anting with hot chocolate and soap suds. *Wilson Bull.* 67: 64.

Pitelka, F. A. 1946. Age in relation to migration in the Blue Jay. *Auk* 63: 82–84.

Smith, K. G. 1978. Range extension of the Blue Jay into western North America. *Bird-Banding* 49: 208–14.

Van Horn, D., and Toweill, D. E. 1977. Recent records of the Blue Jay (*Cyanocitta cristata*) in Oregon. *Murrelet* 58: 83–84.

Weber, J. W. 1977. Blue Jay influx into Washington during the 1976-77 winter. *Murrelet* 58: 84–86.

Weisbrod, A. R. 1971. Grooming behaviors of the Blue Jay. *Living Bird* 10: 271–84.

Black-capped Chickadee

Dixon, K. L., and Stefanski, R. A. 1970. An appraisal of the song of the Black-capped Chickadee. *Wilson Bull.* 82: 53–62.

Ficken, M. S. 1981. Food finding in Black-capped Chickadees: altruistic communication? *Wilson Bull.* 93: 393–94.

Ficken, M. S., and Ficken, R. W. 1974. Is the Golden-winged Warbler a social mimic of the Black-capped Chickadee? *Wilson Bull.* 86: 468–71.

Ficken, M. S.; Ficken, R. W.; and Witkin, S. R. 1978. Vocal repertoire of the Black-capped Chickadee. *Auk* 95: 34–48.

Ficken, M. S., and Witkin, S. R. 1977. Responses of Black-capped Chickadee flocks to predators. *Auk* 94: 156–57.

*Glase, J. C. 1973. Ecology of social organization in the Black-capped Chickadee. *Living Bird* 12: 235–67.

Grossman, A. F., and West, G. C. 1977. Metabolic rate and temperature regulation of winter acclimatized Black-capped Chickadees *Parus atricapillus* of interior Alaska. *Ornis Scand.* 8: 127–38.

Hamerstrom, F. 1942. Dominance in winter flocks of chickadees. *Wilson Bull.* 54: 32–42.

Hartzler, J. E. 1970. Winter dominance relationship in Black-capped Chickadees. *Wilson Bull.* 82: 427–34.

Kessel, B. 1976. Winter activity patterns of Black-capped Chickadees in interior Alaska. *Wilson Bull.* 88: 36–61.

Krebs, J. R. 1973. Social learning and the significance of mixed-species flocks of chickadees (*Parus* spp.). *Can. J. Zool.* 51: 1275–88.

Krebs, J. R.; Ryan, J. C.; and Charnov, E. L. 1974. Hunting by expectation or optimal foraging? A study of patch use by chickadees. *Anim. Behav.* 22: 953–64.

Lawrence, L. de K. 1973. *Black-capped Chickadee*.

Canadian Wildlife Service Hinterland Who's Who series.

Mueller, E. 1973. Chickadees at adjacent feeding sites: the effects of food deprivation. *Auk* 90: 520–32.

Odum, E. P. 1941-42. Annual cycle of the Black-capped Chickadee. *Auk* 58: 314–33, 518–35; 59: 499–531.

Samson, F. B., and Lewis, S. J. 1979. Experiments on population regulation in two North American parids. *Wilson Bull.* 9: 222–33.

Smith, S. M. 1967. Seasonal changes in the survival rate of the Black-capped Chickadee. *Condor* 69: 344–59.

———. 1976. Ecological aspects of dominance hierarchies in Black-capped Chickadees. *Auk* 93: 95–107.

Stefanski, R. A. 1967. Utilization of the breeding territory in the Black-capped Chickadee. *Condor* 69: 259–67.

Weise, C. M., and Meyer, J. R. 1979. Juvenile dispersal and development of site-fidelity in the Black-capped Chickadee. *Auk* 96: 40–55.

Witkin, S. R., and Ficken, M. S. 1980. Chickadee alarm calls: does mate investment pay dividends? *Anim. Behav.* 27: 1275–76.

House Wren

Baldwin, S. P. 1921. The marriage relations of the House Wren (*Troglodytes a. aëdon*). *Auk* 38: 237–44.

Baldwin, S. P., and Bowen, W. W. 1928. Nesting and local distribution of the House Wren (*Troglodytes aëdon aëdon*). *Auk* 45: 186–99.

Bent, A. C. 1948. *Life histories of North American nuthatches, wrens, thrashers and their allies.* U.S. National Museum Bull. 195.

Brackbill, H. 1970. A polygynous House Wren. *Bird-Banding* 41: 118–21.

Dunn, E. H. 1976. The relationship between brood size and age of effective homeothermy in nestling House Wrens. *Wilson Bull.* 88: 478–82.

*Kendeigh, S. C. 1941. Territorial and mating behavior of the House Wren. *Illinois Biol. Monog.* 18, No. 3.

McCabe, R. A. 1965. Nest construction by House Wrens. *Condor* 67: 229–34.

Sherman, A. R. 1925. The problem of the House Wren. *Bird-Lore* 27: 97–100.

Bluebirds

Barash, D. P. 1976. Male response to apparent female adultery in the Mountain Bluebird (*Sialia currucoides*): an evolutionary interpretation. *Am. Nat.* 110: 1097–1101.

Bent, A. C. 1949. *Life histories of North American thrushes, kinglets and their allies.* U.S. National Museum Bull. 196.

Conner, R. N., and Adkisson, C. S. 1974. Eastern Bluebirds nesting in clearcuts. *J. Wildl. Manage.* 38: 934–35.

Criddle, N. 1927. Habits of the Mountain Bluebird in Manitoba. *Can. Field-Nat.* 41: 40–44.

Goldman, P. 1975. Hunting behavior of Eastern Bluebirds. *Auk* 92: 798–801.

Hartshorne, J. M. 1962. Behavior of the Eastern Bluebird at the nest. *Living Bird* 1: 131–49.

Kibler, L. F. 1969. The establishment and maintenance of a bluebird nest-box project: a review and commentary. *Bird-Banding* 40: 114–29.

*Krieg, D. C. 1971. The behavioral patterns of the Eastern Bluebird (*Sialia sialis*). *N.Y. State Museum Bull.* 415.

Laskey, A. R. 1939. A study of nesting Eastern Bluebirds. *Bird-Banding* 10: 23–33.

Miller, W. 1970. Factors influencing the status of Eastern and Mountain Bluebirds in southwestern Manitoba. *Blue Jay* 28: 38–46.

Peakall, D. P. 1970. The Eastern Bluebird: its breeding season, clutch size, and nesting success. *Living Bird* 9: 239–55.

Pinkowski, B. C. 1971. Some observations on the vocalizations of the Eastern Bluebird. *Bird-Banding* 42: 20–27.

———. 1975. Yearling male Eastern Bluebird assists parents in feeding young. *Auk* 92: 801–2.

———. 1976. Use of tree cavities by nesting Eastern Bluebirds. *J. Wildl. Manage.* 40: 556–63.

———. 1977a. Breeding adaptations in the Eastern Bluebird. *Condor* 79: 289–302.

———. 1977b. Foraging behavior of the Eastern Bluebird. *Wilson Bull.* 89: 404–14.

———. 1978. Feeding of nestling and fledgling Eastern Bluebirds. *Wilson Bull.* 90: 84–98.

Power, H. W., III. 1966. Biology of the Mountain Bluebird in Montana. *Condor* 68: 351–71.

———. 1980. The foraging behavior of Mountain Bluebirds with emphasis on sexual foraging differences. *Orniphol. Monogr.* No. 28.

Preston, F. W., and McCormick, J. M. 1948. The eyesight of the bluebird. *Wilson Bull.* 60: 120–21.

Rounds, R. C., and Munro, H. L. 1982. A review of hybridization between *Sialia sialis* and *S. currucoides*. *Wilson Bull.* 94: 219–23.

Scott, L. 1979. *Mountain Bluebird*. Canadian Wildlife Service Hinterland Who's Who series.

Swenson, J. E. 1968. The Deer Mouse as a nest competitor and possible predator of the Mountain Bluebird. *Blue Jay* 26: 214–15.

Tate, J., Jr., and Tate, D. J. 1982. The Blue List for 1982. *Amer. Birds* 36: 126–35.

Thomas, R. H. 1946. A study of Eastern Bluebirds in Arkansas. *Wilson Bull.* 58: 143–83.

Welty, J. C. 1980. The geography of birds. In *Birds: Reprints from Scientific American*, ed. Barry W. Wilson, pp. 14–22. San Francisco: W. H. Freeman.

Wetherbee, K. B. 1933. Eastern Bluebirds in juvenal plumage feed young of second brood. *Bird-Banding* 4: 199–200.

American Robin

Beaver, D. L. 1980. Recovery of an American Robin population after earlier DDT use. *Brit. Birds* 51: 220–28.

Bent, A. C. 1949. *Life histories of North American thrushes, kinglets, and their allies*. U.S. National Museum Bull. 196.

*Eiserer, L. A. 1976. *The American Robin: a backyard institution*. Chicago: Nelson Hall.

———. 1980. Effects of grass length and mowing on foraging behavior of the American Robin (*Turdus migratorius*). *Auk* 97: 576–80.

Heppner, F. 1965. Sensory mechanisms and environmental clues used by the American Robin in locating earthworms. *Condor* 67: 247–56.

Hirth, D. H.; Hester, A. E.; and Greeley, F. 1969. Dispersal and flocking of marked young robins (*Turdus m. migratorius*) after fledging. *Bird-Banding* 40: 208–15.

*Howard, D. V. 1967. Variation in the breeding season and clutch-size of the robin in the northeastern United States and the Maritime provinces of Canada. *Wilson Bull.* 79: 432–40.

Howell, J. C. 1942. Notes on the nesting habits of the American Robin (*Turdus migratorius* L.) *Amer. Midl. Nat.* 28: 529–603.

Long, R. C. 1973. *American Robin*. Canadian Wildlife Service Hinterland Who's Who series.

McNicholl, M. K. 1978. Mid-March singing by American Robin and Varied Thrush in southwestern Alberta. *Blue Jay* 36: 118–19.

Morton, E. S. 1968. Robins feeding on hairy caterpillars. *Auk* 85: 696.

Nickell, W. P. 1944. Studies of habitats, locations and structural materials of nests of the robin. *Jack-Pine Warbler* 22: 48–64.

Pettingill, O. S., Jr. 1963. All-day observation at a robin's nest. *Living Bird* 2: 47–55.

Schantz, W. E. 1939. A detailed study of a family of robins. *Wilson Bull.* 51: 157–69.

Willson, G. D. 1978. Reproductive biology of American Robins following a Dutch Elm disease control program. *Proc. Iowa Acad. Sci.* 85: 91–96.

Young, H. 1955. Breeding behavior and nesting of the eastern robin. *Amer. Midl. Nat.* 53: 329–52.

Waxwings

Allen, A. A. 1930. Cherry bird—the Cedar Waxwing. *Bird-Lore* 32: 298–307.

Bent, A. C. 1950. *Life histories of North American wagtails, shrikes, vireos, and their allies*. U.S. National Museum Bull. 197.

Crouch, J. E. 1936. Nesting habits of the Cedar Waxwing (*Bombycilla cedrorum*). *Auk* 53: 1–8.

Gross, W. A. 1929. A Cedar Waxwing study in northern Michigan. *Bird-Lore* 31: 178–82.

Lea, R. B. 1942. A study of the nesting habits of the Cedar Waxwing. *Wilson Bull.* 54: 225–37.

Leck, C. F., and Cantor, F. L. 1979. Seasonality, clutch size, and hatching success in the Cedar Waxwing. *Auk* 96: 196–98.

McCoy, H. 1927. A waxwing ceremony. *Bird-Lore* 29: 188–89.

Nice, M. M. 1941. Observations on the behavior of a young Cedar Waxwing. *Condor* 43: 58–64.

*Putnam, L. S. 1949. The life history of the Cedar Waxwing. *Wilson Bull.* 61: 141–82.

Rogers, T. H. 1976. Northern Rocky Mountain-Intermountain Region. *Amer. Birds* 30: 742–45.

Rothstein, S. I. 1971. High nest density and non-random nest placement in the Cedar Waxwing. *Condor* 73: 483–86.

Saunders, A. A. 1911. A study of the nesting of the Cedar Waxwing. *Auk* 28: 323–29.

Shrikes

Anderson, R. M. 1976. Shrikes feed on prey remains left by hawks. *Condor* 78: 269.

Anderson, W. L., and Duzan, R. E. 1978. DDE residues and eggshell thinning in Loggerhead Shrikes. *Wilson Bull.* 90: 215–20.

Applegate, R. D. 1977. Possible ecological role of food caches of Loggerhead Shrike. *Auk* 94: 391–92.

Bent, A. C. 1950. *Life histories of North American wagtails, shrikes, vireos, and their allies.* U.S. National Museum Bull. 197.

Busbee, E. L. 1976. The ontogeny of cricket killing and mouse killing in Loggerhead Shrikes (*Lanius ludovicianus* L.) *Condor* 78: 357–65.

———. 1977. The effects of dieldrin on the behavior of young Loggerhead Shrikes. *Auk* 94: 28–35.

Cade, T. J. 1967. Ecological and behavioral aspects of predation by the Northern Shrike. *Living Bird* 6: 43–86.

Chapman, B. R., and Casto, S. D. 1972. Additional vertebrate prey of the Loggerhead Shrike. *Wilson Bull.* 84: 496–97.

Craig, R. B. 1978. An analysis of the predatory behavior of the Loggerhead Shrike. *Auk* 95: 221–34.

Kridelbaugh, A. 1983. Nesting ecology of the Loggerhead Shrike in central Missouri. *Wilson Bull.* 95: 303–8.

*Miller, A. H. 1931. Systematic revision and natural history of American shrikes (*Lanius*). *U. Calif. Pub. Zool.* 38: 11–242.

Morrison, M. L. 1980. Seasonal aspects of the predatory behavior of Loggerhead Shrikes. *Condor* 82: 296–300.

———. 1981. Population trends of the Loggerhead Shrike in the United States. *Amer. Birds* 35: 754–57.

Porter, D. K.; Strong, M. A.; Giezentanner, J. B.; and Ryder, R. A. 1975. Nest ecology, productivity, and growth of the Loggerhead Shrike on the shortgrass prairie. *Southwestern Nat.* 19: 429–36.

Smith, S. M. 1972. Ontogeny of impaling behavior in the Loggerhead Shrike, *Lanius ludovicianus* L. *Behaviour* 42: 232–47.

———. 1973a. An aggressive display and related behavior in the Loggerhead Shrike. *Auk* 90: 287–98.

———. 1973b. A study of prey-attack behaviour in young Loggerhead Shrikes, *Lanius ludovicianus* L. *Behaviour* 44: 113–41.

Wemmer, C. 1970. Impaling behaviour of the Loggerhead Shrike, *Lanius ludovicianus* Linnaeus. *Z. f. Tierpsychol.* 26: 208–24.

Yellow Warbler

Bankwitz, K. G. and Thompson, W. L. 1979. Song characteristics of the Yellow Warbler. *Wilson Bull.* 91: 533–50.

Bent, A. C. 1953. *Life histories of North American wood warblers.* U.S. National Museum Bull. 203.

Berger, A. J. 1955. Six-storied Yellow Warbler nest with eleven cowbird eggs. *Jack-Pine Warbler* 33: 84.

Biermann, G. C., and Sealy, S. G. 1982. Parental feeding of nestling Yellow Warblers in relation to brood size and prey availability. *Auk* 99: 332–41.

Bowman, I., and Chamberlain, D. 1980. Kirtland's Warbler *Dendroica kirklandii* (Baird). Endangered Canadian Wildlife fact sheet. Committee on the Status of Endangered Wildlife in Canada.

Clark, K. L., and Robertson, R. J. 1981. Cowbird parasitism and evolution of anti-parasite strategies in the Yellow Warbler. *Wilson Bull.* 93: 249–58.

Ficken, M. S., and Ficken, R. W. 1962. The comparative ethology of the wood warblers: a review. *Living Bird* 1: 103–22.

———. 1965. Comparative ethology of the Chestnut-sided Warbler, Yellow Warbler, and American Redstart. *Wilson Bull.* 77: 363–75.

———. 1970. Responses of four warbler species to playback of their two song types. *Auk* 87: 296–304.

Goossen, J. P., and Sealy, S. G. 1982. Production of young in a dense nesting population of Yellow Warblers, *Dendroica petechia,* in Manitoba. *Can. Field-Nat.* 96: 189–99.

Griscom, L., and Sprunt, A., Jr. 1979. *The warblers of America: a popular account of the wood warblers as they occur in the Western Hemisphere.* Garden City, N.Y.: Doubleday.

Lemon, R. E.; Struger, J.; and Lechowicz, M. J. 1983. Song features as species discriminants in American warblers (*Parulidae*). *Condor* 85: 308–22.

Lywood, C. 1981. Yellow Warblers: nest biology and philopatry. *Ontario Bird Banding* 14: 23–29.

Mayfield, H. 1977. Brown-headed Cowbird: agent of extermination? *Amer. Birds* 31: 107–13.

Morse, D. H. 1966. The context of songs in the Yellow Warbler. *Wilson Bull.* 78: 444–55.

Robertson, R. J., and Norman, R. F. 1977. Function and evolution of aggressive host behavior towards the brown-headed cowbird (*Molothrus ater*). *Can. J. Zool.* 55: 508–18.

Rothstein, S. I. 1975. An experimental and teleonomic investigation of avian brood parasitism. *Condor* 77: 250–71.

Schrantz, F. G. 1943. Nest life of the eastern Yellow Warbler. *Auk* 60: 367–87.

Song Sparrow

Borror, D. J. 1965. Song variation in Maine Song Sparrows. *Wilson Bull.* 77: 5–37.

Eberhardt, C., and Baptista, L. F. 1977. Intraspecific and interspecific song mimesis in California Song Sparrows. *Bird-Banding* 48: 193–205.

Halliburton, R., and Mewaldt, L. R. 1976. Survival and mobility in a population of Pacific coast Song Sparrows (*Melospiza melodia* Gouldii). *Condor* 78: 499–504.

Harris, M. A., and Lemon, R. E. 1972. Songs of song sparrows (*Melospiza melodia*): individual variation and dialects. *Can. J. Zool.* 50: 301–9.

———. 1974. Songs of song sparrows: reactions of males to songs of different localities. *Condor* 76: 33–44.

———. 1976. Response of male Song Sparrows *Melospiza melodia* to neighboring and non-neighboring individuals. *Ibis* 118: 421–25.

Kroodsma, D. E. 1976. The effect of large song repertoires on neighbor "recognition" in male Song Sparrows. *Condor* 78: 97–99.

———. 1977. A re-evaluation of song development in the Song Sparrow. *Anim. Behav.* 25: 390–99.

Lemon, R. E. 1975. How birds develop dialects. *Condor* 77: 385–406.

Mulligan, J. A., S. J. 1963. A description of Song Sparrow song based on instrumental analysis. *Proc. XIII Intern. Ornithol. Congr.*: 272–84.

———. 1966. Singing behavior and its development in Song Sparrow *Melospiza melodia*. *U. Calif. Pub. Zool.* 81: 1–76.

———. 1980. Song Sparrows have top ten song preference list. *Amer. Zool.* 20: 725.

*Nice, M. M. 1964. *Studies in the life history of the Song Sparrow*. Reprint edition, 2 vol. New York: Dover.

Searcy, W. A., and Marler, P. 1981. A test for responsiveness to song structure and programming in female sparrows. *Science* 213: 926–28.

Smith, J. N. M. 1978. Division of labour by song sparrows feeding fledged young. *Can. J. Zool.* 56: 187–91.

———. 1981. Cowbird parasitism, host fitness, and age of the host female in an island Song Sparrow population. *Condor* 83: 152–61.

Smith, J. N. M., and Merkt, J. R. 1980. Development and stability of single-parent family units in the song sparrow. *Can. J. Zool.* 58: 1869–75.

Smith, J. N. M., and Roff, D. A. 1980. Temporal spacing of broods, brood size, and parental care in song sparrows (*Melospiza melodia*). *Can. J. Zool.* 58: 1007–15.

Tompa, F. S. 1962. Territorial behavior: the main controlling factor of a local Song Sparrow population. *Auk* 79: 687–97.

Red-winged Blackbird

Albers, P. H. 1978. Habitat selection by breeding Red-winged Blackbirds. *Wilson Bull.* 90: 619–34.

Beer, J. R., and Tibbitts, D. 1950. Nesting behavior of the Red-wing Blackbird. *Flicker* 22: 61–77.

Beletsky, L. D. 1983. An investigation of individual recognition by voice in female Red-winged Blackbirds. *Anim. Behav.* 31: 355–62.

Bird, R. D., and Smith, L. B. 1964. The food habits of the Red-winged Blackbird, *Agelaius phoeniceus*, in Manitoba. *Can. Field-Nat.* 78: 179–86.

Blakley, N. R. 1976. Successive polygyny in upland nesting Red-winged Blackbirds. *Condor* 78: 129–33.

Bray, O. E.; Kennelly, J. J.; and Guarino, J. L. 1975. Fertility of eggs produced on territories of vasectomized Red-winged Blackbirds. *Wilson Bull.* 87: 187–94.

Case, N. A., and Hewitt, O. H. 1963. Nesting and productivity of the Red-winged Blackbird in relation to habitat. *Living Bird* 2: 7–20.

Dolbeer, R. A. 1976. Reproductive rate and temporal spacing of nesting of Red-winged Blackbirds in upland habitat. *Auk* 93: 343–55.

Holcomb, L. C. 1974. The question of possible surplus females in breeding Red-winged Blackbirds. *Wilson Bull.* 86: 177–79.

Lenington, S. 1980. Female choice and polygyny in Red-winged Blackbirds. *Anim. Behav.* 28: 347–61.

Miller, R. S. 1968. Conditions of competition between Redwings and Yellowhead Blackbirds. *J. Anim. Ecol.* 37: 43–67.

*Nero, R. W. 1984. *Redwings*. Washington, D.C.: Smithsonian Institution Press.

Orians, G. H. 1961. The ecology of blackbird (*Agelaius*) social systems. *Ecol. Monogr.* 31: 285–312.

————. 1980. *Some adaptations of marsh-nesting blackbirds.* Princeton, N.J.: Princeton University Press.

Peek, F. W. 1971. Seasonal change in the breeding behavior of the male Red-winged Blackbird. *Wilson Bull.* 83: 383–95.

Roberts, T. A., and Kennelly, J. J. 1980. Variation in promiscuity among Red-winged Blackbirds. *Wilson Bull.* 92: 110–12.

Searcy, W. A. 1979a. Female choice of mates: a general model for birds and its application to Red-winged Blackbirds (*Agelaius phoeniceus*). *Amer. Nat.* 114: 77–100.

————. 1979b. Male characteristics and pairing success in Red-winged Blackbirds. *Auk* 96: 353–63.

Smith, L. B., and Bird, R. D. 1969. Autumn flocking habits of the Red-winged Blackbird in southern Manitoba. *Can. Field-Nat.* 83: 40–47.

Somers, J. D.; Gartshore, R. G.; Gilbert, F. F.; and Brooks, R. J. 1981. Movements and habitat use by depredating red-winged blackbirds in Simcoe County, Ontario. *Can. J. Zool.* 59: 2206–14.

Weatherhead, P. J. 1981. Coming home to roost. *Nature Canada* 10 (5): 38–40, 43.

————. 1981. The dynamics of Red-winged Blackbird populations at four late summer roosts in Quebec. *J. Field Ornithol.* 52: 222–27.

Wittenberger, J. F. 1981. Male quality and polygyny: the "sexy son" hypothesis revisited. *Amer. Nat.* 117: 329–38.

Yasukawa, K. 1981. Song repertoires in the Red-winged Blackbird (*Agelaius phoeniceus*): a test of the Beau Geste hypothesis. *Anim. Behav.* 29: 114–25.

Yasukawa, K., and Searcy, W. A. 1981. Nesting synchrony and dispersion in Red-winged Blackbirds: is the harem competitive or cooperative? *Auk* 98: 659–68.

Meadowlarks

Bent, A. C. 1958. *Life histories of North American blackbirds, orioles, tanagers, and allies.* U.S. National Museum Bull. 211.

D'Agincourt, L. G., and Falls, J. B. 1983. Variation of repertoire use in the eastern meadowlark, *Sturnella magna. Can. J. Zool.* 61: 1086–93.

Falls, J. B., and D'Agincourt, L. G. 1982. Why do meadowlarks switch song types? *Can. J. Zool.* 60: 3400–3408.

Falls, J. B., and Krebs, J. R. 1975. Sequence of songs in repertoires of western meadowlarks (*Sturnella neglecta*). *Can. J. Zool.* 53: 1165–78.

Fish, W. R.; Nelson, K.; and Issac, D. 1962. The temporal patterning of meadowlark song. *Amer. Zool.* 2: 409.

Lanyon, W. E. 1956. Ecological aspects of sympatric distribution of meadowlarks in the north-central states. *Ecology* 37: 98–108.

*————. 1957. *The comparative biology of the meadowlarks* (Sturnella) *in Wisconsin.* Publ. Nuttall Ornithol. Club No. 1.

————. Geographical variation in the vocalizations of the Western Meadowlark. *Condor* 60: 339–41.

————. 1966. Hybridization in meadowlarks. *Bull. American Museum Natural History* 134: 5–25.

————. 1979. Hybrid sterility in meadowlarks. *Nature* 279: 557–58.

McNicholl, M. K. 1983. Early fledging record of Western Meadowlark in Manitoba. *Blue Jay* 41: 201–4.

Ordal, J. M. 1976. Effect of sympatry on meadowlark vocalizations. *Condor* 78: 100–101.

Rohwer, S. A. 1972a. A multivariate assessment of interbreeding between the meadowlarks, *Sturnella. Syst. Zool.* 21: 313–38.

————. 1973. Significance of sympatry to behavior and evolution of Great Plains meadowlarks. *Evolution* 27: 44–57.

Roseberry, J. L., and Klimstra, W. D. 1970. The nesting ecology and reproduction performance of the Eastern Meadowlark. *Wilson Bull.* 82: 243–67.

Schroeder, R. L., II. 1974. A study of the nesting behavior of Western Meadowlarks near Fort Collins, Colorado. *Colo. Field Ornithol.* 21/22: 6–10.

Szijj, L. J. 1963. Morphological analysis of the sympatric populations of meadowlarks in Ontario. *Proc. XIII Intern. Ornithol. Congr.*: 176–88.

————. 1966. Hybridization and the nature of the isolating mechanism in sympatric populations of meadowlarks (*Sturnella*) in Ontario. *Z. f. Tierpsychol.* 6: 677–90.

Northern Oriole

Anderson, B. W. 1971. Man's influence on hybridization in two avian species in South Dakota. *Condor* 73: 342–47.

Beletsky, L. D. 1982. Vocal behavior of the Northern Oriole. *Wilson Bull.* 94: 381–85.

————. Vocalizations of female Northern Orioles. *Condor* 84: 445–47.

*Bent, A. C. 1958. *Life histories of North American blackbirds, orioles, tanagers, and allies.* U.S. National Museum Bull. 211.

Erickson, J. E. 1969. Banding studies of wintering Baltimore Orioles in North Carolina, 1963-66. *Bird-Banding* 40: 181–97.

Miller, A. H. 1931. Notes on the song and territorial habits of Bullock's Oriole. *Wilson Bull.* 43: 102–8.

Rising, J. D. 1970. Morphological variation and evolution in some North American orioles. *Syst. Zool.* 19: 315–51.

Schaefer, V. H. 1976. Geographic variation in the

placement and structure of oriole nests. *Condor* 78: 443–48.

Sealy, S. G. 1979. Prebasic molt of the northern oriole. *Can. J. Zool.* 57: 1473–78.

Sibley, C. G., and Short, L. L. 1964. Hybridization in the orioles of the Great Plains. *Condor* 66: 130–50.

Metric conversion table

Metric		Imperial
Length		
1 centimeter	=	0.3937 inch
1 meter	=	3.281 feet
1 meter	=	1.094 yards
1 kilometer	=	0.6214 mile
Weight		
1 gram	=	0.035 oz.
1 kilogram	=	2.205 lbs.
1 tonne	=	1.102 tons
Volume		
1 liter	=	0.220 gallon (Imperial)
1 liter	=	0.264 gallon (American)
Area		
1 square centimeter	=	0.155 square inch
1 square meter	=	10.76 square feet
1 square meter	=	1.196 square yards
1 square kilometer	=	0.386 square mile

Photography
Credits

Front Cover: Blue Jay
by Wayne Lankinen
Back Cover: Bohemian Waxwing
by Arthur Savage

4	Tim Fitzharris
7	Wayne Lankinen
9	Mildred McPhee/Valan Photos
12	Dennis W. Schmidt/Valan Photos
13	Dennis W. Schmidt
15	George K. Peck
16	Arthur Savage
17	Jeanne Brakefield
19	George K. Peck
22	Robert McCaw
23	Robert McCaw
26	Wayne Lankinen/Valan Photos
27	Rita Summers
28	Wayne Lankinen
30	Fred Bruemmer
31	Leonard Lee Rue III
34	Tim Fitzharris
35	Lorne Scott
37	Leonard Lee Rue III
38	Rolf Kraiker
39	Dennis W. Schmidt
41	Wilfried D. Schurig
42	Jeff Foott
43	Stephen J. Krasemann/Valan Photos
46	J. A. Barrie
47	Tom W. Hall
49	Wayne Lankinen/DRK Photo
50	Stephen J. Krasemann/DRK Photo
51	Leonard Lee Rue III
53	Stephen J. Krasemann/DRK Photo
57	Rolf Kraiker
58	Tom A. Schneider/DRK Photo
60	Lyn Hancock
61	Craig Blacklock
63	Arthur Savage
65	Tom Brakefield
66	Arthur Savage
67	Albert Kuhnigk/Valan Photos
68	Norman Lightfoot
70	Stephen J. Krasemann/Valan Photos
71	Tim Fitzharris
75	Arthur Savage
76	Alvin E. Staffan
77	Jeff Foott
79	Arthur Savage
80	Jeff Foott
81	Tom Brakefield
82	Charles G. Summers Jr.
85	Charles G. Summers Jr.
86	Tom W. Hall

87	Jeanne Brakefield
89	Robert McCaw
91	Michael Hopiak/Cornell Laboratory of Ornithology
93	Rolf Kraiker
95	Fred Bruemmer
97	Leonard Lee Rue III
98	Stephen J. Krasemann/Valan Photos
101	Leonard Lee Rue III
103	Robert McCaw
107	Tom Brakefield
108	Arthur Savage
109	Leonard Lee Rue III
111	Gary R. Jones
112	Fred Bruemmer
114	Stephen J. Krasemann/Valan Photos
115	Arthur Savage
117	Wayne Lankinen
119	Albert Kuhnigk
120	John Gerlach/DRK Photo
123	Isidor Jeklin
124	Tom W. Hall
126	Michael Hopiak/Cornell Laboratory of Ornithology
129	Robert McCaw
132	Alvin E. Staffan
135	Dennis W. Schmidt/Valan Photos
136	Alvin E. Staffan
140	Anthony J. Bond, FRPS/Valan Photos
142	Robert McCaw
144	Wayne Lankinen
146	Harold V. Green/Valan Photos
148	Dennis W. Schmidt
150	Alvin E. Staffan
151	Arthur Savage
153	Arthur Savage
154	Jeff Foott
155	Charles G. Summers Jr.
156	Stephen J. Krasemann/DRK Photo
158	Arthur Savage
159	Wayne Lankinen/DRK Photo
160	Gary R. Jones
163	Wilfried D. Schurig
164	Arthur Savage
166	Tim Fitzharris
168	Wayne Lankinen
169	Tom and Pat Leeson
170	Michael Hopiak/Cornell Laboratory of Ornithology
172	Edgar T. Jones
173	Robert McCaw
175	Robert C. Simpson/Valan Photos
176	F. Hublitz/Cornell Laboratory of Ornithology

Index